Ultimate Neural Network Programming with Python

Create Powerful Modern AI Systems by Harnessing Neural Networks with Python, Keras, and TensorFlow

Vishal Rajput

Orangeava.com

First published: November 2023
Published by: Orange Education Pvt Ltd, AVA™
Address: 9, Daryaganj, Delhi, 110002

ISBN: 978-93-91246-54-9
www.orangeava.com

Dedicated to

My ideals who kept me on the path of learning:

Swami Vivekananda

Bhagat Singh

JP

and

My Friends and Family

About the Author

Vishal Rajput, an ardent explorer and practitioner of Artificial Intelligence, is honored as a three-time top-50 AI writer on Medium. He has earned an advanced master's in AI from KU Leuven, Belgium, a university renowned globally as one of the top 50. Since his foray into AI in 2016, Vishal has amassed over six years of experience, balancing academic rigor and industrial applicability, and has contributed to eight research papers in international journals and book chapters. His journey has included collaborations with eminent research labs such as SONY R&D and MIRZ UZ Leuven, providing opportunities to explore and contribute to the myriad facets of AI. Vishal's relentless passion and multifaceted involvement in this transformative field have culminated in a comprehensive book aimed at unraveling the intricate tapestry of AI, bridging its profound depths and vast breadth. This endeavor is a scholarly pursuit and a holistic exploration reflecting his diverse experiences and insights, particularly emphasizing adversarial robustness and fraud detection in AI. Beyond his professional and academic engagements, Vishal actively participates in various AI meetups and events as a speaker, serves as a mentor in AI, and leads innovation and AI development at a drone-based startup. With a palette of rich experiences and a reservoir of knowledge, he invites you with anticipation and excitement to embark on this enlightening journey through the boundless landscapes of Artificial Intelligence, fostering a collaborative exploration and enriched appreciation of this unprecedented field.

About the Technical Reviewers

Nehaa Bansal is a trailblazing thought leader and data scientist, driven by a relentless passion for early innovation. With a wealth of experience spanning multiple industries including banking, finance, telecom, and insurance, Nehaa has mastered the art of developing predictive models that drive impactful outcomes. Her ability to excel both as an independent contributor and a collaborative team player sets her apart in the field.

Nehaa's academic journey showcases a string of remarkable achievements. Graduating at the top of her class, she obtained a bachelor's degree in computer science, laying a strong foundation for her future endeavors. Building upon her academic success, she further honed her skills by earning a master's in data science from the esteemed BITS Pilani.

At the core of Nehaa's professional ethos lie values that shape her every action. She thrives on taking ownership, putting people first, and asking the fundamental question of "why" before embarking on any endeavor. Her agile mindset propels her to act swiftly, embrace failure as a learning opportunity, iterate continuously, and always strive to play fair.

Driven by her deep-rooted passion for solving user problems, Nehaa leverages her expertise in analytics capabilities, product strategy, and leadership to craft innovative solutions. She approaches every challenge with unwavering dedication, consistently pushing the boundaries of what is possible.

Beyond her professional pursuits, Nehaa finds fulfillment in various personal interests. She relishes the power of continuous learning and remains at the forefront of emerging trends in her field. Furthermore, she is an avid advocate for creating a more inclusive and diverse work environment, fostering collaboration and empathy among team members.

With an indomitable spirit and a commitment to excellence, Nehaa Bansal continues to inspire and pave the way for others in the realm of technology and data science. Her unwavering dedication to her craft, coupled with her deep empathy for others, has solidified her as a thought leader and a catalyst for positive change.

Pradeepta Mishra is the Co-Founder and Chief Architect of Datasafeguard.ai a California headquartered start-up, leading a group of data scientists, computational linguistics experts, and machine learning and deep learning experts in building artificial intelligence-driven products for data privacy and synthetic fraud prevention. He was awarded "India's Top - 40Under40DataScientists" by Analytics India Magazine for two years in a row in 2019 and 2020. As an inventor, he has filed 14 patents in different global locations, out of which 4 are granted. He is the author of nine books; his first book has been recommended in the HSLS center at the University of Pittsburgh, PA, USA. His 4th book #PytorchRecipes was published by Apress and added to Buswell Library, IL, USA. His fifth Book #Practical Explainable AI using Python was recently published by Apress and has been recognized as a textbook for Barcelona Technology School's (BTS) big data analytics course. He delivered a keynote session at the Global Data Science Conference 2018, CA, USA. He has delivered a TEDx talk on "Can Machines Think?", available on the official TEDx YouTube channel. Many of his books are translated and published in Japanese, Spanish, and Chinese on popular demand from authors. He has delivered 500+ tech talks on data science, ML, DL, NLP, and AI in various Universities, meetups, technical institutions, and community-arranged forums. He is visiting faculty and academic advisory board for AI-ML in M. Tech in AI course and Cyber Security course at Reva University, Bangalore, India, and also various other universities. Has mentored and trained over 2000 plus data scientists and AI engineers in last 18 years."

Welcome note

Welcome and greetings! We are delighted to have you here as we embark on an exhilarating exploration of the vast world of artificial intelligence. AI is an extraordinary technology that has revolutionized our understanding and interaction with the world around us. Numerous experts anticipate AI will profoundly impact humanity, rivaling the transformative effects of monumental inventions such as fire, the wheel, and agriculture.

The influence of AI permeates every aspect of our lives, often without us even realizing it. Take, for instance, Google Maps, which has long employed classical AI techniques to provide accurate and efficient directions. Additionally, the Amazon marketplace, weather forecasts, and the formidable Google Search Engine rely on intricate AI systems to enhance their functionalities.

Within the pages of this remarkable book, we will delve into the fundamental principles that underpin these intricate AI systems and explore the mathematical approaches behind them. Together, we will embark on an exhilarating journey into the depths of AI, uncovering its immense potential and unveiling the mysteries that lie within. Thank you for joining me on this thrilling expedition into the captivating world of AI.

Is this book for me?

Since you're here, the answer is a resounding yes! So, let's dive deeper into the details. Whether you're intrigued by the fundamentals of Python, eager to construct neural networks from the ground up, curious about the mathematical optimizations that drive these unique AI systems, or keen on building an entire AI pipeline, this book has got you covered on all fronts.

Our comprehensive guide aims to demystify the core concepts of Neural Networks, providing you with a deep understanding while ensuring an engaging learning experience. We believe in learning by doing, so this book incorporates hands-on sessions to actively involve and captivate our readers.

Prepare to embark on a captivating journey that will empower you with the knowledge and skills needed to comprehend the inner workings of AI. With a focus on practicality and a firm foundation in Python, this book will equip you with the tools necessary to build, optimize, and deploy neural networks and bring your AI projects to life.

Join us on this enlightening adventure as we unravel the intricacies of Neural Networks and ignite your passion for AI. So, get ready to explore, experiment, and excel!

Software Engineers

This book perfectly fits software engineers looking to dive into AI. It provides ample opportunities to explore and practice AI concepts while leveraging the Python programming language. You'll gain valuable insights and practical skills from algorithms to real-life product implementation. Discover how to create AI-powered solutions and unleash your potential in the exciting field of AI.

Machine Learning Enthusiasts and Engineers

This book will advance your understanding if you're already well-versed in AI and have a solid foundation. It offers an opportunity to delve deeper into AI concepts, providing hands-on training that allows you to build projects from scratch. By engaging in practical exercises, you'll gain a more comprehensive understanding of AI and sharpen your skills. Prepare to expand your knowledge and expertise as you embark on a hands-on exploration and learning journey.

AI Researchers

This book caters to AI researchers by offering clear explanations of mathematical concepts used in AI algorithms. It also guides writing production-level code, addressing a common challenge researchers face. Expand your understanding of AI and enhance your ability to apply it effectively in real-life scenarios with this valuable resource.

What is the book's goal?

- Introduce our readers to the basics of Python and how to use it for AI purposes.

- Help readers understand complex mathematical concepts by giving them an easy breakdown of mathematical equations, which can later be applied to understand the complex mathematics behind modern AI systems.

- Enable our readers to write mathematical concepts behind AI algorithms in a code format by implementing things from scratch without using high-level libraries such as TensorFlow or PyTorch.

How is this book structured?

This book aims to comprehensively understand Artificial Neural Networks (ANN) and guide readers in building ANN models using Python. In addition, it explores the practical applications of ANN in various industries and academic fields.

The book begins with an introduction to Neural Networks and then covers the fundamentals of Python and the relevant libraries used in ANN modeling. Next, it gradually introduces the theoretical concepts that serve as the foundation for the rest of the book, including one-layer and multilayer neural networks, vectors and weights, and Linear Regression Models.

The core section of the book focuses on the construction of ANN models. It starts with building neural networks from scratch, including detailed coding examples. Then, the addition of input and output layers to the ANN model and techniques for saving, restoring, and fine-tuning the model's hyperparameters are discussed. Later, we discover the excellent TensorFlow library and how to write NN models using a high-level library.

In the book's final part, readers will delve into training and compilation of DL models. Finally, the book concludes by demonstrating real-world applications of AI, providing readers with the necessary knowledge to grasp new AI concepts and engage in AI research while enabling them to implement and comprehend cutting-edge AI technologies.

By completing this book, readers will acquire the skills to effectively apply ANN in practice and develop a solid foundation for exploring advanced AI concepts and techniques.

Do I need to know anything else before getting started?

Basic knowledge of Python and AI is excellent, but don't worry; we will cover everything from setting up your machine to building things that can be utilized in a real-world application.

The tools and technologies we will cover in this book include Python, Neural Networks, Mathematical Operations, Image Processing, TensorFlow, Keras, Numpy, and VS Code.

Without further ado, let's get started.

Acknowledgments

Vishal Rajput: It is with immense gratitude and heartfelt appreciation that I extend my acknowledgments to the individuals and institutions that have significantly contributed to the creation of this book on AI.

First and foremost, I express deep gratitude to my friends through this book who have consistently engaged with me in insightful AI discussions. Bhuppi, Sooraj, Venkatesh, and Venkatraman, your involvement and shared enthusiasm have been invaluable in shaping the concepts presented within these pages.

I am indebted to my alma mater, KU Leuven, for providing me with a rich educational foundation. A special debt of gratitude is owed to the research collaboration I had the privilege of undertaking with Dr. Irshad Ahmad Ansari, whose guidance and mentorship significantly influenced the depth and quality of this work.

The unwavering support of all my friends and family has been a constant source of inspiration. Their encouragement and belief in my pursuit of knowledge have been instrumental in bringing this project to fruition.

I extend my special thanks to renowned institutions such as Stanford and MIT, whose lectures have expanded my understanding of AI. Additionally, platforms like MLST and other exceptional YouTube channels, featuring luminaries such as Hinton, Bengio, and Andrew Ng, have been instrumental in imparting profound insights into the realm of AI.

Finally, with profound gratitude and appreciation, I like to thank the **reviewer** and **Team AVA**.

Preface

This book provides a comprehensive exploration of Artificial Intelligence (AI), beginning with a foundational understanding of its history, significant developments, and evolution into various sub-fields. The initial chapters lay down the theoretical groundwork, delineating between AI and Deep Learning and elucidating the basic concepts and models like neuron-inspired networks. Progressing sequentially, it offers practical insights into setting up Python workflows for AI development, focusing on installing essential packages and configuring development environments. It introduces foundational Python libraries and programming concepts crucial for AI development and data science, enhancing comprehension through web scraping, regex, and multithreading discussions.

Moving forward, the book delves deeper into advanced topics, covering effective neural network training concepts, dimensionality reduction techniques, and unsupervised learning. The readers are guided through building neural networks from scratch, emphasizing understanding various data structures and implementing multi-layer networks using NumPy. Subsequent chapters intensively explore Convolutional Neural Networks (CNN) and provide insights into TensorFlow and Keras, highlighting the contrasts between TensorFlow and other deep learning frameworks. The concluding chapters center on structuring deep learning code, constructing end-to-end image segmentation pipelines, and presenting the latest advancements and techniques in AI, ensuring the readers are well-acquainted with cutting-edge developments in the field.

Chapter 1: This chapter introduces AI, highlighting its evolutionary phases and sub-fields. The goal is to impart an understanding of AI history and how it diverged into various domains, emphasizing intelligent behavior like learning, reasoning, and language. It discusses differences between AI and Deep Learning, illustrates early neuron-inspired network models, and mentions significant developments like ChatGPT.

Chapter 2: This chapter serves as a practical guide to setting up the Python environment for AI development, including installing necessary packages and configuring environments like Anaconda and VS Code. It also introduces the concepts of Object-Oriented Programming (OOP) crucial for development.

Chapter 3: This chapter discusses various Python libraries and techniques essential for Data Scientists, focusing on web scraping, regular expressions, multi-threading, multi-processing, and introducing the basics of Pandas.

Chapter 4: This chapter dives into the fundamental concepts vital for training neural networks, such as activation functions, overfitting, bias-variance trade-off, and the principle of universal approximators. It introduces concepts like Radial Bias Function and the curse of dimensionality, providing insights into the realm of neural networks.

Chapter 5: This chapter elucidates dimensionality reduction techniques and unsupervised learning, touching upon topics like PCA, clustering, semi-supervised learning, and self-supervised learning. It also explores version space and optimization through SVM, shedding light on different SVM forms and the Kernel Trick.

Chapter 6: This chapter takes a hands-on approach to illustrate building neural networks from scratch. It discusses the coding of neurons, understanding various data structures like lists, arrays, and tensors, and provides insights into creating multi-layer networks using NumPy.

Chapter 7: This chapter delves deep into the optimization of weights through derivatives and backpropagation. It details the mathematics and implementation of backpropagation and introduces various optimizers like SGD and Adam, emphasizing training networks end-to-end.

Chapter 8: This chapter elaborates on Convolutional Neural Networks (CNN), detailing their operation, feature extraction, and types, and introduces various CNN-based networks like VGG 16, ResNet, and others. It discusses different convolution types and provides insights into scaling conv networks through the Efficient Net Architecture.

Chapter 9: This chapter provides an overview of TensorFlow and Keras, contrasting TensorFlow with other deep learning frameworks like PyTorch and Theano. It provides insights into TensorFlow's internals and various components, discussing layers, activations, optimizers, and loss functions, and illustrates building a multi-input single-output network with custom callbacks.

Chapter 10: This chapter focuses on structuring deep learning code and building an end-to-end image segmentation pipeline. It emphasizes project structure, documentation, debugging, and logging, and introduces segmentation techniques like UNet and Attention Gates.

Chapter 11: The final chapter delves into advanced AI concepts and models, including RNN, LSTM, self-attention mechanisms, object detection with YOLO, and generative models like VAE and GANs. It provides a detailed understanding of different AI models like DALLE-2 and explains the use of self-attention for transformers in Natural Language Processing (NLP).

This book serves as a comprehensive guide, starting from the basics and history of AI, delving into practical aspects and foundational concepts, and concluding with the latest advancements in the field.

Downloading the code bundles and colored images

Please follow the link to download the
Code Bundles of the book:

https://github.com/OrangeAVA/Ultimate-Neural-Network-Programming-with-Python

The code bundles and images of the book are also hosted on
https://rebrand.ly/553a52

In case there's an update to the code, it will be updated on the existing GitHub repository.

Errata

We take immense pride in our work at **Orange Education Pvt Ltd,** and follow best practices to ensure the accuracy of our content to provide an indulging reading experience to our subscribers. Our readers are our mirrors, and we use their inputs to reflect and improve upon human errors, if any, that may have occurred during the publishing processes involved. To let us maintain the quality and help us reach out to any readers who might be having difficulties due to any unforeseen errors, please write to us at :

errata@orangeava.com

Your support, suggestions, and feedback are highly appreciated.

DID YOU KNOW

Did you know that Orange Education Pvt Ltd offers eBook versions of every book published, with PDF and ePub files available? You can upgrade to the eBook version at **www.orangeava.com** and as a print book customer, you are entitled to a discount on the eBook copy. Get in touch with us at: **info@orangeava.com** for more details.

At **www.orangeava.com**, you can also read a collection of free technical articles, sign up for a range of free newsletters, and receive exclusive discounts and offers on AVA™ Books and eBooks.

PIRACY

If you come across any illegal copies of our works in any form on the internet, we would be grateful if you would provide us with the location address or website name. Please contact us at **info@orangeava.com** with a link to the material.

ARE YOU INTERESTED IN AUTHORING WITH US?

If there is a topic that you have expertise in, and you are interested in either writing or contributing to a book, please write to us at **business@orangeava.com**. We are on a journey to help developers and tech professionals to gain insights on the present technological advancements and innovations happening across the globe and build a community that believes Knowledge is best acquired by sharing and learning with others. Please reach out to us to learn what our audience demands and how you can be part of this educational reform. We also welcome ideas from tech experts and help them build learning and development content for their domains.

REVIEWS

Please leave a review. Once you have read and used this book, why not leave a review on the site that you purchased it from? Potential readers can then see and use your unbiased opinion to make purchase decisions. We at Orange Education would love to know what you think about our products, and our authors can learn from your feedback. Thank you!

For more information about Orange Education, please visit **www.orangeava.com**.

Table of Contents

## CHAPTER 1

Understanding AI History

Knowing the historical background and context is important to fall in love with any technology or subject. Without sufficient background and context, you may always ask yourself, why am I even reading this? Throughout this chapter, we cover who this book is meant for and how it is going to help you, whether you are an AI researcher, developer, or enthusiast. From understanding the earliest inspiration to the first set of mathematical blocks to build neural networks, this chapter gives you all.

Structure

This chapter covers the following topics:

- How AI evolved over decades
- Different AI uses cases
- Differentiating AI, ML, and DL
- Multi-layer Perceptron

Evolution of AI

While many are familiar with the concept of the AI winter, the complete narrative of AI's evolution over the decades remains to be discovered by most. To grasp the intricacies of the field, it is crucial to comprehend the foundations and the remarkable journey that has brought us here. The inception of AI can be traced back to the 1960s when pioneering researchers delved into the realm of creating intelligent machines. While the Dartmouth Conference in 1956 is widely regarded as the birth of AI, it was during the 1960s that substantial strides were made, propelling the field forward.

The early history of AI

Early AI researchers focused on creating systems that could solve problems **symbolically, using logical reasoning and rule-based approaches**. One of the key developments was the General Problem Solver (GPS) created by Allen Newell and Herbert A. Simon. GPS was an early attempt at building a problem-solving system that could reason and plan its actions. The idea was that they could represent the entire world through symbols and perfect logic, and if one could do that, one could train a system to navigate that world, but it was almost impossible to build such a system due to the inherent random nature of things. For example, so many things can't be written using perfect logic; thus, creating a world model with excellent reasoning capabilities was doomed to fail in at least certain areas. Another notable achievement was the creation of the ELIZA program by Joseph Weizenbaum. ELIZA was a computer program that simulated a conversation with a human and demonstrated natural language processing capabilities.

Let us try to understand this in more detail through a concept called **Combinatorial explosion**. It is a phenomenon in AI where the number of possible states or combinations grows exponentially as the problem size increases. It refers to the rapid expansion of the search space or the complexity of a problem as more variables or options are introduced.

In AI, combinatorial explosion poses a significant challenge because it leads to computational intractability and makes it difficult to explore all possible solutions reasonably. As the number of variables, constraints, or choices increases, the number of potent states grows exponentially. This explosion in possibilities often exceeds the computational resources available to solve the problem effectively. Planning and search, and drug discovery are a few problems that represent the combinatorial explosion problem. Let's understand this problem through an example and why the early AI system failed.

Example to understand the concept

Consider a photo of a chair represented by a 10x10 feature matrix. Each point in this matrix can take on a value ranging from 0 to 256. Consequently, the total number of possible combinations in this search space is calculated by multiplying 256 by itself 100 times (256¹⁰⁰). This astronomical number signifies the sheer magnitude of the search space.

To put it into perspective, the enormity of this space surpasses the number of atoms present in the entire universe. In other words, more atoms in the universe must be needed to draw sufficient samples from this vast search space to comprehend the underlying distribution.

In essence, attempting to explore and analyze the entire 256¹⁰⁰ space is an insurmountable task due to its incomprehensible size, exceeding the limitations of current resources and feasibility. But we still somehow do it through Neural Networks.

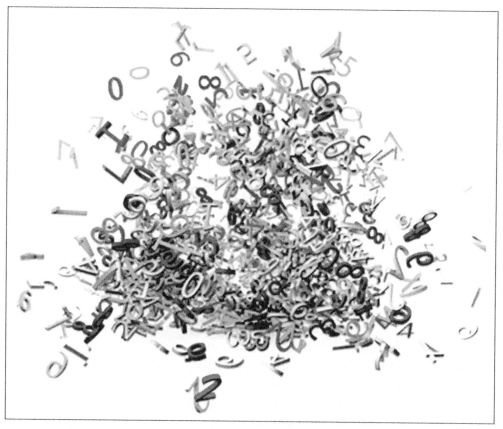

Figure 1.1: *Combinatorial explosion (Img Src)*

During the 1970s, a significant development in AI was the advent of knowledge-based systems and the ascent of expert systems. Researchers' primary objective was to encapsulate human expertise within rule-based systems, employing them for medical diagnosis and decision-making. A notable achievement during this period was the creation of MYCIN, an expert system devised by Edward Shortliffe specifically for diagnosing infectious diseases. MYCIN showcased the potential of AI in tackling complex problem domains. Nevertheless, progress in the field was impeded by limitations in computational power and the need for more available data. As a result, interest in AI research dwindled towards the end of the decade.

Towards the end of the **1970s and early 1980s**, a groundbreaking discovery was on the horizon, poised to revolutionize the field of AI. During this time, scientists began exploring alternative approaches to training AI systems. But unfortunately, while significant efforts had been invested in creating AI systems that mimicked the human brain, all these endeavors had yet to achieve the desired success.

The most crucial development in the History of AI

However, a significant turning point arrived when Geoff Hinton proposed an entirely revolutionary idea: **The backpropagation of errors**. Departing from the notion of teaching machines to behave like the human brain, Hinton advocated for a results-oriented approach. Instead of expecting machines to make correct predictions from the outset, the concept involved allowing the machine to make incorrect predictions and then improving upon them iteratively.

This paradigm shift marked a pivotal moment in AI. The concept of **Backpropagation [1]**, further developed by Rumelhart, Hinton, and Williams, formed the backbone of the entire AI field. Today, it is widely recognized as the backpropagation algorithm, a fundamental technique in training neural networks.

The introduction of backpropagation brought about a new perspective, emphasizing the iterative correction of machine predictions. This breakthrough approach unlocked unprecedented possibilities for AI systems, enabling them to learn and adapt from their mistakes. As a result, the field of AI embarked on a transformative trajectory that continues to shape its advancements. In later chapters of this book, we will delve much deeper into the Backpropagation algorithm and look into its inner workings by implementing it from scratch.

Throughout the book, we will keep giving you links to great lectures and video series for building intuition upon the ideas presented in this book. Here's one such great mini-video series from the 3blue1brown YouTube channel to understand the core ideas behind NN: **3Blue1Brown NN series [2]**.

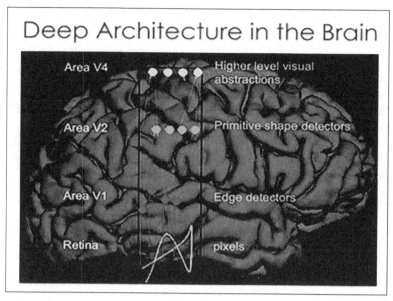

Figure 1.2: *Drawing inspiration from Neural Nets from Brain (Img Src)*

AI started evolving into new fields

During the **1990s**, AI research shifted towards practical applications and integrating AI technologies across diverse domains. Machine learning techniques, including decision trees, support vector machines, and Bayesian networks, gained significant prominence during this era. Simultaneously, advancements in natural language processing (NLP) propelled the development of systems like IBM's Watson, which achieved fame by winning the **Jeopardy** game show in 2011.

The fields of robotics and computer vision also experienced remarkable progress, finding applications in industrial automation and developing autonomous vehicles. The advent of the internet and the abundance of available data led to the emergence of data-driven approaches and data mining. AI techniques found practical use in diverse areas, ranging from fraud detection and recommendation systems to improving search engines. During this period, we witnessed a notable transition from rule-based AI systems to statistical and probabilistic methods, facilitating the development of more scalable and adaptable solutions.

AI starts taking its modern form

In the early **2000s**, AI experienced a convergence with fields like computational neuroscience and cognitive science, fostering interdisciplinary research. During this period, we witnessed a significant breakthrough with the emergence of deep learning, a subfield of machine learning that utilizes neural networks with multiple layers. As a result, deep learning revolutionized AI capabilities, achieving unprecedented success in tasks like image recognition, speech recognition, and natural language processing. Furthermore, the availability of extensive labeled datasets and advancements in graphics processing units (GPUs) accelerated the development and adoption of deep learning algorithms, enhancing AI's potential for solving complex problems and driving further advancements in the field.

With a little more historical context, we are ready to delve deeper into the technical subject matter.

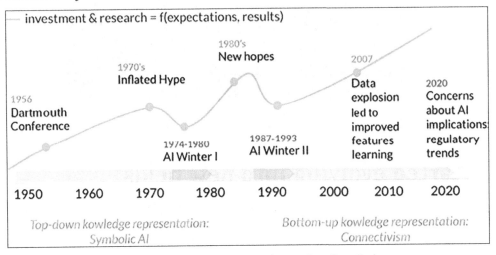

Figure 1.3: *How AI progressed over time (Img Src)*

Understanding Intelligent Behavior

The goal of every AI system is to behave intelligently; defining what intelligence is a big task. Nonetheless, we try to associate different tasks as signs of intelligence. The true nature of intelligence is still a mystery, but there are several outcomes or behaviors that we can say are generated from some form of intelligence; chess and reasoning are two such examples. In this section, we touch upon the role of AI in Chess, reasoning, poker, and so on, which we consider an outcome of intelligent behavior.

AI beats humans at chess

Before delving into AI's technical definition and components, it is essential to ponder some fundamental questions. First, what do we truly consider intelligent? Is playing chess a definitive proof of intelligent behavior? Does conversing like a human or the ability to reason qualify as a form of intelligence? The concept of intelligence remains elusive, and defining it proves trickier than most realize. When AI achieves significant breakthroughs, they are often attributed to clever hacks or increased computing power. However, this can also be the case for human intelligence. Present-day can undoubtedly display intelligent behavior, but whether it can be deemed truly intelligent remains uncertain. A notable example is the 1997 match where Gary Kasparov, the chess world champion, was defeated by IBM's system named Deep Blue system. Deep Blue relied on human involvement and chess-specific rules; it demonstrated behavior that can be considered intelligent, albeit not necessarily intelligence itself. Here's the video of Kasparov playing chess with AI: **AI vs. Kasparov Chess [3]**.

Figure 1.4: *Gary Kasparov (Chess World Champion) vs. Deep Blue (Img Src)*

AI learning reasoning and language

On a separate occasion, IBM again showcased an intelligent system to the world called Watson; it became famous by winning a trivia game show called Jeopardy! in 2011. By outperforming human champions, Watson showcased the potential of AI systems to understand and process natural language at a level that surpassed human capabilities. This groundbreaking accomplishment captured global attention and sparked widespread interest in AI. Watson's core technology was natural language processing and data analytics. This later ushered in the era of cognitive computing. It demonstrated the ability of AI systems to analyze vast amounts of unstructured data, understand complex questions, and provide accurate answers. This breakthrough paved the way for AI systems to excel in tasks requiring cognitive abilities, such as language comprehension, reasoning, and decision-making. Here's the video of AI playing Jeopardy released by IBM research: **IBM AI Jeopardy [4]**.

Figure 1.5: IBM Watson *playing and winning the game of Jeopardy against humans (Img Src)*

AI starts playing poker

In 2017, an AI system called **Libratus** beat human players in Poker. Researchers at Carnegie Mellon University developed it for playing heads-up, no-limit Texas hold 'em poker. Poker is a game of incomplete information, unlike chess or Go, making it a significant challenge for AI. Libratus has been a landmark in this realm, as it was the first AI to beat professional poker players in a complete tournament setting in 2017. Its approach includes three modules: a reinforcement learning module for strategy, an endgame solver for specific scenarios, and a self-improver module that reviews the AI's strategy to seal potential leaks. The success of Libratus represents a significant achievement in AI's ability to manage uncertainty and complex decision-making scenarios. Here's a video from Engadget explaining AI poker: **Libratus AI Poker [5]**.

Figure 1.6: *Libratus AI beating humans at Poker (Img Src)*

Conquering GO and Dota 2

AlphaGo and OpenAI Five are the other two excellent AI systems that make quite a lot of noise worldwide. We suggest giving a read to both Original **Alpha GO [6]** and **OpenAI Five [7]** papers, as both achieved something remarkable and introduced many new ideas to train intelligent systems that can beat humans in GO and Dota 2. For those who don't know about AlphaGo, it's an AI system to play a game called GO; it's an enormously complex game with 10^{300} possible combinations, much greater than the number of atoms in the universe. On the other hand, OpenAI Five is a system to play a multiple-player Online game called DOTA2. The game of Dota 2 presents novel challenges for AI systems, such as extended time horizons, imperfect information, and complex, continuous state-action spaces, all challenges which will become increasingly central to more capable AI systems.

Note: Humans have again beaten machines at **GO** by leveraging information from adversarial attacks; go and read this **paper [8]** from MIT.

Figure 1.7: *GO Board game (Img Src)*

An experience with ChatGPT

Lastly, I'm sure you're already familiar with or have encountered ChatGPT. I had an intriguing experience with ChatGPT when I asked it to interview me about one of my papers. Surprisingly, the conversation turned out quite well. Although AI systems like ChatGPT aren't flawless, their comprehension capabilities have significantly improved in recent years. I share this to provide you with a broader perspective of the field before delving into the fundamental aspects of AI. It's essential to grasp the overall landscape and acknowledge the advancements made thus far.

Interview me about my recent paper titled "Robustness of different loss functions and their impact on networks learning capability". Do not write answers for me. Ask me a question and wait for my answer. Once you get my answer, ask me next question.

 What was the main motivation for conducting this research?

The main motivation for conducting this research was to explore the robustness of different loss functions and their impact on the learning capability of neural networks. We were interested in understanding how different loss functions can affect the performance of neural networks, and whether certain loss functions are better suited for certain types of tasks or data.

 I asked to ask me questions not answer them, do it correctly this time

 Okay, sure. Can you describe the methodology you used in this study? How did you evaluate the robustness of different loss functions and their impact on networks learning capability?

 I changed the pixels belonging to the highest gradient and then looked at their segmentation maps.   ↻ Try again

 Can you elaborate on that? What do you mean by changing the pixels belonging to the   highest gradient and looking at the segmentation maps? How did this help you evaluate the robustness of different loss functions?

 So, we trained three models, one with Binary loss, second with Dice loss and third one with binary + dice loss. The model trained with Binary + Dice loss can preserve the segmentation maps much better than other two models.

 I see. So you trained these three models on the same data, but with different loss functions,   and then evaluated the performance of each model on a segmentation task by looking at the quality of the segmentation maps they produced. Can you provide more details on this process and how you quantified the performance of the different models? What were the main findings from this experiment?

 Dice metric was used to evaluate it. And the main finding was Dice loss gives more precise segmentation maps, and binary loss gives much more robustness. And combining the two loss functions gives more accurate and more robust results.

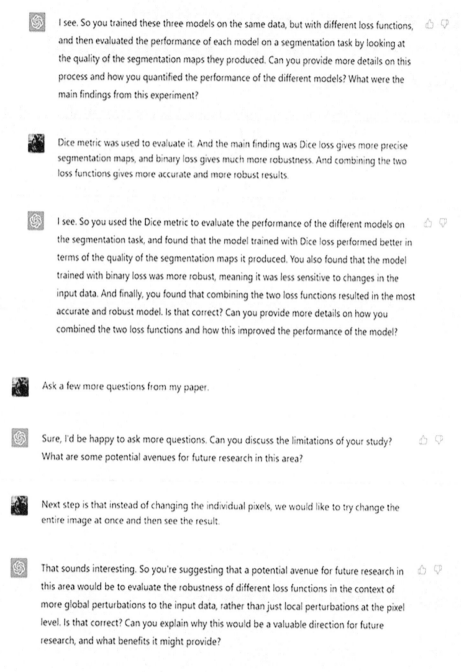

Figure 1.8: *My Interview with ChatGPT*

This covers the history, and some old and recent exciting developments over the past few decades.

Difference between Artificial Intelligence, Machine Learning, and Deep Learning

In the last sections, we looked into the historical context of AI and what are different use cases where AI is being used or has already beaten humans in displaying intelligent behavior. From this chapter, we will go more technical and build a mathematical and practical understanding of these concepts. So, let's first start by defining the terms Artificial Intelligence, Machine Learning, and Deep Learning.

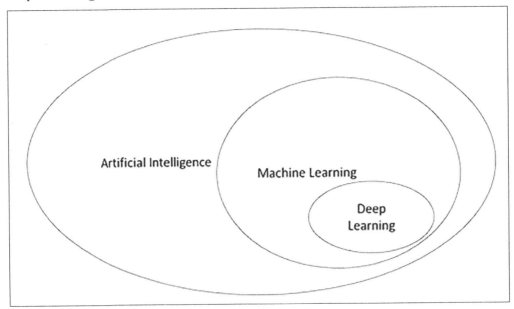

Figure 1.9: *Deep learning is a subset of Machine Learning, and Machine Learning is a subset of Artificial Intelligence*

Formally defining AI terms

In reality, there are many ways to define or understand these terms. Still, I see them as a subset within a subset, with the top layer being artificial intelligence and the last layer being deep learning. For example, a concise definition of **Artificial Intelligence**: *the effort to automate intellectual tasks usually performed by humans*. AI is a general field encompassing machine learning and deep learning, but it includes many more approaches that don't involve learning.

Machine learning emerges from whether a computer can surpass the limitations of explicitly programmed instructions and autonomously learn how to perform a given task. Can a computer exhibit unexpected behavior? Instead of programmers manually crafting rules for data processing, can a computer automatically learn these rules by analyzing data? This question introduces a new programming paradigm. In traditional symbolic AI programming, humans input rules (a program) and data to be processed according to those rules, yielding answers. However, humans input data and the expected solutions in machine learning, and the system generates the rules. These rules can then be applied to new data to create novel and original answers.

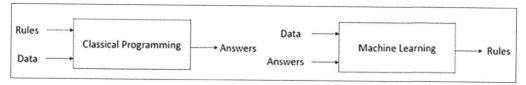

Figure 1.10: *Difference between Classical programming and Machine learning*

Machine learning operates through training rather than explicit programming. Instead of being given predefined instructions, a machine-learning system is exposed to numerous examples relevant to a specific task. By analyzing these examples, the system identifies *statistical patterns and structures that enable it to formulate rules for automating the task at hand*. For example, if you wanted to automate the process of tagging your vacation pictures, you could provide a machine-learning system with a large dataset of pictures already tagged by humans. The system would then learn statistical rules to associate specific images with corresponding tags, allowing for automated tagging in the future.

Machine learning and mathematical statistics share a strong connection but diverge in crucial aspects. Unlike traditional statistics, machine learning mainly focuses on handling large, intricate datasets. These datasets can be vast, containing millions of images, each composed of tens of thousands of pixels. Consequently, classical statistical techniques like Bayesian analysis become impractical in such scenarios. As a result, machine learning, particularly deep learning, tends to have a limited emphasis on mathematical theory, potentially needing more in-depth theoretical foundations. Instead, it takes an engineering-oriented approach, prioritizing hands-on experimentation and empirical validation over rigorous theoretical proofs. In essence, machine learning is a discipline that heavily relies on practical demonstrations and empirical evidence to support its idea of learning and intelligence. Examples of Machine learning algorithms include Support Vector Machines, Logistic Regression, Decision Trees, and so on.

Deep learning is a specific machine learning subfield and a relatively new concept. It takes an entirely new stance on learning; instead of learning statistical rules directly, it creates a representation of data fed through multiple layers, subsequently creating deeper and deeper representations, thus the name 'Deep Learning'. Other appropriate names for the same are layered representations learning and hierarchical representations learning. Modern deep learning often involves tens or even hundreds of successive layers of representations—and they're all learned automatically from exposure to training data. Meanwhile, other approaches to machine learning tend to focus on learning only one or two layers of representations of the data; hence, they're sometimes called shallow learning. As we move forward in the book, we'll create a deep neural network from scratch.

Learning representations from data

Deep learning is a subset of machine learning that focuses on learning useful representations of input data through exposure to known examples. To perform machine learning, three elements are required:

- Input data points (like sound files or images)
- Examples of the expected output (such as human-generated transcripts or image tags like a cat image or a dog image)
- A way to measure the algorithm's performance to provide feedback for adjustment and learning

The central idea in machine learning and deep learning is to transform the input data so that the generated representation can be mapped to a particular output. In other words, transform the data so that the difference between the actual and predicted output is minimal. At its core, it's a different way of representing or encoding data. For instance, we can write two in so many ways: 2 (Decimal), II (Roman), and 10 (Binary); all of these are just different ways of representing the same idea of two. The distinction between AI-generated encodings and traditional ML or DL representations lies in their structure and human interpretability. ML or DL representations may not adhere to a rigid or easily readable format, as they are influenced by the input data and the algorithm employed to generate them. For instance, consider color images that can be encoded in formats such as RGB or HSV. While these formats represent the same data, they offer distinct advantages for specific tasks. For example, RGB facilitates the selection of red pixels, while HSV simplifies adjusting brightness. Machine learning models identify appropriate representations that enhance the data's suitability for the given task, such as classification. Refer to the following figure for the disparity between fixed and learned encodings.

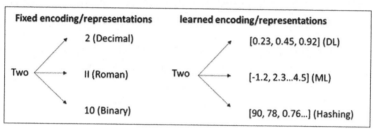

Figure 1.11: *Representing Two using fixed and leaned encoding/representations*

It is crucial to recognize that learned representations can exhibit substantial variation in size and value, contingent upon the algorithm employed for their generation. Even when applying the same algorithm, the representations may diverge for different data points, especially if alterations are made to the remaining dataset. Within learned representations, the value assigned to a particular data point is influenced by encoding other data points, thus emphasizing the interconnectedness and interdependence of the learned representation space.

Example to understand the concept

To illustrate this, let's consider an example using a machine learning algorithm for image recognition. Suppose we have a dataset of images containing different animals, such as dogs, cats, and birds. The algorithm aims to learn representations that can accurately classify these images into their respective categories.

During the training process, the algorithm analyzes the features of the images and creates learned representations for each data point. These representations are numerical values that capture essential characteristics of the images relevant to the classification task. For instance, certain learned representations might emphasize the presence of fur or feathers, the shape of the ears, or the arrangement of wings.

The learned representations can change if we modify the dataset by adding or removing images. For instance, if we introduce new images of fish into the dataset, the algorithm may adjust its learned representations to accommodate this new category. Consequently, the representations assigned to previously seen animals like dogs, cats, and birds may also be influenced by including the additional images.

Furthermore, within these learned representations, the encoding of a specific data point can depend on the encodings of other data points. For example, in a deep neural network where representations are hierarchically learned, encoding an image at a higher layer can be influenced by the encodings of multiple images at lower layers. This interdependence allows the model to capture complex relationships and dependencies within the dataset.

In summary, learned representations can vary in size and value depending on the algorithm used and can be sensitive to changes in the dataset. Moreover, encoding a particular data point can rely on the encodings of other points, enabling the model to capture intricate relationships within the data.

Sub-Fields of AI

AI is a broad term, and we tried to give a clear difference between its three main components: AI, ML, and DL. But we must still dive deeper and further categorize these systems to complete our mental map AI subdomains. Even though all three: Artificial Intelligence (AI), Machine Learning (ML), and Deep Learning (DL) are interconnected fields, we can still try to organize them into their subcategories:

Artificial Intelligence (AI)

AI can be broken down into two main types: Narrow AI, which is designed to perform a narrow task (for example, facial recognition or voice commands), and General AI, which is intended to perform any intellectual task that a human being can do. Here are some subfields:

- **Expert Systems:** Mimic the decision-making ability of a human expert.
- **Natural Language Processing (NLP):** Computers interacting with human language. In recent times the entire NLP has moved over to DL-based methods.
- **Speech Recognition:** Translating spoken language into written form.
- **Computer Vision:** Enabling computers to understand and interpret visual information from the real world.
- **Robotics:** Designing machines capable of carrying out complex actions autonomously or semi-autonomously.

- **Planning and Navigation:** Algorithms for planning and navigation in AI systems, often used in robotics.

Machine Learning (ML)

Machine Learning is a method of data analysis that automates the building of analytical models. It's a branch of AI based on the idea that systems can learn from data, identify patterns, and make decisions with minimal human intervention. Here are some subfields:

- **Supervised Learning:** The model learns from label ed data. Examples include regression, support vector machines, decision trees, and random forests.

- **Unsupervised Learning:** The model learns from unlabeled data. Examples include clustering algorithms (like k-means) and dimensionality reduction techniques (like PCA).

- **Semi-supervised Learning:** The model learns from labeled and unlabeled data.

- **Reinforcement Learning:** The model learns to make decisions by receiving rewards for good choices and penalties for bad ones. It's often used in games and robotics.

- **Ensemble Methods:** These combine multiple machine learning models to improve results. Examples include bagging, boosting, and stacking.

Deep Learning (DL)

Deep Learning is a subfield of machine learning concerned with algorithms inspired by the structure and function of the brain, called artificial neural networks. It's a technique for implementing machine learning that uses artificial neural networks with multiple layers (hence the *deep* in deep learning). Here are some subfields:

- **Convolutional Neural Networks (CNNs):** Primarily used for image processing tasks like image recognition.

- **Recurrent Neural Networks (RNNs):** Designed for sequence prediction problems and tasks that require memory of past information, like time series forecasting and language translation.

- **Long Short-Term Memory Networks (LSTMs):** A type of RNN that can learn and remember over long sequences, widely used in language modeling and translation.

- **Generative Adversarial Networks (GANs):** Composed of two networks, one generates and evaluates data. They are typically used to generate realistic images, but can also be used for various purposes.

- **Autoencoders:** Used for tasks like anomaly detection and dimensionality reduction, as well as learning efficient data representations.

- **Transformers:** Primarily used in natural language processing tasks, they have significantly improved text translation and generation.

Remember, these fields overlap and intersect in many ways, and advancements in one often lead to improvements in others. Going over all these sub-topics is a book in itself. But I still want to give a sense of what is happening in AI. All of today's AI developments are happening in **DL** primarily. **GANs** and **Transformers** are the crazes of the industry right now. Regarding statistical analysis, like the banking sector, drug trials, and so on, ML-based methods are still the king. However, DL is relatively very poor in explaining its behavior. Thus, people in industries with strong regulations still prefer ML over DL because of their result's explainability or interpretability.

In later chapters of the book, we will look into the basics of Transformers and GANs. Both of these are making huge waves in the industry. As a result, all you come across is highly likely to be based on either of the two, from DALL-E to ChatGPT.

Early Models of Neuron-Inspired Networks

The idea of mimicking brain neurons to make intelligent systems is not new. But formalizing this idea to actually make it work was quite difficult. Making the networks trainable and learn through the Backpropagation algorithm was nothing less than a stroke of genius from Hinton's side. Let's start our journey with understanding the development of the earliest Neuron-Inspired Networks.

Understanding biological neurons

If you'll go and do a quick search on the internet, you will find some articles stating that artificial neurons are just like biological neurons. I want to clarify that artificial neurons are not similar to biological ones but are mathematical representations of biological neurons. Though I'm not a biologist, I'm certain that biological neurons don't use backpropagation to learn things. Biological neurons inspire artificial neurons, and that's where the similarity ends.

One estimate is that the human brain contains over 10^{11} neurons and 10^{14} synapses in the human nervous system. Biological neuron switching is much slower than a computer's transistor switching, but the connectivity is higher than in today's supercomputers.

A biological neuron has three main parts:

- Neuron cell body
- Branching extensions called dendrites for receiving inputs
- An axon that carries the neuron's output to the dendrites of other neurons

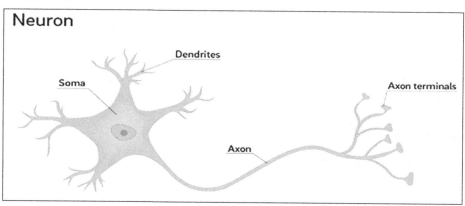

Figure 1.12: *Biological neurons (Img Src)*

McCulloch-Pitts model of a neuron

A simple and popular model for neurons is the McCulloch-Pitts model. However, one should know that this is a strong mathematical abstraction of reality. So, let's understand this model in more detail.

Components of the McCulloch-Pitts Model:

- **Input:** The MCP neuron receives binary input (either 0 or 1) from multiple other neurons, just like a biological neuron receives signals from multiple other neurons.
- **Weights:** These inputs are each associated with a **weight**, which can be positive (excitatory) or negative (inhibitory). In the simplest form of the model, these weights are not adjustable, unlike in modern artificial neural networks, where the weights are adjustable and learned through training.
- **Activation Function:** The neuron computes a weighted sum of its inputs and then applies a thresholding function. If the sum is greater than or

equal to the threshold, the neuron fires (outputs a 1); if the sum is less than the threshold, the neuron does not fire (outputs a 0).

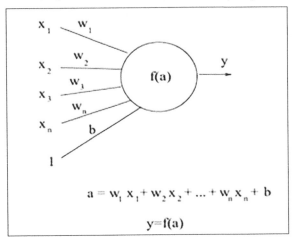

Figure 1.13: *McCulloch–Pitts model of neuron (w_1, w_2..., w_n are non-trainable here)*

Example to understand the concept

Let us consider a simple MCP neuron with three input signals. Let us assume the threshold is set to 2.

1. *We have three inputs: $I_1 = 1$, $I_2 = 0$, $I_3 = 1$.*

2. *These inputs are associated with weights: $W_1 = -1$ (inhibitory), $W_2 = 1$ (excitatory), $W_3 = 2$ (excitatory).*

3. *The neuron calculates the weighted sum of the inputs: $\text{Sum} = I_1*W_1 + I_2*W_2 + I_3*W_3 = 1*(-1) + 0*1 + 1*2 = 1$.*

4. *The weighted sum (1) is compared to the threshold (2). Since $1 < 2$, the neuron's output is 0, that is, the neuron does not fire.*

This is a very basic example of an MCP neuron. Remember that the model drastically simplifies biological neurons and modern artificial neural networks. For instance, weights in an MCP neuron are static and do not change, while in modern neural networks, weights are adjusted during training through a process called backpropagation. Furthermore, the binary nature of the MCP model's inputs, outputs, and weights is also a simplification. In most modern artificial neural networks, these quantities are real-valued.

So, MCP started the idea of neural networks, but because of its non-trainable weight, it is a useless model in most real-world scenarios. So, they needed to transform this idea making the weights adaptable and trainable.

Multilayer Perceptron (MLP)

A Multilayer Perceptron (MLP) is an artificial neural network composed of multiple layers of neurons (also called nodes or perceptron's), where each neuron in a layer is connected to all neurons in the previous layer. It consists of at least three layers – an input layer, one or more hidden layers, and an output layer.

MLPs are used in supervised learning problems for regression (predicting a continuous output) and classification (predicting a discrete output).

Example to understand the concept

Consider a simple MLP with two input neurons, one hidden layer with two neurons, and one output neuron. Let's assume we're trying to solve a binary classification problem. Here's how it might work:

1. *We have two inputs, x_1 and x_2.*

2. *These inputs are passed to the hidden layer, where each neuron applies weights w to the inputs and adds a bias b. The weights and biases are parameters that the MLP will learn during training. Each neuron j in the hidden layer computes a weighted sum: $z_j = w^1_j * x_1 + w^2_j * x_2 + b_j$.*

3. *Each neuron in the hidden layer then applies an activation function to the weighted sum to introduce non-linearity into the model. A common choice of activation function is the ReLU (Rectified Linear Unit) function, which is $\max(0, z)$. For example, let's denote the output of neuron j in the hidden layer after applying the activation function as h_j.*

4. *The hidden layer outputs h_1 and h_2 are then passed to the output neuron, which applies its weights and bias to compute a weighted sum: $output = w^1_{output} * h_1 + w^2_{output} * h_2 + b_{output}$.*

5. *For a binary classification problem, the output neuron often uses the sigmoid activation function to squash the output between 0 and 1: $output = 1 / (1 + \exp(-z_{output}))$. This output can be interpreted as the probability of the positive class.*

Let's write the preceding points concisely mathematically, with two inputs and two hidden neurons with one output neuron.

Let us denote the weights from the inputs to neuron j in the hidden layer as w^1_j and w^2_j, and the biases as b_j. Also, weights from the hidden layer to the output as w^1_{output} and w^2_{output}, and the bias as b_{output}.

1. $Z^1_{hidden} = w^1_1 * x_1 + w^2_1 * x_2 + b_2$

2. $h_1 = max(0, z^1_{hidden})$ **(ReLU activation)**

3. $z^2_{hidden} = w^1_2 {}^*x_1 + w^2_2 {}^*x_2 + b_2$

4. $h_2 = max(0, z_{hidden})$ **(ReLU activation)**

5. $z_{output} = w^1_{output} {}^*h_1 + w^2_{output} {}^*h_2 + b_{output}$

6. $output = 1 \, / \, (1 + exp(-z_{output}))$ **(Sigmoid activation)**

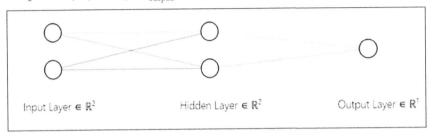

Figure 1.14: *Simple NN with two inputs and two hidden neurons*

This diagram shows the representation of neural networks described in the preceding equations. But the real-world networks have hundreds and thousands of neurons with several layers in it, the following diagram shows a much more realistic neural network that can solve simple tasks like classification or regression on some simple input arrays.

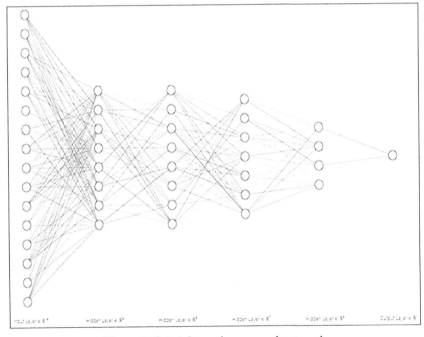

Figure 1.15: A 4-layer deep neural network

I want the readers to understand this not only with examples but also with generalized mathematical equations. So, let's look at how to define it in a generalized mathematical way.

We know that neural networks work with matrices, and here's what the matrix-vector notation of the preceding definition looks like. Here the input is $x \in R^m$, the output is $y \in R^l$ and the interconnection matrices are $W \in R^{l \times n\_h}$, $V \in R^{n\_h \times m}$ for the output layer and hidden layer, respectively. Finally, the bias vector is $\beta \in R^{n\_h}$ and consists of the threshold values of the n_h hidden neurons.

$$Y = W\sigma(Vx + \beta)$$

Many people struggle to grasp mathematical equations, so let's understand what these representations mean.

$x \in R^m$: R represents the set of real numbers, and the superscript m indicates that x is a vector of length **m**. Each element of the vector x is a real number.

$W \in R^{l \times n\_h}$: represents that the variable W belongs to the set of real-valued matrices with dimensions l rows and n_h columns.

$V \in R^{n\_h \times m}$: R represents the set of real numbers, and the superscript n_h x m indicates that "V" is a matrix with n_h rows and **m** columns. Each element of the matrix V is a real number.

n_h : n hidden neurons.

$\sigma(X)$: Activation function for input X.

The preceding notation is more compact than the elementwise notation. For example, here's the same equation represented in the elementwise notation.

$$y_i = \sum_{r=1}^{n_h} w_{ir}\sigma\left(\sum_{j=1}^{m} v_{rj}x_j + \beta_r\right), i = 1, n...l.$$

Given above is a simple example of an MLP with one hidden layer. In practice, MLPs can have many hidden layers and many neurons in each layer. Also, different types of activation functions can be used.

The parameters of the MLP (the weights and biases) are learned during training by minimizing a loss function that measures the difference between the MLP's predictions and the true outputs. This is typically done using an optimization algorithm like stochastic gradient descent, which we will see in the upcoming chapters.

Note: You can visit all the links and references mentioned in this chapter by scanning the QR code given at the end. We highly recommend visiting the mentioned references as we try to keep them to a minimum and only add them in places where we feel that users should dive deeper into those topics.

Conclusion

Welcoming the readers and explaining how to utilize the book aptly, followed by AI developments during different decades and how they propelled the field in a given direction. Formally defining AI, ML, and DL are often used interchangeably, so it's essential to know the difference between them. Next, we discuss the data representation/encodings followed by AI, ML, and DL subfields. This highlights how these models manipulate data to give us the desired results. Finally, we introduce the MCP and MLP and explain the math behind it using simple examples. These were the earliest forms of present-day neural networks.

In the next chapter, we will discuss Python and its essential components. Python is the major language for AI development, so gaining the skill and knowledge for real-life project development is super important. We will also set up the necessary environments to work with AI-related libraries. See you soon!!!

"The goal of AI is to replace human intuition with machine algorithms, but to do so in a way that respects the complexities and subtleties of human intelligence." - Fei-Fei Li

https://github.com/OrangeAVA/Ultimate-Neural-Network-Programming-with-Python

CHAPTER 2
Setting up Python Workflow for AI Development

When people start working in AI, they often tend to go for a non-optimal setup for AI development, leading to increased complexity and production time. Setting up a proper Python-based workflow is essential for building real-world AI projects, especially when working with others. Often, beginners need more time to learn the right practices and thus need clarification when working in a dynamic environment. This chapter aims to provide enough context for our readers to set up their workflow properly.

Structure

This chapter covers the following topics:

- Setting up Python environment for AI development
- Setting up the Anaconda environment
- Integrating GitHub with VS Code
- Understanding the concept of OOPS

Let's start this chapter by giving a brief introduction to Python. Python is a high-level, interpreted programming language that has gained significant popularity in many fields, including artificial intelligence (AI), machine learning (ML), data science, web development, and more. The language was designed by Guido van Rossum and first released in 1991. It emphasizes readability and ease of use, with a clear and straightforward syntax that often reads like English. This makes Python particularly popular for beginners.

Python's popularity in AI and related fields, such as machine learning and data science, can be attributed to several factors:

- **Ease of Learning and Use:** Python is recognized for its clean and readable syntax, making it particularly accessible for beginners. This readability allows developers to focus on problem-solving rather than struggling with complex syntax.

- **Powerful Libraries and Frameworks:** Python has a rich ecosystem of libraries and frameworks that simplify complex tasks. For AI and ML, libraries such as TensorFlow, PyTorch, Keras, and Scikit-learn provide ready-to-use algorithms and tools for data preprocessing, machine learning, deep learning, and more. In addition, library libraries like Pandas, NumPy, and Matplotlib are commonly used for data science and analysis.

- **Community and Support:** Python has a large and active community that continually contributes to its development. If developers encounter issues, they can often find solutions or ask for help from community forums, Stack Overflow, and more. This support is a significant advantage for Python users.

- **Interoperability:** Python can easily integrate with C, C++, or Java. This is particularly beneficial when performance-intensive tasks must be offloaded to lower-level languages.

- **Versatility:** Python is a general-purpose programming language used for various tasks outside AI and ML, such as web development, scripting, automation, and more. This versatility makes Python a practical and valuable language to learn.

Python's widespread usage and popularity are reflected in various surveys and studies. For example, according to recent surveys, Python has become the most popular programming language among professional developers, and the top language developers want to learn. The results of the same are shown in the following figure:

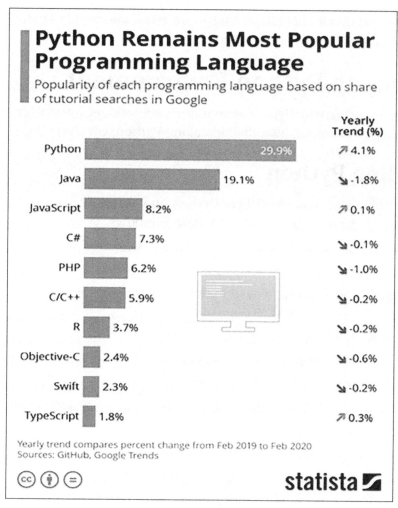

Figure 2.1: *The popularity of Python compared to other languages (Img Src)*

Python's simplicity and extensive library support in AI and machine learning have made it the language of choice for many researchers and practitioners. Furthermore, its ability to seamlessly integrate with other languages allows for the efficient implementation of performance-critical code, making it a versatile choice for high-level algorithm design and low-level performance optimization.

This chapter aims to avoid going deep into Python but teach our readers to use Python for AI projects.

Note: If you already have sufficient knowledge of Python, you can skip this chapter except for the last part, where it explains the deep internal structure of Python's compiler. That section is reserved for Python enthusiasts only.

We are going to divide this chapter into various components of Python that are often used in AI software development.

Setting up Python Environment

After understanding why Python is so important, let's get into the environment setup for AI development, including installing Python, Git, and VS Code.

Installing Python

Before anything else, you should get Python on your machine. You can refer to the Step-by-Step Guide to Install Python on Windows.

- Step 1: Download Python binaries from python.org
- Step 2: Install the binaries
- Step 3: Add Python to system environment variables (click a small box when the below window pops up)
- Step 4: Install pip

Avoid installing the latest version (one version before the latest is usually good), as it causes many dependencies to break.

Note: Remember to add Python to System PATH as shown in the following diagram:

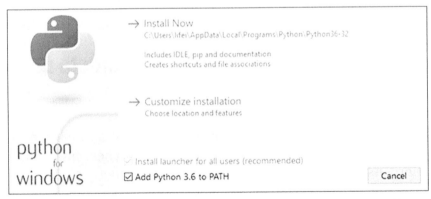

Figure 2.2: *Add Path variable to system environment during Python installation*

Getting Anaconda for Data Science Environment Setup

Anaconda is a Python distribution for data science and machine learning. It is free and open-source and makes managing and deploying packages simple.

Anaconda ships with a virtual environment manager- the Anaconda Navigator. Anaconda lets you bypass the command-line commands.

Anaconda will give you two package managers- **pip** and **conda**. When some packages aren't available with conda, you can use pip to install them. Note that using pip to install packages also available to conda may cause an installation error.

To download an Anaconda distribution, you can use the official download page:

https://www.anaconda.com/download/ [9]

Here, you can select your platform and then choose the installer. You can choose which version you want, and whether 32-bit or 64-bit.

To install a package with conda, you can use the following command–

```
conda install <package name>
```

Setting up a Virtual Environment

A virtual environment lets us create different Python versions with the packages we want or as the project needs. Moreover, such an environment helps us ensure no clashes between the versions of packages and those of Python and its package managers.

Let's see how we can create one with Anaconda. Use the following command in your **Anaconda prompt** (it's similar to CMD or Terminal; search in your navigation bar):

```
# To create environment
conda create --name custom_python_env python3
# To activate environment
conda activate custom_python_env
# To deactivate
conda deactivate
```

Installing packages

A few important packages that are often used for Data Science developments are:

- NumPy (for numerical computations)
- Pandas (for handling data sets)
- Matplotlib (for visualization and graphs)

- SciPy (scientific computation)
- Scikit-learn (most ML algorithms implementation)

```
# All of these packages can be installed by running the following command
in CMD or Terminal
```

```
pip install <package name>
```

Note: Many more advanced packages can help you run better visualizations or computations. This is the most basic setup.

Another thing that you should check out is the **Jupyter notebook.** This makes code experimentation very easy and convenient. It has a very simple UI and is often used for testing purposes.

```
# To install jupyter notebooks
```

```
pip install jupyter
```

```
# To activate jupyter notebook
```

```
jupyter notebook
```

Setting up VS Code

We need an editor to write proper production-level code integrated with Git, and VS Code is one such choice. Here's the link to download it:

https://code.visualstudio.com/download [10]

Note: Don't forget to add it to the path while installing.

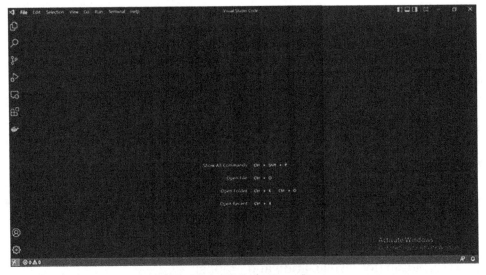

Figure 2.3: VS Code Home Page

To run the Python in VS Code smoothly, we need to install the Python extension provided by Microsoft. It offers IntelliSense (Pylance), linting, debugging, code navigation, code formatting, refactoring, variable explorer, test explorer, and more!

Steps to install it:

- First, click the four dots menu on the left side called `Extensions`.
- Then type Python in the search bar (it requires an internet connection).
- Look for Python by Microsoft.
- Click it and look on the right side for the install button.
- Click the install button.

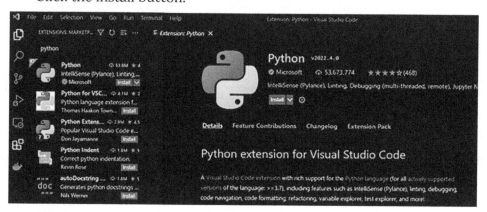

Figure 2.4: *Microsoft extension page*

Next press `Ctrl + Shift + P`, it will open the Command Palette. The command palette is the options menu from where any functionality of VS Code can be set or altered.

- Next, type in the search `Select Interpreter`. Once it shows the option, click it and wait a few seconds.

Using the following command, we must install the ipykernel library to run the Jupyter notebook inside VS Code.

```
# To run conda in VS Code, install ipykernel by typing the below command
in Anaconda Prompt

conda install ipykernel
```

Note: You can set up both Git and Conda environments inside the VS Code, which is usually a good practice.

You can either use the base Python environment or the Conda environment inside VS Code. As mentioned above, open the VS Code and enter `Ctrl + Shift + P` to open the command palette. Then, type `Select Interpreter`, click it, and wait a few seconds.

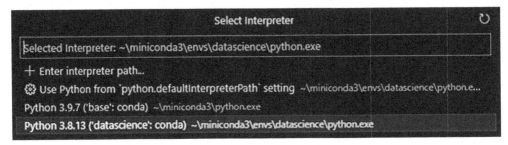

Figure 2.5: *Selecting Conda (Miniconda) environment*

Installing Git

Version control has been a blessing for programmers, and Git is the most widely used version control system. It permits us to track our progress. We have a log of what we did when we did it, allowing us to go back to the previous state of our project.

GitHub is a cloud-based code hosting service that helps you track your source code history. If we want to keep track of our project locally, we don't need to use GitHub. But if you're working with a team or want to showcase your project and skills, you can build a strong profile on GitHub by putting your projects in repositories.

Here's the link to install Git for your respective machines:

https://git-scm.com/book/en/v2/Getting-Started-Installing-Git [11]

Here's how you can install Git on both Windows and Linux:

Windows:

- Go to the Git website: https://git-scm.com/downloads.
- Click the download link for Windows and download the .exe file.
- Once downloaded, double-click the .exe file to start the installation process.
- You can accept the default settings during installation. First, however, consider the step that asks you to choose the default editor. If you have a preference (for example, Notepad++ or Visual Studio Code), you can select it here.
- Click on `Install` to start the installation.

- Once the installation is complete, you can open the Git Bash program to start using Git.

Linux (Ubuntu/Debian):

You can install Git on Ubuntu or any other Debian-based distribution using the apt package manager from the terminal:

First, update your package list:

```
# Type the following command in terminal
sudo apt update
```

Installing and Configuring Git:

```
# Type the following command in terminal
sudo apt install git
## Configuring Git
git config --global user.name "give your name here"
git config --global user.email "give your email id here"
# Create the key
ssh-keygen -t rsa -C your_name@githuub.com
#copy the key to your keyboard
cat ~/.ssh/id_rsa.pub
# Then go to your GitHub account in the browser -> Account settings -> ssh
keys and add the ssh key you just copied
#If everything works fine
ssh -T git@github.com
```

It's possible that some of the steps might break here, but you can always work with GUI version of GitHub. Also, if something doesn't work here, do not shy away from looking on the internet.

Setting up GitHub with VS Code

GitHub is a version control software, as in our production journey we go through a lot of iterations, it is important that our platform where we write our code and GitHub are integrated together to keep track of all the changes that happened over the time. Thus, integrating VS Code with GitHub is a really good practice.

- **Create a New Repository (Repo for short):** You should've created a GitHub account and have Git installed. If you haven't done that, then head over here. Once done, head to the `Repositories` section and click `New`.

Figure 2.6: *GitHub Main Page*

- **Add a Repo name and description**: After navigating to the `Create a new repository` page, add in your desired repository name, choose if you want your repo to be `Public` or `Private`, and you could (optionally) describe what your project is all about.

It is recommend to leave the others unchecked to prevent errors when committing later. So, when you're done with that, tap the `Create repository` button at the bottom of the page to open up a `Quick setup` page.

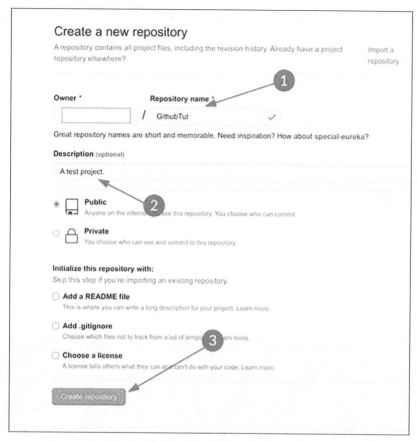

Figure 2.7: *Creating GitHub repository*

- **Setting up VS Code with GitHub integration:** Open up VS Code and hold `Ctrl + Shift + P` (Windows) or `Cmd + Shift + P` (if you're on a Mac) which would open up the Command Palette, then type in `Git clone` and select `Git: Clone`.

Figure 2.8: *VS Code Main Page*

Return to the Quick Setup page, and copy the highlighted link to your clipboard.

Figure 2.9: *Copy the GitHub repository link*

Then paste it into the VSCode tab, and select Clone from GitHub.

An authorization screen should pop up, accept and enter your GitHub password, then you'd be redirected back to VSCode.

Select the directory where you want the repo to be 'cloned' and follow the guided prompt.

You should see a prompt asking if to open the repository folder. Still, if you didn't see it, you could select the File shortcut to the far left, click Open Folder, and navigate to the folder where your cloned repo is stored and Confirm.

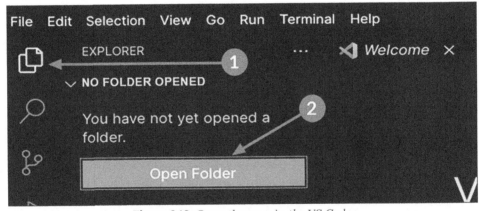

Figure 2.10: *Open the repo in the VS Code*

Create a file in your empty project folder; let's call it the README.md file.

Now, we can type in anything we want, but for the sake of this tutorial let's type in 'Hello world!' in the README.md file, and then save it.

Right-click the current folder and select Open in Integrated Terminal which should now load up a terminal window in your working directory.

Figure 2.11: *Opening terminal window in VS Code*

Type in `git status`, and if all goes well, you should see something like this:

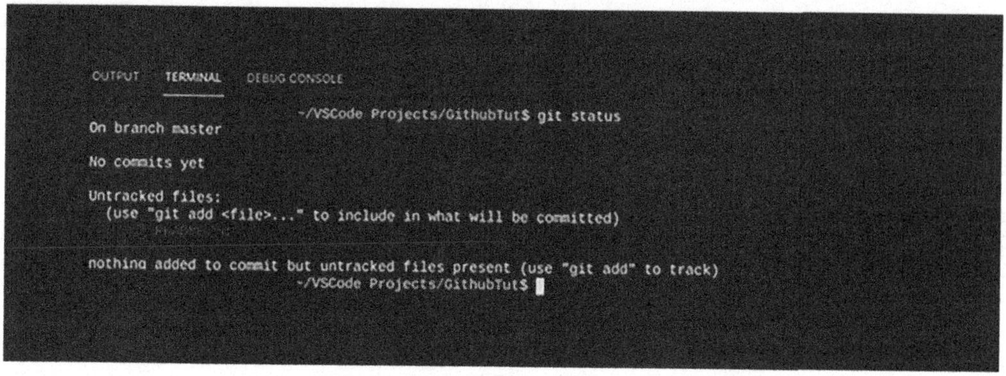

Figure 2.12: *Checking Git Status in Terminal Window*

Ensure you correctly navigated to the folder where you cloned your repo.

Now if all that works, run the following commands in your terminal:

```
# Run these commands one by one
git add README.md
git commit -m "My first commit"
git branch -M master
git push -u origin master
```

Suppose you get an error after typing in the git branch -M master, change master to main. Then, go back to GitHub on your browser and refresh the page, and if all that was successful, you will see all the changes reflected in your GitHub repo.

Note: Most package installation is easy, but setting up VS Code might be tricky, so we tried to show all the steps involved in GitHub and Conda integrations. Now we are fully set to write production-level code.

Concepts of OOPS

Ole-Johan Dahl and Kristen Nygaard designed the first object-oriented programming language (Simula 67) in 1967, the first language to support the concepts of classes and objects. Object-oriented programming (OOP) is a programming paradigm that uses objects, instances of c lasses, to represent real-world entities and their interactions. In OOP, a c lass is a blueprint for creating objects (instances) with attributes and methods.

- **Attributes:** The characteristics of an object, such as its name, color, or size, are represented by variables.
- **Methods:** The actions an object can perform, such as moving, speaking, or calculating, are represented by functions. Some popular programming languages that support OOP include Java, C++, Python, C#, and Ruby.

OOP is a widely used programming paradigm that allows for creating more modular, maintainable, and scalable software by modeling real-world entities as objects with specific properties and behaviors.

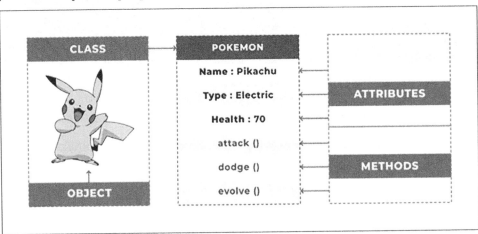

Figure 2.13: *Explaining the attributes and methods of a class object*

Let's look at the main features of Object-oriented programming

- Classes and objects
- Data hiding
- Encapsulation
- Inheritance
- Polymorphism
- Abstraction

Classes and objects: In OOP, classes are the blueprint for creating objects, and objects are instances of classes. Each object has its own properties and methods.

Data hiding: Data hiding is a technique used to prevent direct access to an object's internal state, which helps to ensure data integrity and security.

Encapsulation: refers to hiding an object's internal details and exposing only the necessary information to the outside world through an object's methods.

This allows for a more secure and stable code by protecting the internal state of an object from external changes.

Inheritance: It allows one class to inherit properties and methods from a parent class.

This allows for a hierarchical structure in which a subclass can inherit and extend the properties and methods of its parent class.

Inheritance enables more efficient and organized code by breaking down complex systems into smaller, more manageable classes.

It also establishes a clear hierarchy of classes, making it easier to understand and navigate the code.

Polymorphism: Polymorphism allows objects of different classes to be treated as objects of a common superclass. This allows for more dynamic and flexible code, as the specific object type can be determined at runtime.

It allows for more efficient code by reducing the need for multiple if-else statements or switch cases to handle different types of objects.

Abstraction: The process of identifying the essential characteristics of an object and ignoring non-essential details. It allows for the creation of classes with simplified interfaces that can be used to represent complex real-world systems.

It enables efficient and organized code by breaking down complex systems into smaller, more manageable classes.

With the understanding of these features of the oops, let's summarize their benefits and drawbacks. The benefits of using an Object-Oriented Paradigm for the development of software are:

Increased abstraction: making the code easier to understand and maintain.

Reusability of objects: allowing for efficient and effective code reuse.

Modularity: allows for separating code into distinct objects, making identifying and resolving bugs easier.

Encapsulation: allows for hiding complex code details, making it easier to understand and modify the code.

However, despite being the most followed way of implementation for developing most, if not all of the software, OOP has some drawbacks. Let's understand a few of them.

Increased complexity, as the code becomes more structured and harder to understand for novice programmers. **Increased overhead**, as more resources are required to manage the objects and their interactions. **Decreased performance**, as the creation and management of objects, can slow down program execution. **Inflexibility**, as code written in OOP, can be difficult to adapt to changes in the requirements of a program.

Encapsulation

Let's look at some class code in Python and understand Encapsulation:

```python
# Class BankAccount

class BankAccount:
    def __init__(self, balance):
        self.__balance = balance  # Initialize the private balance variable


    def get_balance(self):
        return self.__balance  # Return the current balance


    def deposit(self, amount):
        self.__balance += amount # Increase the balance by the specified amount


    def withdraw(self, amount):
        if self.__balance >= amount:
            self.__balance -= amount  # Decrease the balance by the specified amount
        else:
```

```
        print("Insufficient balance.")  # Print an error message if the
balance is insufficient


# Create a BankAccount instance with an initial balance of 1000
account = BankAccount(1000)


print(account.get_balance())  # Print the initial balance (1000)


account.deposit(500)  # Deposit 500 into the account
print(account.get_balance())  # Print the updated balance (1500)


account.withdraw(2000)  # Attempt to withdraw 2000 (insufficient balance)
print(account.get_balance())  # Print the balance after the withdrawal
attempt (1500)
```

This code defines a class called `BankAccount` that represents a basic bank account. It has the following methods:

- `__init__(self, balance)`: The constructor method initializes a `BankAccount` object with a starting balance passed as an argument. It assigns the balance to the private instance variable `__balance`.

- `Get_balance(self)`: A method that returns the account's current balance.

- `Deposit(self, amount)`: A method used to deposit an amount into the account. It increases the balance by the specified amount.

- `Withdraw(self, amount)`: A method to withdraw an amount from the account. First, it checks if the account has sufficient balance and deducts the specified amount if it does. If the balance is insufficient, it prints a message stating `Insufficient balance`.

The class uses **encapsulation** by making the `__balance` variable private. It can only be accessed and modified through the getter (`get_balance`) and setter (deposit and withdraw) methods.

The code creates an instance of BankAccount called account with an initial balance 1000. It then calls the get_balance method to retrieve and print the initial balance (1000). Next, it deposits 500 into the account using the deposit method and prints the updated balance (1500). Finally, it attempts to withdraw

2000 using the withdraw method, but since the balance is insufficient, it prints `Insufficient balance` and the balance remains unchanged (1500).

Accessing Variables

Let's look at the concept of **public** and **private** variables and try to identify the error in the below code:

```python
class Player:
    def __init__(self, name, sport):
        self.name = name  # Initialize the player's name
        self.sport = sport  # Initialize the player's sport


    def __run(self):
        return "Running!"  # Private method that returns "Running!"



class Coach:
    def __init__(self, name, player):
        self.name = name  # Initialize the coach's name
        self.player = player  # Initialize the coach's player


    def command_player(self):
        return self.player.__run()  # Calls the private __run() method of
the player


player = Player("Michael Jordan", "Basketball")  # Create a Player in-
stance with name "Michael Jordan" and sport "Basketball"
coach = Coach("Phil Jackson", player)  # Create a Coach instance with
name "Phil Jackson" and the player object as an argument
print(coach.command_player())  # Prints the result of the command_play-
er() method of the coach
```

In this code, we have two classes: Player and Coach.

The `Player` class represents a player and has a constructor `__init__` that takes the player's name and sport as arguments and assigns them to the instance variables name and sport, respectively. It also has a private method __run, which returns the string "Running!". However, since the method name starts with double underscores, it is intended to be a private method and should not be accessed directly outside the class.

The Coach class represents a coach with a constructor __init__ that takes the coach's name and a Player object as arguments. It assigns the coach's name to the instance variable name and the player object to the instance variable player. The Coach class also has a method command_player that calls the player object's private __run method and returns its result.

There is an error in the above code, can you identify it?

The error is in the line return self.player.__run() within the command_player method of the Coach class.

In Python, when a method or variable name starts with double underscores (for example, __run), it is treated as a name mangling mechanism to make the method or variable private within the class. This means the name gets modified to include the class name, making it harder to access outside the class. However, the name mangling does not work when accessing the method or variable outside the class.

Therefore, when trying to access the __run method of the Player object using self.player.__run(), an AttributeError will be raised, indicating that the Player object has no attribute named __run.

To fix the error, you can change the method name from __run to a single underscore, indicating that it's intended to be a private method but accessible within the class. Alternatively, you can make it public by removing the underscores altogether.

```python
class Player:
    def __init__(self, name, sport):
        self.name = name
        self.sport = sport


    def _run(self):   # Changed from __run to _run
        return "Running!"


class Coach:
    def __init__(self, name, player):
```

```
        self.name = name
        self.player = player


    def command_player(self):
        return self.player._run()   # Access the public _run method


player = Player("Michael Jordan", "Basketball")
coach = Coach("Phil Jackson", player)
print(coach.command_player())
```

Now some of you might be wondering what this has to do with AI, believe me, when you start working on real-life projects, they will become increasingly complex and big, and the time following this structure will be helpful.

Note: Often, you will see people working in AI use something like **Jupyter,** it is a great tool for experimentation but not meant for writing production-level code

Inheritance

Let's understand another concept of **inheritance**, let's say you want to program software that stores the details of football players, but you might extend it to other sports too in the future.

To efficiently design the software for storing football player details and potentially extending it to other sports in the future, we can follow the Object-Oriented Programming (OOP) paradigm and utilize inheritance.

By analyzing the requirements, we can identify two entities: the general sports player details and the football player details. This suggests that we should have separate classes for these entities, with the football player class inheriting from the sports player class.

The `SportsPlayer` class will contain attributes such as:

- Name
- Sport
- Height
- Weight

- Country
- Date of Birth (private attribute)

We can implement methods in the `SportsPlayer` class to provide flexibility and data encapsulation to update these attributes and retrieve their values. Additionally, it's important to use private attributes for information that should not be directly modified or accessed outside the class.

The `FootballPlayer` class will inherit from the `SportsPlayer` class and include additional attributes specific to football players, such as:

- Position
- Jersey Number
- Club
- Goals
- Assists

With this design, we can reuse the attributes and methods from the `SportsPlayer` class without duplication. In addition, the `FootballPlayer` class can also introduce its specific methods or override inherited methods to provide customized behavior.

By utilizing inheritance and encapsulation, we achieve a modular and extensible design allowing easy management of player details across different sports.

The previously provided code demonstrates this design by implementing the `SportsPlayer` and `FootballPlayer` classes accordingly.

Let's see what the full implementation will look like.

```python
class SportsPlayer:
    def __init__(self, name, sport, height, weight, DOB, country):
        self.name = name  # Player's name
        self.sport = sport  # Sport played
        self.height = height  # Player's height
        self.weight = weight  # Player's weight
        self.__DOB = DOB  # Player's date of birth (private)
        self.__country = country  # Player's country (private)


    def change_name(self, new_name):
```

```python
        self.name = new_name  # Change the player's name


    def change_sport(self, new_sport):
        self.sport = new_sport  # Change the player's sport


    def change_height(self, new_height):
        self.height = new_height  # Change the player's height


    def change_weight(self, new_weight):
        self.weight = new_weight  # Change the player's weight


    def get_all_details(self):
        return [
            self.name,
            self.sport,
            self.height,
            self.weight,
            self.__DOB,
            self.__country,
        ]  # Return all player details as a list


    def print_details(self):
        print("Name:", self.name)
        print("Sport:", self.sport)
        print("Height:", self.height)
        print("Weight:", self.weight)
        print("Date of Birth:", self.__DOB)
        print("Country:", self.__country)


class FootballPlayer(SportsPlayer):
```

```python
    def __init__(
        self,
        name,
        sport,
        height,
        weight,
        DOB,
        country,
        position,
        jersey_number,
        club,
        goals,
        assists,
    ):
        SportsPlayer.__init__(self, name, sport, height, weight, DOB, country)
        self.position = position  # Player's position
        self.jersey_number = jersey_number  # Player's jersey number
        self.club = club  # Player's club
        self.goals = goals  # Player's goals
        self.assists = assists  # Player's assists


    def set_position(self, position):
        self.position = position  # Set the player's position


    def set_jersey_number(self, jersey_number):
        self.jersey_number = jersey_number  # Set the player's jersey number


    def set_club(self, club):
        self.club = club  # Set the player's club
```

```python
    def set_goals(self, goals):
        self.goals = goals  # Set the player's goals


    def set_assists(self, assists):
        self.assists = assists  # Set the player's assists


    def print_details(self):
        print(
            f"The player's name is {self.name} plays the sports of {self.sport}. \nHis height and weight are {self.height}cm and {self.weight}kg. \nHe plays in the position of {self.position} and for the club {self.club} with Jersey number {self.jersey_number}"
        )


footy = FootballPlayer(
    "Cristiano Ronaldo",
    "Football",
    "187",
    "85",
    "05/02/1985",
    "Portugal",
    "ST",
    "7",
    "Man United",
    "820",
    "273",
)
footy.print_details()
```

The above is the implementation of storing football players with the possibility of extending to every other sport. So, with these, we have reused common methods and attributes of the parent class.

The output of the above code is:

"The player's name is Cristiano Ronaldo plays the sport of Football.

His height and weight are 187cm and 85kg.

He plays in the position of ST and for the club Man United with Jersey number 7"

We want to give you the best resources available across the entire internet. Thus, we don't shy away from sharing additional external materials from different sources that you can watch by scanning the QR code given below. There is a great video on OOPS in Python from a YouTube channel called Tech with Tim: **OOPS in Python [12].**

Now, let's move on to some key points to remember about OOP in the context of data science:

- OOP provides a way to organize code and data into reusable structures called objects.
- A class is a blueprint for creating objects that define their properties and methods.
- Encapsulation is bundling data and methods within a class to restrict direct access and enforce data integrity.
- Inheritance allows classes to inherit properties and methods from a superclass, enabling code reuse and creating hierarchical relationships.
- Polymorphism enables objects of different classes to be treated as objects of a common superclass, allowing for interchangeable usage.
- Abstraction is the process of simplifying complex systems by breaking them down into manageable, abstract representations.
- OOP facilitates modularity, making code easier to understand, maintain, and extend.
- OOP can enhance code readability and reusability, leading to more efficient development and collaboration in data science projects.

Note: You can visit all the links and references mentioned in this chapter by scanning the QR code given below. We highly recommend visiting the mentioned references, as we try to keep them to a minimum and only add them in places where users should dive deeper into those topics.

Conclusion

In this chapter, the focus is on setting up a Python environment for real-world development. The concept of environments is introduced, emphasizing their importance and practicality in real-world scenarios. Additionally, the chapter highlights the benefits of integrating GitHub with VS Code, as it serves as an excellent starting point for building AI products in real-life applications.

After setting up Python for AI development, we are ready to test different Python Libraries. The next chapter will look into various libraries and tools that are often part of post or pre-processing data, like Regex, Pandas, Multi-Threading, and Multi-Processing.

"The potential benefits of artificial intelligence are huge, so are the dangers." ~Dave Waters.

https://github.com/OrangeAVA/Ultimate-Neural-Network-Programming-with-Python

CHAPTER 3

Python Libraries for Data Scientists

The meteoric rise of Python would not have happened if not for its vast array of libraries like Pandas, Regex, Multi-threading, and so on. Python has libraries for all processes, whether game development, image processing, data management, or web scraping.

Structure

This chapter covers the following topics:

- Introduction to Web Scrapping
- Extracting patterns using Regex
- Parallel processing using Multi-Threading and Multi-Processing
- Basics of Pandas

Web Scraping

Why do we need website scrapping? The Internet is a collection of millions of websites, and every site doesn't provide an API to access its data in a structured way. So to access data from these sites, we need website scrapping. It provides an automated solution to access unstructured web data in a structured format.

The technical definition of Website or Web scrapping: Web scraping is an automatic method to obtain large amounts of data from websites. Most of this data is unstructured in an HTML format, then converted into structured data in a spreadsheet or database for use in various applications.

Uses of web scraping:

- News Monitoring
- Sentiment Analysis
- Market Research
- Sport Alerts

To delve into the libraries utilized for web scraping, it is essential to grasp the concept of HTML. HTML serves as a markup language, enabling the creation and design of web content. It encompasses an assortment of tags and attributes that delineate the layout and structure of a web document, presenting data in an organized format. HTML documents commonly carry the file extension .htm or .html. Now, how can we extract data from various websites? This task necessitates the assistance of specific libraries.

- Beautiful soup
- Selenium
- Scrapy

Let's also understand another important term related to Web scraping called XML. It is a markup language that is designed to store data. It is popularly used for the transfer of data. It is case-sensitive. XML offers you the ability to define markup elements and generate customized markup language. The basic unit in XML is known as an element. The extension of the XML file is .xml.

Let's explore the distinctions between XML and HTML. XML and HTML differ in their fundamental nature and purpose. XML, which stands for Extensible Markup Language, serves as a framework for defining markup languages that facilitate data storage and transfer. On the other hand, HTML, short for Hypertext Markup Language, is a predefined markup language specifically designed to describe the structure and presentation of webpages.

Here are some key contrasts between XML and HTML:

1. **Terminology:** XML focuses on extensibility, while HTML concentrates on hypertext.

2. **Data vs. Presentation:** XML primarily deals with the transfer and storage of data, whereas HTML is primarily concerned with how the data is presented.

3. **Content vs. Format:** XML is driven by content, emphasizing the organization and meaning of the data, while HTML is format-driven, focusing on how the content is visually rendered.

4. **Case Sensitivity:** XML is case sensitive, meaning that tags and attributes are distinguished by case, while HTML is case insensitive, allowing more flexibility in tag and attribute names.

5. **Namespace Support:** XML supports namespaces, allowing for the differentiation of elements and attributes with the same names, while HTML does not offer namespaces support.

6. **Tag Closure:** XML enforces strict tag closure, requiring all tags to be properly closed, whereas HTML is more lenient.

7. **Tag Flexibility:** XML allows for the extensibility of tags, meaning that users can define their own tags, whereas HTML has a limited set of predefined tags.

8. **Predefined Tags:** XML does not have predefined tags, whereas HTML comes with a predefined set of tags for various purposes.

By understanding these distinctions, we can appreciate how XML and HTML serve different roles in managing and presenting data on the web. Let's look at a simple code example of HTML:

```
# Most Basic Example of a HTML code
<!DOCTYPE html>
<html>
<head>
<title> Page title </title> </head>
<body>
<h1> First Heading</h1> <p> First paragraph.</p> </body>
</html>


# Most Basic Example of a XML code
<book>
  <title>Introduction to XML</title>
```

```
<author>John Doe</author>
<publication_year>2023</publication_year>
</book>
```

Now, let's look into some of these website-scraping libraries. The first library we are going to look into is called **Beautiful Soup**. Beautiful Soup is a Python package. As the name suggests, it parses unwanted data. It helps to organize and format the web data by fixing bad HTML and presenting it to us in easily traversable XML structures. In short, it is a Python package allowing us to pull data from HTML and XML documents.

To install beautiful soup as a Python package, we must execute its pip command `pip install bs4` in Command Prompt. In practice, bs4 is imported into the Python code with the name of its main class BeautifulSoup `from bs4 import BeautifulSoup`.

Another Python module used in practice along with BeautifulSoup is `requests`. It is installed with the pip command `pip install requests`. The requests module allows you to send HTTP requests using Python. The HTTP request returns a Response Object with all the response data (content, encoding, status, and so on).

Let's look at how to utilize BeautifulSoup to access and parse HTML content.

```
# Making the most basic request using beautiful Soup package
soup = BeautifulSoup(html_request_variable, "html.parser")
```

In this snippet, we're creating an instance of the BeautifulSoup class, passing in the markup (in this case, an HTML request) and the parser (in this case, an HTML parser) as arguments to the BeautifulSoup constructor. Once initialized, this soup object will contain all parsed HTML tags/elements as attributes, allowing us to interact with the HTML content programmatically.

For a more comprehensive understanding of the capabilities of BeautifulSoup, let's examine some parameters we can pass during its initialization.

- **Markup:** This parameter represents the markup to be parsed. It can be a string or a file-like object.
- **Features:** This parameter specifies the parser to be used. It can either be the name of a specific parser (like "lxml", "lxml-xml", "html.parser", or "html5lib") or the type of markup to be parsed (like "html", "html5", or "xml"). Specifying a particular parser ensures that BeautifulSoup provides consistent results across different platforms and virtual environments.

Next, explore utilizing the soup object to extract all URL links embedded within a webpage.

```python
# Printing all the links in a given page
for link in soup.find_all('a'):
    print(link.get('href'))
```

With the soup object method call find_all we can extract all the html tags belonging to a string. Above, we extract all those elements/tags with the word 'a'. With that, we can look through all the elements extracted and use the method get with the string 'href' to access all the embedded URLs used within the website. Let's see how we can print image source links from a website using the soup object.

```python
# Making the most basic request using beautiful Soup package
tags = soup('img')
for tag in tags:
    print(tag.get('src', None))
```

Similar to the previous approach, we extract all the data under the tag 'img' to fetch all the image data in the webpage. Then we can print the image's source links by looping the data and using the method get with the string src (which implies the source link). Now, let's try to do something even more trivial with the soup object. We want to extract tables using the find attribute and convert it into a data frame using pandas (Not relevant to WebScraping and just used for ease of code).

```python
# Reading a table into pandas data frame
pd.read_html(str(soup.find('table', {'class': 'wikitable'})))[0]
```

The above code finds a table on a website and reads it with a pandas variable. Let's organize the code together for all the above examples.

Let's look at the entire code together:

```python
from bs4 import BeautifulSoup
import requests
import pandas as pd


url = "https://en.wikipedia.org/wiki/List_of_countries_and_dependencies_
and_their_capitals_in_native_languages"
```

```
req = requests.get(url)


soup = BeautifulSoup(req.text, "html.parser")
print(soup.title)


for link in soup.find_all("a"):
    print(link.get("href"))


tags = soup("img")
for tag in tags:
    print(tag.get("src", None))


print(pd.read_html(str(soup.find("table", {"class": "wikitable"}))))[0])
```

All the explained processes can be observed by executing the above code. So, what do we learn from coding using the beautiful soup?

1. We can get the details of a URL with module `requests.get`

2. We can use the BeautifulSoup constructor to parse the requests variable html.

3. Using the Soup object's available methods like find, find_all we can scrape the required tag/element details.

4. Using the element object's get attribute, we can access its details (URL, image line, table, and so on.)

Regex

When we deal with real-life data, it is almost guaranteed to have unwanted elements that need to be cleaned before we feed the data to our algorithm. Regular expression(Regex) is a powerful tool for working with text data. They allow you to match patterns within strings and extract specific information, making them an essential tool for many data-related tasks.

Whether you're working with data for natural language processing (NLP), data analysis, or web development, regular expressions will help you work more efficiently and effectively with text data. In this section, you will learn the basics of regular expression syntax and how to use it in real-world applications. You will discover how to match specific patterns within strings, extract information, and manipulate text data with regular expressions.

Why is Regex Needed?

Text data is ubiquitous, and working with it effectively is crucial in many fields. However, text data can be messy and inconsistent, making extracting specific information or performing certain tasks difficult. Regular expressions are a powerful tool for solving these problems and working with data more efficiently and effectively.

Where Regex is Useful? Regular expressions can be used in a wide range of applications, including

- **Cleaning**: Regular expressions can clean up messy text data, such as removing unwanted characters, formatting data consistently, and transforming data into a more usable form.

- **Natural Language Processing (NLP):** Regular expressions are used in NLP to extract specific information from text data, such as named entities, dates, and email addresses.

- **Web Development:** Regular expressions are used in web development for tasks such as validating user input, searching for specific patterns within web pages, and extracting information from URLs.

- **Data Analysis**: Regular expressions extract specific information from text data, such as identifying trends or patterns within large data sets.

Let's deep dive into the syntax of the regex. These syntaxes are a way for the program to understand what it looks for in a text. These syntaxes vary from very simple to complex representations. However, understanding this syntax will ensure we can create expressions for any use case to extract/mine patterns for the text data. This section will cover the basic syntax of regex and provide examples to illustrate how each component works. The example sentence that will be used to explain this will be.

Example Sentence: "I love to eat pizza and pasta 3 times a day"

- **Literal Characters**

The most basic component of a regex is a literal character, which matches itself. To match specific characters in a string, you can specify those characters in your regex pattern. For example, to match the word "**pizza**" in the example sentence, the regex pattern would be: "**pizza**".

- **Special Characters**

Several special characters in regex have special meanings, including:

- ○ . (dot): Matches any character except a newline character. In the example sentence, The **regex "a.d" would match 'and', 'a d'.**

- ○ (asterisk): Matches zero or more occurrences of the preceding character or group. In the example sentence, to match the words "pizza and pasta" in the sentence, the regex pattern would be: "pi.*ta".

- ○ + (plus sign): Matches one or more occurrences of the preceding character or group. In the example sentence, to match the words "love to eat" in the sentence, the regex pattern would be: "lo.+at"

- ○ ? (question mark): Matches zero or one occurrence of the preceding character or group. In the example sentence, to match the word "pizza" or "piza" the regex pattern would be "piz?za". The character "z" becomes optional in the word.

- ○ ^ (caret): Matches the start of a line. In the example sentence, The regex "^I love" would match, only if it appears at the start of a line.

- ○ $ (dollar sign): Matches the end of a line. For example, to match the last word **"day"** in the sentence, the regex pattern would be: **"day$"**.

- ○ \b (word boundary): Matches the position between a word character (\w) and a non-word character (\W). In the example sentence, to match the space between **"pizza" and "and"** in the sentence, the regex pattern would be: **"\bpizza\b"**.

- ○ \B (non-word boundary): Matches any position that is not a word boundary. In the example sentence, to match the letter "a" in the word **"pizza"**, the regex pattern would be: **"\Ba\B"**.

```
import re
regex_sentence = "I love to eat pizza and pasta 3 times a day"
print(re.findall(r"a.d", regex_sentence))
print(re.findall(r"pi.*ta", regex_sentence))
print(re.findall(r"lo.+at", regex_sentence))
print(re.findall(r"piz?za", regex_sentence))
```

Run all the Python code above at your end to understand the output you would extract from running these special characters.

Let's look into more types of patterns matching available to us in Regex.

- **Character Classes:** Character classes allow you to match any one character from a set of characters. They are specified using square brackets []. In the example sentence given in the code above, the regex **"[aeiou]"** would match any vowel in the string, such as **"o"** in "love" and "a" in "eat", and so on.

- **Character Ranges:** Character ranges allow you to match a range of characters. They are specified using a hyphen **(-)** within square brackets []. In the example sentence, the regex **"[a-z]"** would match any lowercase letter in the string. Likewise, the regex **"[a-f]"** would match any lowercase letters a,b,c,d,e, and f in the example sentence.

- **Shorthand Character Classes:** Several shorthand character classes are frequently used in regex. Some of the most commonly used ones are:

  - \d: Matches any digit. Equivalent to **[0-9]**. In the example sentence, The regex **"\d"** would match the character **"3"**

  - \w: Matches any word character. Equivalent to [a-zA-Z0-9_]. In the example sentence, The regex **"\w"** would match **all** the characters **except the space** between words.

  - \s: Matches any whitespace character, including spaces, tabs, and line breaks. /n In the example sentence, The regex **"pizza\sand\ spasta"** will match the words **"pizza and pasta"**

  - \D: Matches any character that is not a digit. /n In the example sentence, The regex **"\D"** would include all the characters, including the spaces **except "3"**

  - \W: Matches any character that is not a word character.

```
import re

regex_sentence = "I love to eat pizza and pasta 3 times a day"
print(re.findall(r"\d", regex_sentence))
print(re.findall(r"\w", regex_sentence))
print(re.findall(r"pizza\sand\spasta", regex_sentence))
print(re.findall(r"\D", regex_sentence))
print(re.findall(r"\W", regex_sentence))
print(re.findall(r"\S", regex_sentence))
```

Run all the Python code above at your end to understand the output you would extract from running these special characters.

- **Grouping and Capturing:** Grouping and capturing in regular expressions (regex) allow you to group multiple characters and capture the matched text as a single unit, which can be referenced later in your pattern or extracted for use in your code.
- **Grouping:** You use parentheses to group characters in a regex pattern ( ). In the example sentence, to group with the word **"pizza"**, the regex pattern would be: "**(pizza)**".
- **Capturing:** To capture the matched text as a single unit, enclose the characters you want to capture in parentheses ( ). The captured text can be referenced later in the pattern using "\1", "\2", etc. The number represents the position of the capture group in the pattern, starting from 1. For example, to capture the words **"pizza"** or **"pasta"** in a sentence, use the pattern "**((pizza)|(pasta))**".

By grouping and capturing in regex, you can organize your pattern and extract specific parts of the matched text for further processing or manipulation.

```python
import re
regex_sentence = "I love to eat pizza and pasta 3 times a day"


# Using a capture group to extract the words "pizza" and "pasta"
pattern = "((pizza)|(pasta))"
matches = re.findall(pattern, regex_sentence)


print("Captured words:", matches)
# Output: Captured words: [("pizza", "pizza", ""), ("pasta", "", "pasta")]
```

Run all the Python code above at your end to understand the output you would get.

The best way to learn regex is by practicing, here are a few examples of what we discussed above:

```
# The input text to match

text = "The quick brown fox jumps over the lazy dog 123 times."


# Write a regex pattern to match the following:
# All the digits in the text


# Solution: "\d", [0-9]


import re

text = "The quick brown fox jumps over the lazy dog 123 times."


# The re.search() function can be used to search for the first occurrence
# of a pattern in a given string. It returns a Match object if a match is
# found, or None if no match is found.
# Search for a digit in the text

match = re.search(r"\d", text)

if match:
    print("First digit found at position:", match.start())


# Output:
# First digit found at position: 42


# Split the text on punctuation marks
# The re.split() function can be used to split a string into a list of
# strings based on a specified pattern

result = re.split(r"[,;.]", text)

print("Words after splitting:", result)


# Output:
# Words after splitting: ['The quick', ' brown', ' fox jumps', ' over the
lazy dog 123 times', '']
```

```
# Replace all digits with the word 'NUMBER'
# The re.sub() function can replace all occurrences of a pattern in a
string with a specified replacement.
result = re.sub(r"\d+", "NUMBER", text)
print("Text after replacing digits:", result)


# Output:
# Text after replacing digits: The quick brown fox jumps over the lazy dog
NUMBER times


# Find all the words in the text
# The re.findall() function can return a list of all the non-overlapping
occurrences of a pattern in a string.
result = re.findall(r"\b\w+\b", text)
print("Words in the text:", result)


# Output:
# Words in the text: ['The', 'quick', 'brown', 'fox', 'jumps', 'over',
'the', 'lazy', 'dog', '123', 'times']



# Grouping Capturing groups allows us to extract specific parts of the
matching pattern and refer to them later. Capturing groups are created by
enclosing a portion of the pattern in parentheses.
x = re.search("I love to eat (\w+) and (\w+)", text)
print("group 1 is: " + x.group(1) + " group 2 is: " + x.group(2))


#Output:
# group 1 is: pizza group 2 is: pasta
```

```
# Non-capturing groups are similar to capturing groups but don't capture
the matching text. They are indicated by "(?:)"
x = re.search("I love to eat (?:pizza) and (\w+)", text)
print(x.group(1))


# Output: pasta
```

```
# Lookaheads allow you to match a pattern only if another pattern follows
it. Positive lookaheads are indicated by (?=) and negative lookaheads are
indicated by (?!).
x = re.search("\w+(?= times)", text)

print(x.group())
# output: 3
```

```
# Backreferences allow you to reuse the text matched by a capturing group
in the same pattern.
x = re.search("(\\w+) and \\1", text)

print(x.group())
# output: pizza and pizza
```

```
# Non-Capturing Groups
x = re.search("I love to eat (?:pizza) and (\w+)", text)


print(x.group(1))
# output: pasta
```

Note: I know that regex is a complex topic and tough to master, here is one tool that can convert English to regex expression: **https://www.autoregex.xyz/ [13].**

Multi-Threading and Multi-Processing

Python is a versatile language used in various fields, such as web development, data science, artificial intelligence, and more. One reason for Python's versatility is its ability to handle multiple tasks simultaneously. In this section, we'll explore

Python's two principal approaches to concurrent execution: multithreading and multiprocessing.

Multi-Threading

In computing, a thread is the smallest unit of execution. It's a separate flow of execution, and every program has at least one thread. When a program has multiple threads running concurrently within a single process, this is known as multithreading.

Multithreading allows for the parallel execution of tasks. However, there's an important caveat in Python due to the Global Interpreter Lock (GIL). Because of the GIL, Python threads are not truly concurrent on multiple cores or processors; they appear to run in parallel. This is because the GIL only allows one thread to execute in the interpreter at any time.

When to Use Multithreading?

Multithreading is best used for I/O-bound tasks, where the program often waits for input or output from external resources. Examples include web scraping, reading and writing files or interacting with APIs. During the waiting time, the program can switch to other threads and efficiently use its time.

Let's understand this through some code:

```python
import threading
import time


class MyThread(threading.Thread):
    def __init__(self, name, delay):
        threading.Thread.__init__(self)
        self.name = name
        self.delay = delay


    def run(self):
        print('Starting thread %s.' % self.name)
        thread_lock.acquire()
```

```python
            print_numbers(self.name, self.delay)
            thread_lock.release()


def print_numbers(threadName, delay):
    counter = 0
    while counter < 3:
        time.sleep(delay)
        print('%s: %s' % (threadName, time.ctime(time.time())))
        counter += 1


thread_lock = threading.Lock()
threads = []


# Create new threads
thread1 = MyThread("Thread-1", 1)
thread2 = MyThread("Thread-2", 2)


# Start new Threads
thread1.start()
thread2.start()


# Add threads to thread list
threads.append(thread1)
threads.append(thread2)


# Wait for all threads to complete
for t in threads:
    t.join()


print('Exiting Main Thread.')
```

In this example, we create a subclass of `threading.Thread` and override its `run()` method, where the new thread begins. We also introduce `threading.Lock` to prevent threads from interfering with each other, a situation known as a race condition.

Multi-Processing

Multiprocessing refers to the ability of a system to support more than one processor at the same time. Applications in a multiprocessing system are broken to smaller routines that run independently. The operating system allocates these threads to the processors, improving system performance.

Python's multiprocessing module allows for creating separate processes, each with its own Python interpreter and memory space. As a result, multiprocessing can take full advantage of multiple cores, or CPUs.

When to Use Multiprocessing?

Multiprocessing is suitable for CPU-bound tasks that require many computations and can be parallelized. These tasks can be split up and executed concurrently across multiple processors to decrease execution time dramatically.

Let's understand this through an example:

```python
import requests
from multiprocessing import Pool
from bs4 import BeautifulSoup


# Define the list of URLs to be scraped
urls = ["http://www.example.com/page1", "http://www.example.com/page2",
...]


def scrape(url):
    """
    Function to fetch a webpage and extract its title using BeautifulSoup
    """
    response = requests.get(url)
```

```
    soup = BeautifulSoup(response.text, 'html.parser')


    # Assume that the page title is contained within <title> tags
    title = soup.find('title').text
    return title


if __name__ == "__main__":
    # Define the multiprocessing pool
    with Pool(processes=4) as pool:
        # Use the pool's map method to apply the scrape function to every
URL
        results = pool.map(scrape, urls)


    # Print the results
    for url, title in zip(urls, results):
        print(f"Title of {url} is {title}")
```

Explanation of the code:

1. First, we import the necessary libraries. We're using `requests` to fetch the webpages, multiprocessing for parallel processing, and BeautifulSoup to parse the HTML.

2. We define a list of URLs to be scrapped.

3. We define a function `scrape()` that fetches a webpage and extracts its title using BeautifulSoup.

4. In the if `__name__` == "`__main__`" block, we define a multiprocessing pool. The Pool object represents a pool of worker processes. The number of processes is set to 4, meaning up to 4 tasks will be executed in parallel.

5. We use the `map()` method of the `Pool` object to apply the `scrape()` function to every URL in the list. The `map()` method blocks until all tasks are completed.

6. The results are returned as a list of titles in the same order as the corresponding URLs. Finally, we print each URL and its title.

This code effectively parallelizes the web scraping task. Instead of fetching and parsing the web pages one by one, which would be time-consuming, it fetches and parses up to four web pages at a time, which can be significantly faster, especially when dealing with many web pages.

Pandas Basics

What is the Pandas library in Python?

Pandas is a powerful and flexible open-source data analysis and data manipulation library for Python. It provides data structures for efficiently storing large datasets and tools for working with them. Pandas are widely used for data pre-processing and analysis in the data science and machine learning communities.

In this section, you will learn the basics of data analysis using the popular Python library, Pandas. You will learn how to load, manipulate, and analyze data using Pandas data structures such as Series and DataFrames.

Note: The goal here is to introduce the Pandas library such that you can start manipulating your own datasets. To know more details about this, I suggest you read the actual documentation of the Pandas library.

To learn this library, we will split the learning of Pandas into three parts:

- **Introduction to Pandas:** The basics of the Pandas library, including installing the library, loading and saving data, data structures (series and data frames), and indexing and selecting data.

- **Data Pre-processing:** The various methods of cleaning and transforming data, including handling missing values, removing duplicates, and merging and joining data. Additionally, you will learn about data normalization, scaling, and encoding categorical variables.

- **Advanced Pandas Techniques**: This section can cover advanced topics such as groupby operations, pivoting data, time series analysis, and advanced aggregation and grouping techniques.

Introducing Pandas

The first step to start using Pandas is to install it. The easiest way to install Pandas is through the Anaconda distribution, which comes pre-installed with Pandas and many other useful libraries. If you don't have Anaconda installed, you can install it from the official website. If you prefer to install Pandas using pip, you can run the following command in your terminal or command prompt:

```
pip install pandas
```

Let's look at data loading and saving commands:

```
## Loading and Saving Data: Pandas provide several ways to load and save
data into and from a DataFrame:
```

```
import pandas as pd
import sqlite3
```

```
# Loading Data from a CSV File: You can load data from a CSV file using
the "read_csv" function.
df = pd.read_csv('data.csv')
```

```
# Loading Data from an Excel File: You can load data from an Excel file
using the "read_excel" function.
df = pd.read_excel('data.xlsx')
```

```
# Loading Data from a SQL Database: You can load data from a SQL database
using the "read_sql" function.
conn = sqlite3.connect("database.db")
df = pd.read_sql("SELECT * FROM table_name", conn)
```

```
# Loading Data from a Dictionary: You can load data from a dictionary
using the DataFrame constructor.
data = {'col1': [1, 2], 'col2': [3, 4]}
df = pd.DataFrame(data)
```

```
# Saving Data to a CSV File: You can save data to a CSV file using the
"to_csv" method.
# …all df manipulation
df.to_csv('data.csv', index=False)
```

```
#Saving Data to an Excel File: You can save data to an Excel file using
the "to_excel" method.
# …all df manipulation
df.to_excel('data.xlsx', index=False)
```

```
#Saving Data to a SQL Database: You can save data to a SQL database us-
ing the "to_sql" method
conn = sqlite3.connect('database.db')
df = pd.read_sql("SELECT * FROM table_name", conn)
# …all df manipulation
df.to_sql('table', conn, if_exists='replace')
```

Pandas provides two types of Data Structures, namely, Series and DataFrames. A **Series** is a one-dimensional labeled array that can hold any data type. It is similar to a column in a table or a dataset. You can create a Series using the Series constructor or extracting a column from a DataFrame. Likewise, dataFrames can be thought of as a table or a database.

Here are some more basic functionalities of Pandas:

```
import pandas as pd
import numpy as np


# Creating a Series from a list
s = pd.Series([1, 3, 5, np.nan, 6, 8])
print(s)
```

```
# Output:
# 0      1.0
# 1      3.0
# 2      5.0
# 3      NaN
# 4      6.0
# 5      8.0
# dtype: float64


# Creating a Series from a dictionary
s = pd.Series({'a': 1, 'b': 3, 'c': 5})
print(s)


# Output:
# a      1
# b      3
# c      5
# dtype: int64


# Extracting a column from a DataFrame
df = pd.DataFrame({'col1': [1, 2], 'col2': [3, 4]})
s = df['col1']
print(s)


# Output:
# 0      1
# 1      2
# Name: col1, dtype: int64
```

```
# Indexing using Square Brackets: You can select a single column of a
DataFrame by using square brackets and the column name.
df = pd.DataFrame({'col1': [1, 2], 'col2': [3, 4]})
print(df['col1'])
```

```
#Indexing using Dot Notation: You can also access a column using dot no-
tation, but this method is not recommended because it can lead to confu-
sion with the methods and attributes of the DataFrame.
df = pd.DataFrame({'col1': [1, 2], 'col2': [3, 4]})
print(df.col1)
```

```
# Indexing using Row/Column Labels: You can select rows of a DataFrame
using row/column labels using the "loc" attribute.
df = pd.DataFrame({'col1': [1, 2], 'col2': [3, 4]})
df.index = ['row1', 'row2']
print(df.loc['row1','col1'])
```

```
#Indexing using Integer-Based Location: You can select rows/columns of a
DataFrame using integer-based location using the "iloc" attribute.
df = pd.DataFrame({'col1': [1, 2], 'col2': [3, 4]})
print(df.iloc[0:2, 1])
```

```
# output
# 0     3
# 1     4
# Name: col2, dtype: int64
```

```
#Boolean Indexing: You can select rows of a DataFrame based on a condition
using boolean indexing.
df = pd.DataFrame({'col1': [1, 2, 3], 'col2': [4, 5, 6]})
print(df[df['col1'] > 1])
```

Data Pre-processing

It is the process of cleaning and transforming raw data into a suitable format for analysis and modeling. This step is essential in any data analysis or machine learning project, as the data quality and structure significantly impact the results.

Let's directly jump into the code to learn about the available Pandas methods. Most of the code given here is pretty self-explanatory here:

```python
import pandas as pd
import numpy as np
# Creating a sample dataframe with missing values
df = pd.DataFrame({
    'A': [1, 2, np.nan, 4, 5],
    'B': [6, np.nan, 8, 9, 10],
    'C': [11, 12, 13, 14, np.nan]
})

# Display the dataframe
print("Original Dataframe:")
print(df)

# Output
# Original Dataframe:
#      A     B     C
# 0   1.0   6.0   11.0
# 1   2.0   NaN   12.0
# 2   NaN   8.0   13.0
# 3   4.0   9.0   14.0
# 4   5.0   10.0   NaN


# Identifying the missing values
```

```python
print("\nMissing values:")
print(df.isna().sum())
# Output
# Missing values:
# A     1
# B     1
# C     1
# dtype: int64


# Filling the missing values with a constant value (0)
df_fillna = df.fillna(0)
print("\nDataframe after filling missing values with 0:")
print(df_fillna)
# Output
# Dataframe after filling missing values with 0:
#       A     B     C
# 0   1.0   6.0  11.0
# 1   2.0   0.0  12.0
# 2   0.0   8.0  13.0
# 3   4.0   9.0  14.0
# 4   5.0  10.0   0.0


# Dropping the rows containing missing values
df_dropna = df.dropna()
print("\nDataframe after dropping rows with missing values:")
print(df_dropna)
# Output
# Dataframe after dropping rows with missing values:
#       A    B     C
# 0   1.0  6.0  11.0
# 3   4.0  9.0  14.0
```

```
# Dropping the columns containing missing values
df_dropna_col = df.dropna(axis=1)
print("\nDataframe after dropping columns with missing values:")
print(df_dropna_col)
# Output
# Dataframe after dropping columns with missing values:
# Empty DataFrame
# Columns: []
# Index: [0, 1, 2, 3, 4]
```

Data cleaning is important part and here's how you remove the duplicate data

```
import pandas as pd


# Create a sample dataframe
df = pd.DataFrame({'A':[1,2,3,4,5,6,7,8,1,2,3],
                   'B':['a','b','c','d','e','f','g','h','a','b','c']})


# Check the original dataframe
print("Original dataframe:")
print(df)
# Output
# Original dataframe:
#      A  B
# 0    1  a
# 1    2  b
# 2    3  c
# 3    4  d
# 4    5  e
# 5    6  f
```

```
# 6    7  g
# 7    8  h
# 8    1  a
# 9    2  b
# 10   3  c


# Identify the duplicate rows
duplicates = df.duplicated()
print("Duplicate rows:")
print(duplicates)
# Output
# Duplicate rows:
# 0       False
# 1       False
# 2       False
# 3       False
# 4       False
# 5       False
# 6       False
# 7       False
# 8        True
# 9        True
# 10       True
# dtype: bool


# Remove the duplicate rows
df = df.drop_duplicates()


# Check the data frame after removing duplicates
print("Dataframe after removing duplicates:")
print(df)
```

```
# Output
# Dataframe after removing duplicates:
#    A  B
# 0  1  a
# 1  2  b
# 2  3  c
# 3  4  d
# 4  5  e
# 5  6  f
# 6  7  g
import pandas as pd


# Create a sample dataframe
df = pd.DataFrame({'A':[1,2,3,4,5,6,7,8,1,2,3],
                   'B':['a','b','c','d','e','f','g','h','a','b','c']})


# Check the original dataframe
print("Original dataframe:")
print(df)
# Output
# Original dataframe:
#     A  B
# 0   1  a
# 1   2  b
# 2   3  c
# 3   4  d
# 4   5  e
# 5   6  f
# 6   7  g
# 7   8  h
# 8   1  a
```

```
# 9    2  b
# 10   3  c


# Identify the duplicate rows
duplicates = df.duplicated()
print("Duplicate rows:")
print(duplicates)
# Output
# Duplicate rows:
# 0      False
# 1      False
# 2      False
# 3      False
# 4      False
# 5      False
# 6      False
# 7      False
# 8       True
# 9       True
# 10      True
# dtype: bool


# Remove the duplicate rows
df = df.drop_duplicates()


# Check the data frame after removing duplicates
print("Dataframe after removing duplicates:")
print(df)
# Output
# Dataframe after removing duplicates:
#    A  B
```

```
# 0   1   a
# 1   2   b
# 2   3   c
# 3   4   d
# 4   5   e
# 5   6   f
# 6   7   g
```

You will often encounter situations where you must concatenate or join different datasets. Here's how you do it. Run these examples to see and understand the output clearly.

```python
import pandas as pd

# Creating two simple dataframes
df1 = pd.DataFrame({
    'A': ['A0', 'A1', 'A2', 'A3'],
    'B': ['B0', 'B1', 'B2', 'B3'],
    'key': ['K0', 'K1', 'K2', 'K3']
})

df2 = pd.DataFrame({
    'C': ['C0', 'C1', 'C2', 'C3'],
    'D': ['D0', 'D1', 'D2', 'D3'],
    'key': ['K0', 'K1', 'K2', 'K4']
})

print("df1:")
print(df1)
print("\ndf2:")
```

```
print(df2)
```

```
# Concatenation: It is the simplest method of combining data in pandas.
# It is performed using the "pd.concat()" method. This method takes a list
# of data frames as input and concatenates them along the resulting data
# frame's rows (axis=0) or columns (axis=1).
```

```
concat = pd.concat([df1, df2], axis=0)
```

```
print("\nConcatenated dataframe:")
```

```
print(concat)
```

```
# Inner Join: It is the default join in pandas. Only the common rows are
# kept in the resulting data frame in this type of join. All the other
# rows are discarded.
```

```
inner_join = pd.merge(df1, df2, on='key', how='inner')
```

```
print("\nInner Join:")
```

```
print(inner_join)
```

```
# Left Join: In a left join, all the values from the left dataframe are
# combined with those from the right dataframe. The resulting dataframe
# includes all the values from the left dataframe and the matching values
# from the right dataframe. For the missing values in the right dataframe,
# NaN values are used.
```

```
left_join = pd.merge(df1, df2, on='key', how='left')
```

```
print("\nLeft Join:")
```

```
print(left_join)
```

```
# Right Join: In a right join, all the values from the right dataframe
# are combined with those from the left dataframe. The resulting dataframe
# includes all the values from the right dataframe and the matching values
# from the left dataframe. For the missing values in the left dataframe,
# NaN values are used.
```

```
right_join = pd.merge(df1, df2, on='key', how='right')
```

```
print("\nRight Join:")
```

```
print(right_join)
```

```
# Outer Join: In an outer join, all the values from both dataframes are
combined, and the resulting dataframe includes all the values from both
dataframes, even if a value is not present in one of the dataframes
outer_join = pd.merge(df1, df2, on='key', how='outer')
print(«\nOuter Join:»)
print(outer_join)
```

Advanced Pandas Techniques

Often you need to do things like scaling, normalization, encoding, and so on, as a pre-processing step for ML algorithms. Here's an example of how to do that using pandas:

```
import pandas as pd


# Create a sample dataframe
df = pd.DataFrame({
    'A': ['foo', 'bar', 'baz', 'foo', 'bar', 'baz'],
    'B': ['one', 'one', 'two', 'two', 'one', 'one'],
    'C': [1, 2, 3, 4, 5, 6],
    'D': [10, 20, 30, 40, 50, 60]
})


# Encoding categorical variables
df['A_encoded'] = df['A'].astype('category').cat.codes
df['B_encoded'] = df['B'].astype('category').cat.codes


# Normalization - Min-Max scaling (range 0 to 1)
df['C_norm'] = (df['C'] - df['C'].min()) / (df['C'].max() - df['C'].min())
df['D_norm'] = (df['D'] - df['D'].min()) / (df['D'].max() - df['D'].min())


# Advanced groupby operation - group by 'A' and 'B', calculate mean of
'C_norm' and sum of 'D_norm'
```

```
grouped_df = df.groupby(['A', 'B']).agg({'C_norm':'mean', 'D_
norm':'sum'}).reset_index()


print(grouped_df)
```

In the preceding code example:

1. **Encoding Categorical Variables:** We convert the categorical columns 'A' and 'B' into numerical codes. This can be useful for algorithms that require numerical input.

2. **Normalization (Min-Max Scaling):** We perform Min-Max scaling on columns C and D to normalize their values to the range [0, 1]. This can be useful for algorithms sensitive to the input features' scale.

3. **Advanced GroupBy operation:** We group the dataframe by columns 'A' and 'B'; for each group, we calculate the mean of 'C_norm' and the sum of 'D_norm'. The `agg()` function specifies different aggregation functions for different columns. Finally, the `reset_index()` function converts the index created by the groupby operation back into columns.

Note: The other two most commonly used libraries for Data Science are **NumPy** and **OpenCV**. We will take a detailed look at NumPy when we build our Neural Networks from Scratch and OpenCV when we implement Deep learning models in the later chapters.

Conclusion

This chapter focused on extracting data from websites using web scraping libraries. We explored the process of scraping data and learned about the various libraries available for this purpose. Additionally, we delved into the realm of regex, a widely used library that assists in cleaning text data and identifying specific patterns within it. Moving forward, we introduced the concepts of multi-threading and multi-processing, highlighting their significance in enhancing the efficiency of data processing tasks. Finally, as we concluded this chapter, we dedicated our attention to discussing the most frequently utilized functionalities offered by Pandas, a powerful library in the realm of data analysis and manipulation.

After setting up Python for AI development, we are ready to test out different AI components and learn the maths behind them. So, in the next chapter, we will go super technical into the maths behind various AI concepts and components that form the backbone of AI.

"AI is not only for engineers. It's for everyone. If you have an interest in it, you can start learning about it right now." - Andrew Ng

https://github.com/OrangeAVA/Ultimate-Neural-Network-Programming-with-Python

## CHAPTER 4

Foundational Concepts for Effective Neural Network Training

Neural network is not just programming, it's not just engineering, it's not just maths, it's a combination of all three of these. With this chapter we start looking into the maths, code, and ideas behind all the AI technologies. This chapter serves as the foundation for general concepts in AI.

Structure

This chapter covers the following topics:

- Activation functions
- RBF, Universal approximator, and Curse of Dimensionality
- Overfitting, Bias-variance trade-off, and Regularization
- Generalization

Note: We will delve into many mathematical equations in the forthcoming chapters. However, the intention here is to avoid inundating the book with equations, rendering it inaccessible due to an overload of mathematical terminology. Instead, our primary objective is to equip readers with sufficient knowledge and understanding to confidently navigate the often complex mathematical concepts presented in AI research papers. We aim to balance theoretical comprehension and practical applicability, ensuring the content remains engaging and beneficial to our readers.

Activation Functions

An activation function in a neural network is a mathematical function that takes the input signal and generates an output signal for the next layer. It helps to decide whether a neuron should be activated by calculating the weighted sum and adding bias. They are essential for deep learning models and can help introduce non-linear properties to our network, which allows it to learn from more complex data. Having non-linear properties makes neural networks adapt to different problems and scenarios. Later on, we will look into how neural networks form their decision boundary, but for now, know that **non-linearity is the key to neural networks' success**.

Here are some of the most common types of activation functions, keep in mind that you might have specialized activation functions depending upon the problems, but given below are the most common ones you will find:

- **Sigmoid Function:** The sigmoid function takes a real-valued number and squashes it into a range between 0 and 1. In other words, it outputs a new value which translates to the probability of something happening. Because it has a smooth gradient, it's easy for the network to adjust and learn from. However, it can suffer from the vanishing gradient problem, where the gradients are very small, almost negligible, which can slow down the learning during training.

```python
# sigmoid function Python Code
import numpy as np


def sigmoid(z):
  return 1.0 / (1 + np.exp(-z))


# Derivative of sigmoid function
def sigmoid_prime(z):
  return sigmoid(z) * (1-sigmoid(z))
```

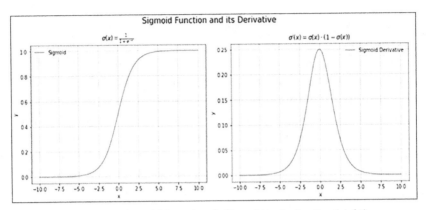

Figure 4.1: *Sigmoid function (left) and its derivative (right)*

- **Tanh (Hyperbolic Tangent) Function:** The tanh function also squashes a real-valued number into the range between -1 and 1. Like the sigmoid function, it's smooth, but unlike the sigmoid, it's zero-centered, making learning easier for the next layer. However, it still suffers from the vanishing gradient problem.

```python
# Tanh activation function Python Code
import numpy as np
def tanh(z):
    return (np.exp(z) - np.exp(-z)) / (np.exp(z) + np.exp(-z))


# Derivative of Tanh Activation Function
def tanh_prime(z):
    return 1 - np.power(tanh(z), 2)
```

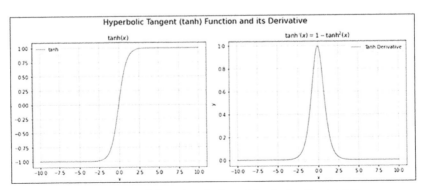

Figure 4.2: *Tanh function (left) and its derivative (right)*

- **ReLU (Rectified Linear Unit) Function:** The ReLU function takes a real-valued input and thresholds it at zero (replaces negative values with zero). So the output is either zero (for all negative inputs) or the original value (for all positive inputs). This makes it computationally efficient and easy to compute without complicated math. In addition, it doesn't suffer from the vanishing gradient problem for positive values. However, negative inputs suffer from the dying ReLU problem, where the neurons become inactive and only output 0.

```python
# ReLU function Python Code
import numpy as np


# ReLU activation function
def relu(z):
  return max(0, z)


# Derivative of ReLU Activation Function
def relu_prime(z):
  return 1 if z > 0 else 0
```

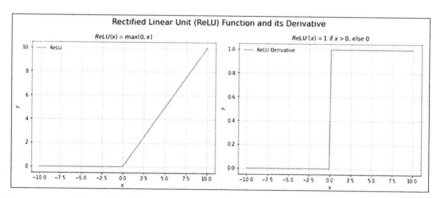

Figure 4.3: *ReLU function (left) and its derivative (right)*

- **Leaky ReLU Function:** This variant of ReLU attempts to fix the dying ReLU problem. Instead of defining the function as zero for negative inputs, it introduces a small slope to keep the updates alive.

```python
# Leaky ReLU activation function
```

```python
import numpy as np

def leaky_relu(z):
    alpha = 0.1
    return z if z > 0 else alpha*z


# Derivative of ReLU Activation Function
def leaky_relu_prime(z):
    alpha=0.1
    return 1 if z > 0 else alpha
```

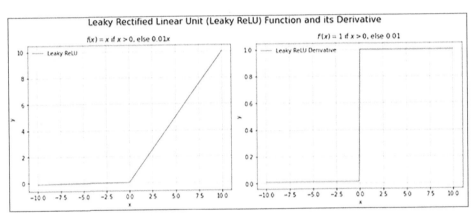

Figure 4.4: *Leaky ReLU function (left) and its derivative (right)*

- **Softmax Function:** The softmax function is primarily used in the output layer of a classifier where we're trying to attain the probabilities to define the output class of the model. It can handle multiple classes and not just binary data, converting scores for each class into probabilities where the sum across all classes is 1. We are not writing the equations and showing the plot of SoftMax because it's the same as Sigmoid. Still, with just one difference: **Sigmoid is used for binary classification methods where we only have 2 classes, while SoftMax applies to multiclass problems. The SoftMax function is an extension of the Sigmoid function.**

Example to understand the concept

Here's *a mental map to think or remember these functions:*

Sigmoid is like a goalkeeper in soccer/football. He can stop the ball (0) or let it pass (1). But most of the time, he deflects the ball to some extent in between.

Tanh is like a tug of war. It can pull the results in both directions, both positive and negative.

ReLU is like an on/off switch. If you send in positive vibes, it passes them on. Send negative vibes, and it shuts off.

Leaky ReLU is like an on/off switch with a night light. Of course, it's mostly off with negative vibes, but still, let's a tiny bit through.

Softmax is like taking a poll. It helps you see which option (or class) is the most popular and gives you the result of a probability distribution.

RBF, Universal Approximators, and Curse of Dimensionality

There are a lot of interesting concepts in and around neural networks that one should be familiar with, few of these concepts include Kernels (like RBF), the idea of universal approximators, and the curse of dimensionality. In this section, we will look at all these topics and build a better understanding of why neural networks work in the first place.

Radial Bias Function

A Radial Basis Function (RBF) is a function whose value depends on the distance from a certain point called the center.

Think of it like throwing a stone into a still pond. The ripples created by the stone in the water get smaller as they move away from the point where the stone was thrown. The place where the stone was thrown is like the center of the Radial Basis Function.

In the pond case, the ripples move in a circular (or radial) pattern, where the **Radial** in the Radial Basis Function comes from. The **Basis** part is there because RBFs can be used as building blocks (or basis functions) to approximate any function.

Imagine you want to create a system that recognizes faces. Faces are complex, but you can think of them as being built up from simpler shapes - circles for the eyes, a triangle for the nose, a curve for the mouth, and so on. Similarly, complex mathematical functions can be approximated by adding many simpler functions, like RBFs.

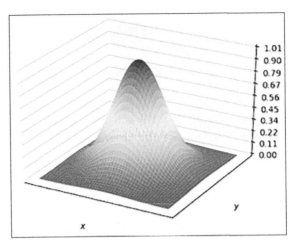

Figure 4.5: *RBF kernel showing function values decreasing as we move away from the center*

So, where do we use this, and why do we need RBFs?

They are used in a type of neural network called a Radial Basis Function Network. Let us go back to our face recognition system. When a new face is presented to the system, it doesn't know who it is. But what it can do is compare this new face to the faces it has seen during training. It does this by measuring how *far* the new face is from the faces it knows;   this **distance** is calculated using RBFs. If the new face is 'close' to a face the system has seen before, it is likely to be the same person.

RBFs are especially good at dealing with problems where the solution involves considering how close or far away the inputs are from each other. This makes them useful in many areas, including image recognition, time-series prediction, and control systems.

Let's look at some basic implementations of RBF. Assume we have a one-dimensional input x and use the Gaussian function as our radial function. Let c = 0 and γ = 1. Our RBF will then look like this:

```python
import numpy as np


def rbf_gaussian(x, z, gamma):
    """"""
    Calculates the Radial Basis Function (RBF) with a Gaussian kernel.
```

Parameters:

x, z: numpy arrays of the same length representing two points in n-dimensional space

gamma: a parameter of the RBF (must be greater than 0)

Returns:

The result of the RBF

«»»

```
distance = np.linalg.norm(x-z)**2
return np.exp(-gamma * distance)


# Example usage:
x = np.array([1, 2, 3])
z = np.array([4, 5, 6])
gamma = 0.1


print(rbf_gaussian(x, z, gamma))
```

Note: Radial Bias function/kernel, when used with SVM (very famous classical machine learning algorithm), gives very powerful results, especially when the data is less.

Neural Networks are universal approximators

The actual talks on artificial neural networks date from the beginning of the previous century, around 1900, when Hilbert formulated a list of 23 challenging mathematical problems for the future century. In his famous 13th problem, he concluded that three variables' analytical functions could not be represented as a finite superposition of continuous functions of only two variables. This conjecture was refuted by Kolmogorov and Arnold in 1957.

Kolmogorov Theorem (1957): Any continuous function $f(x_1, ..., x_n)$ defined on $[0, 1]^n$ ($n \geq 2$) can be represented in the form

$$f(x) = \sum_{j=1}^{2n+1} x_j \left(\sum_{i=1}^{n} \phi_{ij}(x_i) \right)$$

where χ_j, φ_{ij} are continuous functions and φ_{ij} are also monotone.

But why do we care about such an old theorem, and what does it mean?

First and foremost, this theorem introduced the ground-breaking notion that it is possible to construct a system capable of learning any continuous function. The concept of neural networks as *universal approximators* subsequently evolved from a culmination of theorems originating in computational neuroscience and mathematics during the late 1980s and early 1990s. These pivotal theorems establish that a neural network containing at least one hidden layer can approximate any continuous function with remarkable precision, provided many neurons populate the hidden layer. This is why neural networks are frequently called **universal function approximators**.

Two important theorems in this context are:

- **Cybenko's Theorem (1989):** In 1989, George Cybenko demonstrated that a feed-forward network with a single hidden layer containing a finite number of neurons could approximate continuous functions on compact subsets of $\mathbb{R}^n$, under mild assumptions on the activation function. The activation function for the neurons in the hidden layer was assumed to be a sigmoid function, a squashing function that maps its input into a range between 0 and 1 or -1 and 1.

- **Universal Approximation Theorem (1991):** In 1991, Kurt Hornik showed that it is not the specific choice of the activation function but rather the multilayer feedforward architecture that gives neural networks the potential to be universal approximators. The activation function must be a non-constant, bounded, and monotonically increasing continuous function. It does not have to be a sigmoid function.

These theorems have significant implications for neural networks and their applications. Theoretically, they can be used to approximate any function, given an appropriate architecture and training data. This is one of the reasons why they have been so widely used in machine learning and artificial intelligence for tasks such as image recognition, natural language processing, and more.

However, **while these theorems demonstrate the potential power of neural networks, they need to address practical learning issues, such as choosing an appropriate network structure, setting the parameters, or ensuring good generalization from the training data to unseen data**. These remain active areas of research.

The curse of dimensionality

Universal approximation for neural networks is a nice property. However, one could argue that polynomial expansions also possess this property. So should we use neural nets instead of these? The answer is yes. The reason is that neural networks can better cope with the curse of dimensionality. **Barron [14]** showed in 1993 that neural networks could avoid the curse of dimensionality because the approximation error becomes independent from the dimension of the input space (under certain conditions), which is not the case for polynomial expansions.

Let's understand the mathematics and intuition behind the curse of dimensionality. The approximation error for MLPs with one hidden layer is the order of magnitude $O(1/n_h)$, but $O(1/n_p^{2/n})$ for polynomial expansions, where n_h denotes the number of hidden units, n the dimension of the input space, and n_p the number of terms in the expansion. Consider for example $y = f(x_1, x_2, x_3)$. A polynomial expansion with terms up to degree 7 would contain many terms:

$$y = a_1 x_1 + a_2 x_2 + a_3 x_3 + a_{11} x_1^2 + a_{22} x_2^2 + a_{33} x_3^2 + a_{12} x_1 x_2 + a_{13} x_1 x_3 + ... + a_{33} x_3^3 + ...$$
$$+ a_{1111111} x_1^7 + a_{2222222} x_2^7 + ...$$

This means that for a given number of training data, the number of parameters to be estimated is huge (which should be avoided, as we will discuss later in the learning and generalization section). On the other hand, For MLPs This means that for a given number of training data, the number of parameters to be estimated is huge (which should be avoided as we will discuss later in the chapter   on learning and generalization). For MLPs

$$y = w^T tanh\ (V[x_1 x_2 x_3] + \beta)$$

Here V is the weight matrix of the layer, β is the bias, tanh is the activation function, and w is the weight of the output neuron. Here, we can see that MLP grows linearly with an increasing number of input dimensions.

Example to understand the concept

To illustrate this, let's consider a unit square, cube, and hypercube (a "unit" shape means all its sides are 1 unit long).

- **Unit Square (2 dimensions):** Imagine two points randomly placed in a square of side length 1. The maximum distance between any two points is the diagonal, which is $sqrt(1^2 + 1^2) = sqrt(2) \approx 1.41$. The average distance will be less than this.

- **Unit Cube (3 dimensions):** Now imagine two points randomly placed in a *cube of side length 1. The maximum distance is now the space diagonal: sqrt (1² + 1² + 1²) = sqrt(3) ≈ 1.73. So again, the average distance will be less than 1.73 but larger than the average distance in the square.*

- **Unit Hypercube (4 dimensions):** *If we extend to four dimensions, the maximum distance becomes* sqrt(4) = 2. *The average distance will be less than this but even greater than the cube's.*

As we increase the dimensions, the average distance between points increases. This has significant implications in machine learning and data science, especially for algorithms that rely on distance computations, like k-nearest neighbors and support vector machines. Unfortunately, this is one facet of the **curse of dimensionality**. As you add more dimensions, your data becomes sparser and sparser, and distance-based methods become less reliable if you have a massive amount of data.

Why is this a problem?

Many machine learning algorithms rely on measures of distance between points. When dimensions increase, all points appear equally far apart, making it hard for the algorithms to find meaningful patterns in the data. This also means we need exponentially more data to get a good space sampling, and computations become significantly more complex and resource-intensive.

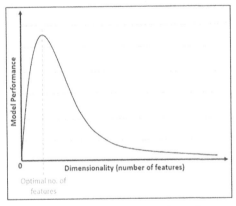

Figure 4.6: *After a certain point model's performance start decreasing after increasing feature space dimensions*

Overfitting, Bias–Variance, and Generalization

Selecting a task appropriate network is crucial, for instance we can always cut an apple with a sword, but we use knives. The same is true for neural networks, we should always use networks that do not over or under utilize the resources. In order to build this understanding, we introduce the concepts of overfitting, bias-variance, and generalization.

Overfitting problem

Overfitting is a common problem in machine learning where a model performs well on the training data but poorly on new, unseen data. When a model is overfitted, it has learned the noise or random fluctuations in the training data rather than the underlying patterns that generalize to new data.

Example to understand the concept

Let us use a simple polynomial regression problem as an example to illustrate overfitting.

We will use the equation of a line, $y = mx + b$, to generate training data, where m is the slope, b is the y-intercept, x is the input, and y is the output.

Let us assume $m = 2$ and $b = 3$, and we generate x values randomly between -10 and 10. We also add some random noise to y to simulate real-world data.

Given this data, we want to fit a polynomial of degree n, $y = a_0 + a_1 * x + a_2 * x^2 + \ldots + a_n * x^n$, where the a_i's are the polynomial coefficients.

If $n = 1$, we're fitting a line to the data, which is the correct model. If we fit the data correctly, our model will generalize well to new data because it has learned the true underlying pattern.

If n is too large, say 20, we fit a 20th-degree polynomial to the data. This model will be flexible and fit the training data almost perfectly, including the random noise. However, when we try to use this model to predict new data, it will likely perform poorly because it has learned the noise in the training data, which does not generalize to new data. This is an example of overfitting.

Now let us define this problem more formally.

Overfitting and the condition of optimality:

In terms of the condition of optimality, overfitting usually means that our model is overly optimized to reduce the loss function on our training data. The loss function (like the mean squared error for regression problems) measures how well our model fits the data. So when a model is overfitted, it's doing a great job minimizing the loss function on the training data, but at the cost of its ability to generalize to new data.

A common way to prevent overfitting is to add a **regularization** term to the loss function. For example, in **Ridge regression**, the loss function is:

$$L = \sum (y - (wX + b))^2 + \lambda w^2$$

Here, y is the actual value, X is the input, w is the weight parameter, b is the bias, and λ is the regularization parameter.

The first term, $\Sigma(y - (aX + b))^2$, is the usual **mean squared error loss**, and the second term, λa^2, is the regularization term, which penalizes large values of the parameters a. This helps to keep the model simpler and reduce overfitting.

In terms of optimality, we want to find the parameters w and b that minimize the loss function L. This is usually done through an optimization algorithm like **gradient descent** (you will learn about this in the coming chapters). **The condition of optimality is that the gradient of L with respect to the parameters is zero, mathematically** $\dfrac{\delta L}{\delta w} = 0$.

However, if the model is overfitted, it needs to be optimized to the training data and generalize better to new data. In this case, the model could be more optimal regarding its predictive performance, even though it minimizes the training loss.

Note: The other side of the overfitting problem is called underfitting problem, this problem arises when your model has two less parameters to capture or represent the underlying parameters. It is shown in the below diagram.

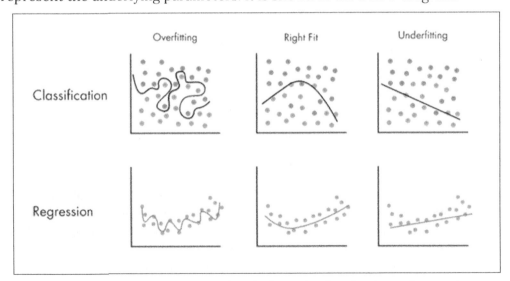

Figure 4.7: *Overfitting, Right Fit and Underfitting for classification and regression*

In order to solve the over/under-fitting problem let's take a look at a few different strategies like **regularization, dropout,** and **early stopping & validation set**.

Regularization and effective parameters

To make our models work on real data, we should understand the concept of regularization in more detail. So let's write the general mathematical form of regularization.

$$\hat{E}(w) = E(w) + v\Omega(w)$$

Here $E(w)$ is the original cost or loss function and $\hat{E}(w)$ is the regularized cost function with $\Omega(w)$ being the regularization term and v a positive real regularization constant. Often, $E(w)$ takes the form of MSE or mean squared error.

$$E(w) = \frac{1}{N}\sum_{1}^{N} [t_n - y(x_n;w)]^2$$

Here t_n is the target variable, and $y(x_n;w)$ is the output of our model with w containing all interconnection weights and bias terms of the neural network model and x_n as inputs. This is also called Ridge Regression or L2 regularization.

$$\Omega(w) = \frac{1}{2}\sum_{i} w_i^2$$

Here $\Omega(w)$ is the regularization term, it can take different forms like $\sum_i w_i$ (Lasso Regression or L1 Regularization) or combination of the $a\sum_i w_i + b\sum_i w_i^2$. This additional regularization term aims at keeping the interconnection weight values small. **Otherwise, the weight matrix can go to $+\infty$ or $-\infty$ during the cost function minimization.**

In simple linear regression, the number of parameters is the number of predictors plus one (for the intercept term). But in ridge regression, due to the shrinkage caused by the λ parameter, each parameter doesn't contribute fully to the model's flexibility, hence the concept of **effective** parameters.

This concept can be extended to other forms of regularized regression, including L1 regularized regression (lasso), although the math becomes more complex. The effective number of parameters generally helps quantify the balance between model fit and model complexity, a key trade-off in machine learning and statistics.

The concept of **effective** parameters can be summarized using the given mathematical equation.

$$\gamma = \sum_j \frac{\lambda_j}{\lambda_j + v}$$

Here λ is the eigen values for our weight matrix. In general, a large regularization constant v large will lead to a smaller model structure giving smaller variance but larger bias. On the other hand, a small value for v will keep the model structure larger, giving large variance but a smaller bias.

Dropout

Another way to regularize a neural network apart from weight based regularization is to reduce its size or add **Dropout**. Dropout is a way to regularize neural networks by randomly dropping neurons.

As the name suggests, Dropout applied to a layer, consists of randomly dropping out (setting to zero) several output features of the layer during training. Let's say that a given layer normally returns a vector [0.2, 0.5, 1.3, 0.8, 1.1] for a given input sample during training. After applying dropout, this vector will have a few randomly distributed zero entries: [0, 0.5, 1.3, 0, 1.1]. The dropout rate is the fraction of the features that are zeroed out; it's usually set between 0.2 and 0.5. At test time, no units are dropped out; instead, the layer's output values are scaled down by a factor equal to the dropout rate, to balance for the fact that more units are active than at training time

Early stopping and validation set

Early stopping is a technique in machine learning that prevents overfitting and improves a model's ability to generalize. When training a model, the aim is to minimize errors in the training data. However, if the model is trained briefly, it can become overly specialized for the training set and perform poorly on new, unseen data.

Early stopping involves monitoring the model's performance on a separate validation dataset during training to tackle this issue. The validation dataset is distinct from the training data and represents unseen data. It helps us estimate how well the model is generalizing.

Throughout training, the model's performance on the validation dataset is evaluated periodically, such as after each epoch or a certain number of training steps. The chosen performance metric can vary depending on the specific problem, like accuracy or loss. This metric is tracked over time, and if the model's performance on the validation dataset stops improving or worsens, early stopping is triggered.

When early stopping is triggered, the training process stops, and the model's parameters are used as the final model. Further training is likely to lead to overfitting, which hampers generalization.

The underlying idea behind early stopping is to find the optimal point during training where the model performs well on both the training and validation datasets. We can capture this optimal point by stopping training before overfitting occurs and obtaining a model that generalizes better to unseen data.

It's important to note that early stopping requires a separate validation dataset different from the training and testing datasets. This validation dataset should resemble the real-world data the model will encounter, ensuring an accurate assessment of its generalization performance.

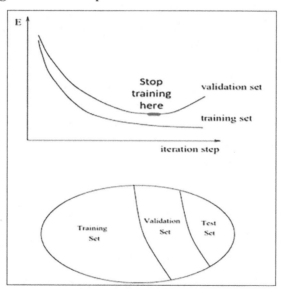

Figure 4.8: *Early stopping and data division in training, validation and test set*

Bias-Variance trade-off

Let's understand the bias-variance trade-off, which is again related to generalization and regularization. The bias-variance trade-off is a fundamental concept in ML that describes the relationship between the complexity of a model and its ability to generalize to unseen data.

Mathematically, we can express the expected prediction error of a model as the sum of three terms: bias, variance, and irreducible error. Here's how:

- **Bias:** This is an error from erroneous assumptions in the model. High bias can cause an algorithm to miss the relevant relations between features and output predictions (underfitting). Mathematically, if f is the true function and $\hat{h}$ is the estimated function, bias is defined as: $\text{Bias}[\hat{h}(x)] = E[\hat{h}(x)] - f(x)$.

- **Variance:** This is an error from sensitivity to small fluctuations in the training set. High variance can cause overfitting by modeling the random noise in the training data, rather than the intended outputs. Mathematically, variance is defined as: $\text{Var}[\hat{h}(x)] = E[(\hat{h}(x) - E[\hat{h}(x)])^2]$.

- **Irreducible Error:** This is the noise term. It's an error we cannot reduce regardless of the algorithm because of the noise in the problem itself.

These three components form the following relationship:

$$\text{Total Error} = \text{Bias}^2 + \text{Variance} + \text{Irreducible Error}$$

The bias-variance trade-off refers to the problem of minimizing these two sources of error that prevent supervised learning algorithms from generalizing beyond their training set.

Increasing the model's complexity will typically increase its variance and reduce its bias. But, conversely, reducing the model's complexity increases its bias and reduces its variance. This is why it's a trade-off. The aim is to find the sweet spot that minimally combines both errors.

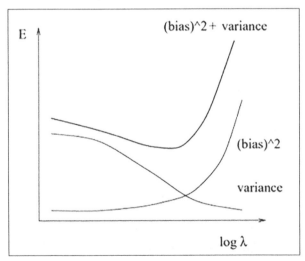

Figure 4.9: *Bias-variance trade-off when adding a regularization term to the cost function. The regularization constant λ is chosen to minimize the sum of bias and variance contributions*

Connection to Overfitting and Underfitting

Underfitting: High bias and low variance. The model makes strong and often incorrect assumptions about the data, resulting in systematic errors no matter how much data you provide.

Overfitting: Low bias and high variance. The model is too flexible and captures the noise in the data, which makes it sensitive to small fluctuations in the training set.

Generalization

When deriving models in general, the goal is not to memorize data but rather to model the underlying generator of the data, characterized by $p(x, t)$, which is the joint probability density of inputs x and targets t.

$$p(x,t) = p(t \mid x)p(x)$$

Deep-learning models generalize locally by morphing inputs into outputs based on their training data. Still, they need help to adapt when the new inputs vary from their training experience. Current DL models can generalize well, but they are still easy to fool and can sometimes classify even a dog as an airplane.

On the other hand, humans possess extreme generalization ability, allowing us to handle hypotheticals, create abstract concepts, and plan for long-term futures. This capability enables us to adapt quickly to radically new situations with little to no new data. Moreover, humans can create abstract models to solve problems efficiently (like rocket science), whereas a deep-learning model would need extensive training data to learn the same task.

Example to understand the concept

If a deep-learning model were trained to navigate a city safely, it would need to experience many dangerous situations (even "dying" numerous times) to learn safe behaviors. However, if moved to a new city, it would have to relearn most of what it knows. In contrast, using abstract modeling and reasoning, humans can learn safe behaviors without such drastic experiences.

In summary, despite advances in machine perception, current AI models still need to be made aware of human-level cognition. They can adapt to new situations resembling past data, while human cognition can quickly adjust to novel situations and future scenarios. Every month you'll keep hearing about new AI models coming into the market, but what do they want to achieve with new models, better **Generalization** so that it performs well in real life test data.

All the new DL architecture development is geared towards creating a more generalized model for a given task.

Note: To improve the generalization performance of the trained models, one can remove irrelevant interconnection weights. This procedure is called **pruning**. We will not look at the maths behind this, but you can read the recent paper called **Recent Advances on Neural Network Pruning at Initialization [15]**.

Note: Researchers have recently discovered that teaching them multiple tasks is better than training neural networks for a particular task. By doing so, we create a better-generalized model. Have a read about this concept from one of the recent papers called **GATO [16]** from Google.

Conclusion

This chapter serves as an in-depth exploration of various components within the realm of artificial intelligence (AI). It begins by examining the significance of activation functions in neural networks, providing an understanding of their different types, and introducing the Radial Bias Function. As activation functions form the core of neural networks, this knowledge is essential for comprehending their functioning and application in diverse scenarios.

The chapter then moves on to discuss the concept of neural networks as universal approximators, showcasing their ability to solve a wide range of problems. It also addresses the challenge of the curse of dimensionality, shedding light on the implications of high-dimensional data, and the relevance of dimensionality reduction techniques for effective visualization. Additionally, the chapter highlights key concepts such as overfitting, bias-variance trade-off, early stopping, and generalization, all of which are vital for training neural networks that can effectively operate in real-life situations.

These concepts pave the way for the subsequent chapters, which will delve into dimensionality reduction techniques, supervised learning, and mathematical optimizations, further expanding the reader's knowledge in the field of AI.

"Artificial intelligence is the new electricity. It has the potential to transform every industry and every aspect of human life." - Sundar Pichai

https://github.com/OrangeAVA/Ultimate-Neural-Network-Programming-with-Python

CHAPTER 5

Dimensionality Reduction, Unsupervised Learning and Optimizations

Neural networks are vast and have so many components within and around them. Learning all of them is quite impossible, but we can surely build some intuition about what we might need to learn. Having a grasp on mathematical optimization gives you a tool to read more papers and build a strong foundation.

Structure

This chapter covers the following topics:

- Dimensionality reduction: linear and non-linear
- Unsupervised learning: Clustering
- Semi and self-supervised learning
- Version space
- Learning optimization using SVM

Dimensionality reduction

Neural networks don't work alone in AI pipelines; they are often needed to be combined with a lot of pre and post-processing steps. There is a saying in data science that '80% of work goes in cleaning the data and 20% in actually making the model'. Keeping this in mind, we need to look at some of these pre and post-processing techniques and understand the maths behind them.

Principal component analysis (PCA)

Often the data we deal with in AI applications is huge; before we start training our networks, it's always a good idea to visualize our data, but visualizing high-dimensional data is a tricky bit, and that's why we introduce the idea of PCA that helps us with visualization problem.

The central idea of principal component analysis (PCA) is to reduce the dimensionality of a data set consisting of many interrelated variables, while retaining the variation in the data set as much as possible. This is achieved by transforming a new set of variables, the principal components (PCs), which are uncorrelated and ordered so that the first few retain most of the variation in all of the original variables.

Let's look at the maths behind PCA.

Standardization: Standardize each feature column for a dataset X, with each column representing a feature and each row a data point. The reason we need to start with standardization is to bring all the different scaled features to the same level. Otherwise, in a dataset containing employee information, salary and age will have different scales, and that will cause problems.

$$X_{std} = (X - \mu) / \sigma$$

Here, μ is the mean, and σ is the standard deviation.

Compute Covariance Matrix: We need a covariance matrix as it captures the relationships and variability among different features (variables) in a dataset. Each element in the covariance matrix represents the covariance between two specific variables. Covariance indicates how two variables change together; a positive covariance suggests that when one variable increases, the other tends to increase as well, while a negative covariance indicates the opposite behavior.

Let's denote the standardized data as X_{std}. Then, the covariance matrix (Σ) is given by:

$$\Sigma = (1 / (n - 1)) X_{std}^{T} X_{std}$$

Here **n** is the number of data points.

Compute Eigenvectors and Eigenvalues: Next, the covariance matrix is used to compute the eigenvalues and eigenvectors of the data. Eigenvectors are directions in the original feature space along which the data varies the most. Eigenvalues quantify the amount of variance along those eigenvectors. The eigenvectors are the principal components of the data, and they represent new coordinate axes that capture the most significant patterns of variability.

Solve the following equation for **eigenvectors (v)** and **eigenvalues (λ)** of the covariance matrix:

$$\Sigma\, v = \lambda\, v$$

You get a list of eigenvalues $[\lambda_1, \lambda_2, \dots, \lambda_d]$ and their corresponding eigenvectors $[v_1, v_2, \dots, v_d]$, where d is the dimension of the feature space.

Sort Eigenvalues and Eigenvectors: Order the eigenvalues in descending order and rearrange them to match the order of their corresponding eigenvalues. We want to capture the new axis with most variations, that's why we have to set eigenvalues in descending order.

$$\lambda_{ordered} = \mathrm{sort}(\lambda,\ descending{=}True)$$

$$v_{ordered} = \mathrm{reorder}(v,\ according\ to\ \lambda_{ordered}\,\})$$

Choose Principal Components: Select the first **k** eigenvectors (where k <= d) from $v_{ordered}$ to form a **d × k** dimensional matrix **P**.

Transform Original Dataset: Finally, transform the original dataset X_{std} to obtain the transformed data **(Y)** using:

$$Y = X_{std}\, P$$

Here, **Y** is the transformed data in the reduced-dimension space.

Let's look at some PCA code implemented in Scikit learn library.

```
import numpy as np
import matplotlib.pyplot as plt
from sklearn.decomposition import PCA


rng = np.random.RandomState(0)
n_samples = 500
```

```
cov = [[3, 3], [3, 4]]
X = rng.multivariate_normal(mean=[0, 0], cov=cov, size=n_samples)
pca = PCA(n_components=2).fit(X)


plt.scatter(X[:, 0], X[:, 1], alpha=0.3, label="samples")
for i, (comp, var) in enumerate(zip(pca.components_, pca.explained_vari-
ance_)):
    comp = comp * var  # scale component by its variance explanation power
    plt.plot(
        [0, comp[0]],
        [0, comp[1]],
        label=f"Component {i}",
        linewidth=5,
        color=f"C{i + 2}",
    )
plt.gca().set(
    aspect="equal",
    title="2-dimensional dataset with principal components",
    xlabel="first feature",
    ylabel="second feature",
)
plt.legend()
plt.show()
```

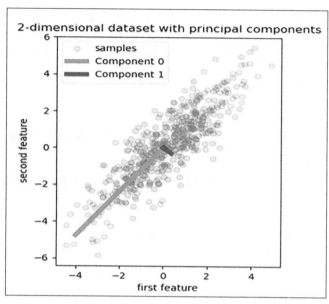

Figure 5.1: *Principal Components for the preceding dataset*
(Example taken from scikit-learn's official website)

T-SNE

T-SNE is a machine learning algorithm for visualizing high-dimensional datasets. Laurens van der Maaten and Geoffrey Hinton developed it. In a nutshell, T-SNE constructs a probability distribution over pairs of high-dimensional objects so that similar objects have a high probability of being picked. In contrast, dissimilar points have an extremely low probability. Then, it creates a similar distribution over the points in the low-dimensional map, and it minimizes the Kullback-Leibler (KL) divergence between the two distributions with respect to the locations of the points in the map.

T-SNE can capture nonlinear structures in the data that PCA might miss. It's especially powerful for visualizing complex real-world datasets with many inherent dimensions and nonlinear relationships. However, it is more computationally intensive than PCA and doesn't provide a deterministic result, that is, running the algorithm multiple times on the same data might yield different results.

Example to understand the concept

Imagine you have a globe and want to create a flat world map. In doing so, you want to preserve the relative distances between cities as much as possible. T-SNE is like the process of flattening the globe into a map. It takes high-dimensional data (like the globe) and reduces it to a lower-dimensional space (like the flat map), trying its best to keep similar data points (cities) close to each other. However, as with any map, some distortion will occur, especially for points far away from each other.

Advantages and limitations of T-SNE and PCA

T-SNE should be preferred over PCA when:

- The data is high-dimensional and has complex, nonlinear structures.
- The primary goal is data visualization.
- Computational resources and time are not major constraints.

On the other hand, PCA should be preferred when:

- The data is linear or linearly separable.
- The primary goal is to remove correlated features or reduce dimensions while preserving as much information as possible.
- Computational resources and time are a constraint.

Note: It's also worth noting that sometimes, T-SNE is used after initial dimensionality reduction with PCA. This is done to speed up the computations and eliminate noise and outliers. Although we will not look into the maths of T-SNE as it is quite complex to understand, having an idea of how it works is more than sufficient to use this technique.

Let's look at the difference between PCA and T-SNE when applied to the MNIST dataset (it's the most common dataset, you can find it anywhere on the internet).

```python
import numpy as np
import pandas as pd
import matplotlib.pyplot as plt
import seaborn as sns


from sklearn import manifold
from sklearn.preprocessing import StandardScaler
from sklearn import decomposition


# Load MNIST dataset, I already had it in csv format
data = pd.read_csv('../input/digit-recognizer/train.csv')
```

```python
# Separating labels and input data
df_labels = data.label
df_data = data.drop('label', axis = 1)

#extracting top 10000 data points
df_data = df_data.head(10000)
df_labels = df_labels.head(10000)
pixel_df = StandardScaler().fit_transform(df_data)

sample_data = pixel_df
pca = decomposition.PCA(n_components = 2, random_state = 42)
pca_data = pca.fit_transform(sample_data)

# Plotting PCA in two dimensions
# attaching the label for each 2-d data point
pca_data = np.column_stack((pca_data, df_labels))
# creating a new data frame for plotting of data points
pca_df = pd.DataFrame(data=pca_data, columns=("X", "Y", "labels"))
sns.FacetGrid(pca_df, hue="labels", size=6).map(plt.scatter, 'X', 'Y').
add_legend()
plt.show()

## Applying T-SNE
tsne = manifold.TSNE(n_components = 2, random_state = 42, verbose = 2,
n_iter = 2000)
transformed_data = tsne.fit_transform(sample_data)

#Creation of new dataframe for plotting of data points
tsne_df = pd.DataFrame(
    np.column_stack((transformed_data, df_labels)),
    columns = ['x', 'y', 'labels'])
```

```
tsne_df.loc[:, 'labels']= tsne_df.labels.astype(int)

# Plotting MNIST in two dimensions
grid = sns.FacetGrid(tsne_df, hue='labels', size = 8)
grid.map(plt.scatter, 'x', 'y').add_legend()
```

Please have a look at one of the very interesting videos on PCA from the YouTube channel called StatsQuest: **https://www.youtube.com/watch?v=FgakZw6K1QQ&ab_channel=StatQuestwithJoshStarmer [17]**

Note: All the video links are in the QR code at the end of every chapter.

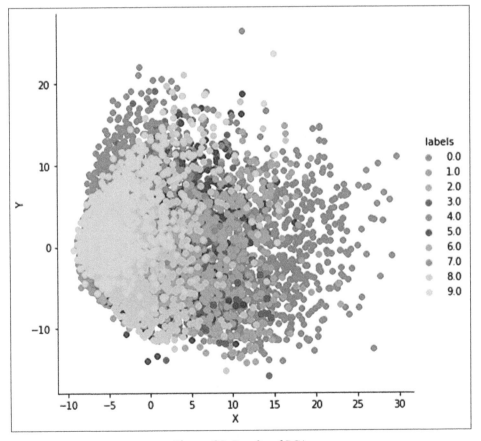

Figure 5.2: Results of PCA

The preceding figure shows the results of PCA on the MNIST data, we can see that using the PCA doesn't give us a clear separation between all the classes.

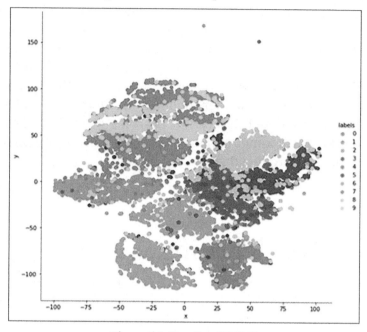

Figure 5.3: *Results of* T-SNE

In the preceding case of MNIST, we can see that T-SNE works better than PCA in showing a clear separation between the different classes of the MNIST dataset, as shown in the preceding figures. But keep in mind that's not always the case; the performance of both of these can totally change based on the distribution of the data.

Non-linear PCA

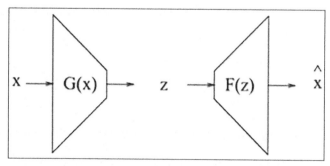

Figure 5.4: *Information bottleneck in dimensionality reduction. Linear PCA is obtained for linear mappings F(·) and G(·). Nonlinear PCA analysis is obtained by considering nonlinear mappings that MLPs can parameterize*

Another non-linear mapping method uses a simple Multi-Layer Perceptron or MLPs structure in encoder-decoder format. A Multilayer Perceptron (MLP) is a feedforward artificial neural network consisting of input, hidden, and output layers used for various machine learning tasks by transforming input data through interconnected nodes with learnable weights. The idea behind this technique is that we take our input x and pass it through an MLP $G(x)$, which reduces the size or dimensions of the input by passing it through hidden layers of neurons and creating an encoder mapping. In *Chapter 1: Understanding* AI *History*, we already discussed the idea of Learning representations from data. Finally, we take these encodings and pass them through another set of decoder MLP $F(z)$ to produce the reduced version of our input data .

Note: It can be mathematically proven that we can get the exact same results as PCA using MLPs

Unsupervised learning

In the real world, you will often encounter scenarios where you don't have unlabeled or partially labeled data only. Although there are several ways to deal with such scenarios, a few common techniques are clustering, semi-supervised learning, self-supervised learning, and so on.

Clustering

Clustering is unsupervised learning that aims to group similar instances. Clustering algorithms identify the inherent groupings in data. Here are a few common types of clustering algorithms and their underlying math:

K-means clustering: This is one of the simplest and most popular unsupervised machine learning algorithms. K-means' objective is simple: group similar data points together and discover underlying patterns. Here's a high-level explanation of the algorithm:

1. Choose the number "K" of clusters.

2. Select the centroids at random K points (not necessarily from your dataset).

3. Assign each data point to the closest centroid, which forms K clusters.

4. Compute and place the new centroid of each cluster.

5. Reassign each data point to the new closest centroid. If any reassignment occurs, go to step 4; otherwise, the model is ready.

K-means is equivalent to the **expectation-maximization** algorithm with a small, all-equal, diagonal covariance matrix.

The algorithm can also be understood through the concept of **Voronoi diagrams**. First, the Voronoi diagram of the points is calculated using the current centroids. Each segment in the Voronoi diagram becomes a separate cluster. Secondly, the centroids are updated to the mean of each segment. The algorithm then repeats this until a stopping criterion is fulfilled. Usually, the algorithm stops when the relative decrease in the objective function between iterations is less than the given tolerance value. However, this is not the case in this implementation: iteration stops when centroids move less than the tolerance.

Given enough time, K-means will always converge; however, this may be to a local minimum. This is highly dependent on the initialization of the centroids. As a result, the computation is often done several times, with different initializations of the centroids.

Another thing to note here is how to decide the number of K's in K-means? One simple way is to use the **elbow method**. The elbow method is a technique used to determine the optimal number of clusters in a K-means clustering algorithm. It involves plotting the sum of squared distances (inertia) between data points and their assigned cluster centers for different values of K (number of clusters). The point where the inertia starts to decrease at a slower rate on the graph resembles an **elbow**, indicating a reasonable number of clusters to choose for the analysis, striking a balance between model complexity and data fitting.

Given below is an example showing the optimum clusters, along with its vornoi diagram.

```python
import numpy as np
import matplotlib.pyplot as plt
from sklearn.cluster import KMeans
from sklearn.decomposition import PCA


# Generate some example data (replace this with your data)
data = np.random.rand(100, 10)


# Perform PCA for dimensionality reduction
reduced_data = PCA(n_components=2).fit_transform(data)
```

```python
# Determine the optimal number of clusters using the elbow method
inertia_values = []
possible_clusters = range(1, 11)  # Test for 1 to 10 clusters
for k in possible_clusters:
    kmeans = KMeans(init="k-means++", n_clusters=k, n_init=4)
    kmeans.fit(reduced_data)
    inertia_values.append(kmeans.inertia_)

# Choose the optimal number of clusters (e.g., where the curve starts to
level off)
optimal_clusters = 3  # Replace with the number of clusters you determine

# Perform K-means clustering with the chosen number of clusters
kmeans = KMeans(init="k-means++", n_clusters=optimal_clusters, n_init=4)
kmeans.fit(reduced_data)

# Plot both images side by side
plt.figure(figsize=(12, 6))

# Elbow curve plot
plt.subplot(1, 2, 1)
plt.plot(possible_clusters, inertia_values, marker='o')
plt.title("Elbow Method for Optimal K")
plt.xlabel("Number of Clusters")
plt.ylabel("Inertia (Sum of Squared Distances)")

# K-means clustering result plot
plt.subplot(1, 2, 2)
h = 0.02
x_min, x_max = reduced_data[:, 0].min() - 1, reduced_data[:, 0].max() + 1
y_min, y_max = reduced_data[:, 1].min() - 1, reduced_data[:, 1].max() + 1
xx, yy = np.meshgrid(np.arange(x_min, x_max, h), np.arange(y_min, y_max,
```

```
h))
Z = kmeans.predict(np.c_[xx.ravel(), yy.ravel()])
Z = Z.reshape(xx.shape)

plt.imshow(Z, interpolation="nearest",
           extent=(xx.min(), xx.max(), yy.min(), yy.max()),
           cmap=plt.cm.Paired,
           aspect="auto", origin="lower")

plt.plot(reduced_data[:, 0], reduced_data[:, 1], "k.", markersize=2)
centroids = kmeans.cluster_centers_
plt.scatter(centroids[:, 0], centroids[:, 1],
            marker="x", s=169, linewidths=3,
            color="w", zorder=10)
plt.title("K-means clustering result (PCA-reduced data)\n"
          "Centroids are marked with white cross")
plt.xlim(x_min, x_max)
plt.ylim(y_min, y_max)
plt.xticks(())
plt.yticks(())

# Adjust layout for better visualization
plt.tight_layout()
plt.show()
```

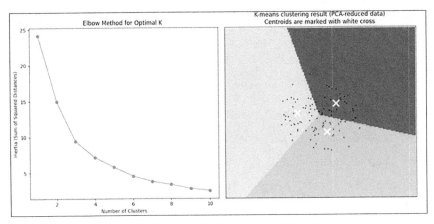

Figure 5.5: *Elbow method for optimal K (left) and
K-Means clustering with its Voronoi diagram (right)*

Hierarchical clustering: This algorithm builds a cluster hierarchy by continuously merging or splitting existing groups. There are two types of hierarchical clustering.

Agglomerative and divisive: Agglomerative follows a bottom-up approach, where each data point starts in its cluster, and pairs of clusters are merged as we move up the hierarchy. Divisive follows a top-down approach, where all observations start in one cluster, and splits are performed recursively as we move down the hierarchy.

The key operation in hierarchical agglomerative clustering is repeatedly combining the two nearest clusters into a larger cluster. There are multiple ways to define the distance between clusters, which lead to different algorithms (single linkage, complete linkage, average linkage, and so on).

No mathematical formula can be universally applied to Hierarchical clustering as it is majorly dependent on the distance metrics (like Euclidean, Manhattan, and so on) and linkage methods used.

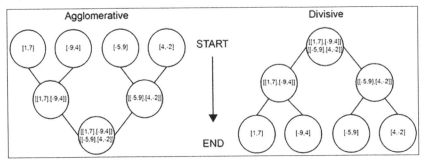

Figure 5.6: *Hierarchal Clustering: Agglomerative and Divisive*

DBSCAN (Density-Based Spatial Clustering of Applications with Noise): This density-based clustering algorithm has the notion of density reachability and connectivity. DBSCAN groups together point packed closely together (points with many nearby neighbors), marking them as outliers point that lie alone in low-density regions.

DBSCAN does not require the user to set the number of clusters a priori. As a result, it can discover clusters of arbitrary shape and is robust to outliers.

Here's a high-level explanation of the algorithm:

- For each point, compute the distance to all other points, and identify which points are within the radius epsilon.

- If a point has at least 'minPts' within the epsilon distance, mark it as a core point.

- Assign each point to a cluster or as noise (an outlier).

There is no specific mathematical formula for DBSCAN clustering. Instead, the algorithm relies on a density-based notion of clusters. It uses the parameters epsilon (the maximum distance between two samples to be considered in the same neighborhood) and **minPts** (the number of samples in a neighborhood for a point to be considered a core point).

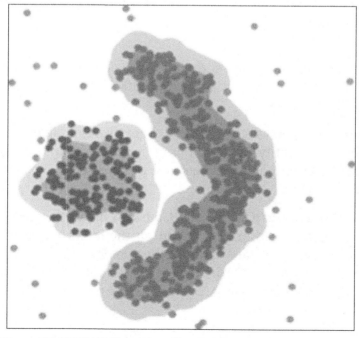

Figure 5.7: DBSCAN Clustering: *Chooses the two most dense clusters*

These are only a few examples of clustering techniques; there are many more.

Other advanced clustering methods:

Affinity propagation: Affinity propagation was first published in 2007 by Brendan Frey and Delbert Dueck in the renowned Science journal. It considers all data points as input measures of similarity between pairs of data points and simultaneously considers them as potential exemplars. Real-valued messages are exchanged between data points until a high-quality set of exemplars and corresponding clusters gradually emerges.

BIRCH (*Balanced Iterative Reducing and Clustering using Hierarchies***):** This technique is very useful when clustering large datasets, as it begins by first generating a more compact summary that retains as much distribution information as possible and then clustering the data summary instead of the original large dataset.

OPTICS (*Ordering Points to Identify the Clustering Structure***):** is a density-based clustering algorithm. It is very similar to the DBSCAN described earlier, but it overcomes one of DBSCAN's limitations: detecting meaningful clusters in data of varying density.

Mini-Batch K-Means: This is a k-means version in which cluster centroids are updated in small batches rather than the entire dataset. When working with a large dataset, the mini-batch k-means technique can be used to minimize computing time.

Mean shift clustering: The mean shift clustering algorithm is a centroid-based algorithm that shifts data points towards centroids to be the mean of other points in the feature space.

Spectral clustering: Spectral clustering is a graph-based algorithm where the approach is used to identify communities of nodes based on the edges. Spectral clustering has grown in popularity because of its ease of implementation and promising performance.

Gaussian Mixture Models (GMM): The Gaussian mixture model extends the k-means clustering algorithm. It is based on the idea that each cluster may be assigned to a different Gaussian distribution. GMM uses soft-assignment of data points to clusters (that is, probabilistic and therefore better) when contrasting with the K-means approach of hard-assignment of data points to clusters.

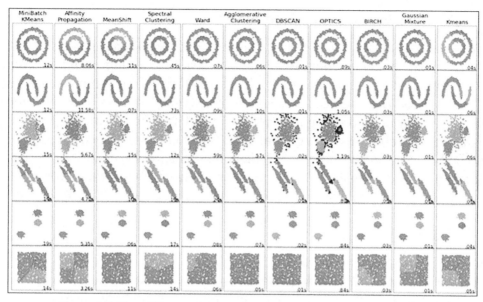

Figure 5.8: *How different clustering algorithm works on the same data*

Semi-supervised learning

Weak supervision, called semi-supervised learning, is a branch of machine learning that deals with partially labeled data. Often, real-world data misses target labels, and models trained under that paradigm fall into semi-supervised learning. Semi-supervised learning falls between unsupervised learning (with no labeled training data) and supervised learning (with only labeled training data). Semi-supervised learning aims to alleviate the issue of having limited amounts of labeled data available for training.

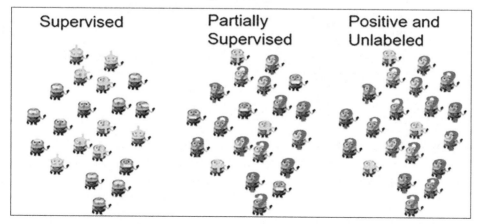

Figure 5.9: *Different scenarios in semi-supervised learning*

Method 1: Using Bagging to find the odd one out

Suppose you possess labels for only a limited number of data points. In such a scenario, what should be your next course of action? One approach is to employ an ensemble technique like **Bagging**, which combines multiple models that learn distinct aspects. This enables the creation of a set of classifiers using the labeled data. Bagging involves training multiple individual models on different subsets of the training data obtained through sampling. The models are trained independently and combined by averaging their predictions (in regression tasks) or voting (in classification tasks) to make the final prediction. Bagging helps reduce the variance of individual models and improves overall prediction accuracy and robustness.

The next step is to classify each unlabeled training example using every model generated. If a consensus is reached among (almost) all classifiers regarding the label of a particular example, it can be added to the training set along with its predicted label. However, it is important to note that this technique may overlook a significant portion of the data points and might not yield optimal results when confronted with substantial amounts of missing data.

Method 2: KNN for label propagation

One alternative approach is to utilize the K-NN algorithm for label propagation. In this technique, we assume that an example with a known label will have nearby neighbors sharing the same label. Labels are then propagated along the edges based on weights, typically determined by the distance between examples. This results in assigning label distributions to unlabeled examples.

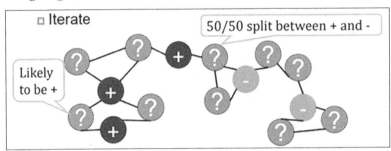

Figure 5.10: Label propagation

By employing the aforementioned K-NN technique, we can derive labels for a substantial amount of unlabeled data, albeit with varying degrees of confidence. However, a challenge arises when encountering a data point with relatively low label confidence. For instance, let's consider a point where, after label propagation, we obtain a confidence of 55% for the positive class and 45% for the negative class. In such cases, we cannot rely on this point alone to form the basis of our final classification model. So, what should be done with such a point? Put that point for manual labeling.

Method 3: Iterate till everything is labeled

Iteratively train a classifier on labeled data, selecting random points for prediction. If high confidence is attained, include those points in the training set for the next iteration. Repeat the process by training a classification model with the original data and the predictions from the previous model. Randomly choose a set number of points and add them to the training set if their confidence level meets the threshold. Continue training models until a sufficiently accurate model is achieved, capable of making highly accurate predictions for every data point.

The iterative approach is adopted based on the assumption that each successive model improves over the previous one, reducing the likelihood of errors. This is also why predictions are made on a few randomly selected points instead of the entire dataset.

Method 4: Active learning is the way forward

Active learning is the optimal approach for addressing the semi-supervised problem. But what exactly is active learning? It is a methodology that involves examining data and strategically selecting specific data points to be labeled by a human operator. This process aids in model improvement by focusing on crucial data points or seeking human input to label them. For example, the following diagram visually illustrates the effectiveness of manually selecting labeled data points instead of random selection in enhancing accuracy.

Note: We also do something called tandem learning for the text-related task. The feature word *puck* indicates the class hockey, and the feature word *strike* indicates baseball. Tandem learning exploits this by asking both instance-label and feature-relevance queries.

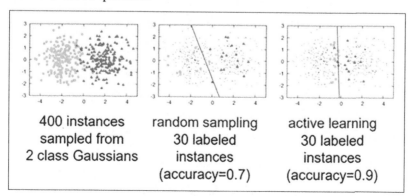

Figure 5.11: *Effect on accuracy after using active learning*

There is one problem with active learning:

We can't identify which data points are important and which aren't every time. So how do we find important data points that a human operator will later label? We have something called uncertainty sampling, train different models, and make predictions on every unlabeled data point; if there is a huge difference in the class confidence or difference in the predicted class, then we choose that point as the important point that needs to be labeled. Think of this in such a way that points that are classified correctly by every model are easy to classify, so we don't need to label that point.

Generalizing active learning to multi-class

Let's now look at the generalized approach towards active learning. In the preceding section, we gave an overview of active learning in method 4 but didn't tell how these techniques achieve what they are set to do. Let's start looking at it one by one, starting with the entropy-based method.

Entropy-based method

$$\varphi_{\mathrm{ENT}}(x) = -\sum_{y} P_{\theta}(x) \log_2 P_{\theta}(x) \quad \theta : model\, weights$$

Let's understand the preceding equation; this is the equation of entropy; when we have three classes, and let's say for every class prediction is 0.33, at that point, it will have the highest value, which means our model is most uncertain about this point, so we need to annotate its label manually. The following diagram shows you what happens to entropy when you have pure leaf nodes or when every point is correctly predicted and when you have impure nodes, that is, when you have a mixture of classes in a node. A point with the highest entropy will need manual annotation of labels.

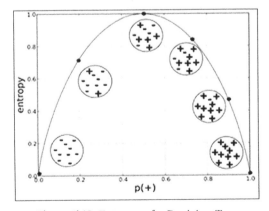

Figure 5.12: *Entropy of a Decision Tree*

Smallest margin

$$\varphi_m(x) = P_\theta(x) - P_\theta(x) \quad \theta : model\ weights$$

Here $P_\theta(x)$ is the probability assigned to the most confident prediction for a given input x (let's say model 1 assigns a point as class 0 with 0.9 confidence) and $P_\theta(x)$ is the probability assigned to the second most confident prediction but a different class for the input x (let's say model 2 assigns the same point as class 1 with 0.88 confidence) (remember we have multiple models predicting for the same data point). So, when the difference between these two points' probability scores is small, we will mark that point for manual annotation of labels.

Least confidence

$$\varphi_{LC}(x) = 1 - P_\theta(x) \quad \theta : model\ weights$$

Here $P_\theta(x)$ is the probability of the highest confidence class for a given input x, and if the probability is high, $\varphi_{LC}(x)$ will be small, which means that point is of no interest to us; we will mark those points for manual annotation, which gives us the high value of $\varphi_{LC}(x)$.

Query by committee

To understand this, we should first talk about a concept that is not often talked about, and it's called **Version Space** (we'll take a detailed look at version space in the next section). Version space in the context of machine learning is a conceptual space containing all the hypotheses consistent with the observed training examples. It is used in concept learning, where the goal is to acquire a Boolean-valued function from training examples.

Initially, the version space includes all possible hypotheses, but as more examples are observed, the space shrinks, excluding hypotheses inconsistent with the new examples. The remaining hypotheses in the version space are those that correctly classify all the observed examples so far. The concept of version space is fundamental to many learning algorithms, such as the Candidate-Elimination algorithm.

In short, version space is the set of all hypotheses consistent with the observed training data.

Coming back to the query by committee, train a committee $C = \{c_1, c_2, c_3...c_n\}$ of classifiers on the labeled data in L. Query instances in U (hypothesis space) for which the committee is in most disagreement, basically the most classifiers can't agree on the same output label. In other words, the following equation represents a criterion for selecting the data point x* that maximizes the committee's disagreement or entropy. The model can refine its predictions and improve performance by querying the labels for these informative data points.

$$x^* = argmax_{x \varepsilon U} - \sum_{i=1}^{|y|} \frac{v(yi)}{|c|} log \frac{v(yi)}{|c|}$$

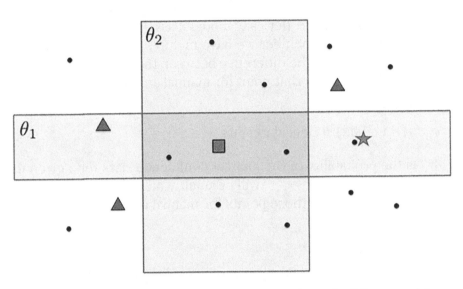

Figure 5.13: Representation of different hypotheses learnt by different models

The key idea here is to reduce version space; with each iteration, we find the points where the two-version space disagrees, and those points are marked as the points that need to be labeled manually. Here we have one point (marked by a *) that disagrees by C1 and C2 classifiers (θ_1 and θ_2) is their version space respectively, we manually mark this label and add it and then again create a version space; iteratively, we find all the important points that are needed to classify the entire dataset.

Note: It's okay if you don't understand every term in the preceding equation; understanding the concepts behind these equations is more important. Having the capacity to read and understand mathematical equations is always an advantage.

Self-supervised learning

Self-supervised learning is a form of unsupervised learning where the data provides the supervision. In other words, it's a type of machine learning where the labels for training are automatically generated from the input data itself.

In traditional supervised learning, you need labeled data, which means you need to know the answer for each example in your training set. This often involves manual labor and can be quite costly and time-consuming. In contrast, self-supervised learning generates its own labels from the input data, eliminating the need for explicit manual labels.

A common approach in self-supervised learning is to predict part of the data given the rest. For example, given a sentence with a missing word, the task could be to predict the missing word. This way, the model can learn useful features from the data, which can benefit downstream tasks like classification even without large amounts of labeled data. The underlying mathematics of self-supervised learning heavily depends on the specific method used. However, the objective function is usually designed to minimize the predicted and actual data differences.

Example to understand the concept

Here's a simple example: suppose you have a sentence, "The cat sat on the ____." A self-supervised learning algorithm could fill in the blank by predicting the missing word, 'mat', using the context provided by the rest of the sentence.

For example, consider an autoencoder, a common self-supervised learning model. An autoencoder aims to learn a compressed representation of the input data and then reconstruct the original data from this compressed form. If x is the input data and x' is the reconstructed data, the objective function, often a form of the loss function, could be something like the Mean Squared Error (MSE):

$$L(x, x') = 1/n * \Sigma (x_i - x'_i)^2$$

where n is the number of instances in the input data.

Self-supervised learning has shown great promise in various fields, including natural language processing, computer vision, and even reinforcement learning, providing a way to leverage the large amounts of unlabeled data available.

Let's now touch upon another concept called **Contrastive learning**; it is one of the very interesting Self-Supervised methods recently gaining much popularity for vision-related challenges. But for now, let's define it: Contrastive Learning is a technique used generally in vision tasks lacking labeled data. Using the principle of contrasting samples against each other, it learns attributes common between data classes and attributes that set apart a data class from another.

The basic idea behind contrastive learning is to teach a model to distinguish between similar and dissimilar pairs of examples in a given dataset. This is done by creating pairs of data samples and then optimizing the model to maximize the similarity between similar pairs and minimize the similarity between dissimilar pairs.

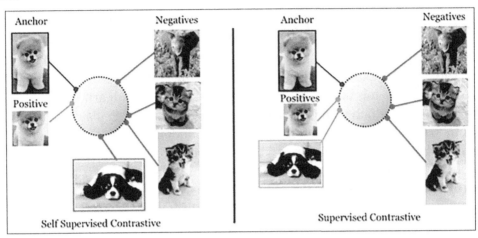

Figure 5.14: *Self-supervised and Supervised Contrastive learning (Img Src)*

Here's how Contrastive learning works:

Data preparation: To start with, a large dataset of unlabeled examples is gathered. These examples can be images, text snippets, or any other type of data.

Data augmentation: Data augmentation techniques are applied to create augmented versions of each example. This helps in increasing the diversity and richness of the dataset. For example, in the case of images, random cropping, rotation, or color jittering can be used to generate augmented versions.

Pair generation: Two augmented versions are randomly selected for each example in the dataset. These two versions form a pair consisting of a *query* example and a *positive* example. The positive example is a transformed version of the query example. The objective is to ensure that the positive example is semantically similar to the query example.

Negative sampling: A *negative* example is chosen to complete the pair. The negative example is typically another example from the dataset that is dissimilar to the query example. The goal is to encourage the model to differentiate between positive and negative examples.

Similarity computation: The next step is to calculate the similarity between the query, positive and negative examples. This is typically done by feeding the examples through a neural network and obtaining their embeddings or feature representations.

Contrastive loss: A contrastive loss function is defined to train the model. The loss function measures the agreement between the predicted similarities and the ground truth labels (1 for positive pairs and 0 for negative pairs). The objective is to maximize the similarity between positive pairs and minimize the similarity between negative pairs.

Optimization: To minimize the contrastive loss, the model parameters are updated using an optimization algorithm, such as stochastic gradient descent (SGD). The process of computing similarities, calculating loss, and updating parameters is repeated over multiple iterations or epochs.

By repeating this process with different pairs of examples, the model learns to extract meaningful representations that capture the underlying structure of the data. These representations can then be used for a variety of downstream tasks, such as image classification, object detection, or text generation.

In summary, contrastive learning leverages the concept of pairing similar and dissimilar examples to train a model without relying on explicit labels. By optimizing a contrastive loss function, the model learns to capture the underlying patterns and structure in the data, leading to effective representation learning.

Version space

Version space is something that is rarely discussed, but it forms the logical structure of learning itself. Understanding the concept of version space makes you see all AI algorithms differently. A version space is a hierarchical representation of knowledge that enables you to keep track of all the useful information supplied by a sequence of learning examples without remembering any of the examples.

The **version space method** is a concept-learning process accomplished by managing multiple models within a version space.

Version space characteristics

Tentative heuristics are represented using version spaces.

A version space represents all the plausible alternative **descriptions** of a heuristic. A plausible description applies to all known positive examples and no known negative examples.

A version space description consists of two complementary trees:

- One that contains nodes connected to overly **general** models, and

- One that contains nodes connected to overly **specific** models.

  Node values/attributes are discrete.

Fundamental assumptions

- The data is correct; there are no erroneous instances.
- A correct description is a conjunction of some attributes with values.

Diagrammatical guidelines

There is a **generalization** tree and a **specialization** tree.

Each **node** is connected to a **model**.

Nodes in the generalization tree are connected to a model that matches everything in its subtree. On the other hand, nodes in the specialization tree are connected to a model that matches only one thing in its subtree.

Links between nodes and their models denote

- generalization relations in a generalization tree and
- specialization relations in a specialization tree.

Diagram of a version space:

In the given diagram, the specialization tree is colored red, and the generalization tree is colored green.

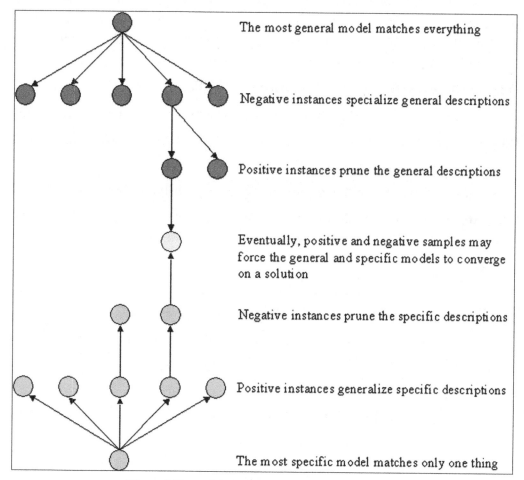

The most general model matches everything

Negative instances specialize general descriptions

Positive instances prune the general descriptions

Eventually, positive and negative samples may force the general and specific models to converge on a solution

Negative instances prune the specific descriptions

Positive instances generalize specific descriptions

The most specific model matches only one thing

Figure 5.15: Explaining the concept of Version space

Generalization and specialization leads to version space convergence

The primary concept behind version space learning revolves around refining broad models through specialization, and simultaneously expanding narrow models through generalization. This dual approach aims to arrive at a singular, accurate model that aligns with all observed positive instances while excluding all negative ones.

Whenever a negative example is introduced, it leads to the specialization of broader models. Consequently, any specific models that align with this negative instance are discarded. On the other hand, introducing a positive example prompts the generalization of narrower models, thereby eliminating any broader models that fail to encompass the positive instance.

Ultimately, the iterative process of encountering positive and negative examples may result in the survival of a single, comprehensive model that is identically representative at both the general and specific levels.

Version space method learning algorithm: candidate-elimination

The version space method handles positive and negative examples symmetrically.

Given:

- A representation language
- A set of positive and negative examples expressed in that language

Compute: a concept description that is consistent with all the positive examples and none of the negative examples.

Method:

1. Initialize G, the set of maximally general hypotheses, to contain one element: the null description (all features are variables).

2. Initialize S, the set of maximally specific hypotheses, to contain one element: the first positive example.

3. Accept a new training example.

   a. If the example is **positive**:
      - Generalize all the specific models to match the positive example, but ensure the following:
        - The new specific models involve minimal changes.
        - Each new specific model is a specialization of some general model.
        - No new specific model is a generalization of some other specific model.
      - Prune away all the general models that fail to match the positive example.

   b. If the example is **negative**:
      - Specialize all general models to prevent a match with the negative example, but ensure the following:
        - The new general models involve minimal changes.
        - Each new general model is a generalization of some specific model.

- ○ No new general model is a specialization of some other general model.
  - Prune away all the general models that fail to match the positive example.
c. If **S** and **G** are both singleton sets, then:
  - If they are identical, output their value and halt.
  - If they are different, the training cases were inconsistent. Output this result and halt.
  - Else continue accepting new training examples.

The algorithm stops when:

- It runs out of data.
- The number of hypotheses remaining is:
  - ○ 0 - no consistent description of the data in the language.
  - ○ 1 - answer (version space converges).
  - ○ 2+ - all descriptions in the language are implicitly included.

Note: The version space method is still a trial-and-error method. The program does not base its choice of examples or learned heuristics on analyzing what works or why, but rather on the assumption that what works will probably work again.

Unlike the decision tree ID3 algorithm,

- Candidate elimination searches an incomplete set of hypotheses (that is, only a subset of the potentially teachable concepts is included in the hypothesis space).
- Candidate elimination finds every hypothesis consistent with the training data, meaning it searches the hypothesis space completely.
- Candidate elimination's inductive bias results from how well it can represent the subset of possible hypotheses it will search. In other words, the bias is a product of its search space.
- No additional bias is introduced through Candidate elimination's search strategy.

Advantages of the version space method:

- Can describe all the possible hypotheses in the language consistent with the data.
- Fast (close to linear).

Disadvantages of the version space method:

- Inconsistent data (noise) may cause the target concept to be pruned.
- Learning disjunctive concepts is challenging.

With so many steps in Version Space, it might take much work to grasp the idea in one go. In summary, think of it as a way to learn concepts, and ultimately every algorithm tries to mimic the same thing in one way or another, **learning concepts and rules**.

Understanding optimization through SVM

SVM, a renowned classical machine learning algorithm, serves as an excellent example of grasping the concept of mathematical optimization. Most AI algorithms revolve around optimizing a cost function or an expression. While numerous articles are available on SVM through a simple Google search, few delve into the underlying mathematical optimization. By acquiring the necessary mathematical proficiency to comprehend this optimization level, you will undoubtedly possess the knowledge to understand various optimizations. The goal here is not to talk about SVM but, more importantly, optimizations.

SVM can be defined in two ways: one is the **dual form,** and the other is the **primal form**. Both get the same optimization result, but how they get it is very different. Just so you know, Primal mode is favored when the dataset is large, the dimension of each data point is small, and there is no need to apply the kernel trick to the data. On the other hand, the dual form is preferred when the data has high dimensionality, and the kernel trick needs to be applied.

Let's understand what we do in SVM. In SVM optimization, we try to maximize the distance of the hyperplane from the **support vectors**; it is the same as minimizing the **L2 norm** of W (weight matrix). As we look at the SVM's math, we will define what a support vector is.

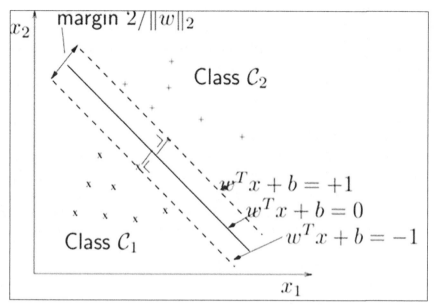

Figure 5.16: *We try to maximize the hyperplane distance to the nearest point in SVM*

The goal of SVM:

- To maximize the margin between the two classes using the Support Vector points, thus the name Support Vector Machines. The margin between the two classes is equal to $2 \,/\, \|w\|_2$ and **this is what we want to optimize.**

Let's mathematically define SVM:

Given a training set $\{x_K, y_K\}_K^N = 1$ input patterns $x_K \in R^n$ output patterns $y_K \in R^n$ where $y_K \in \{-1, +1\}$. Basically, what we defined here is that for input vector x, which is a real number vector of length N, we have an output y with possible values of +1 or -1.

$$\{w^T x_k + b \geq +1, \quad if \ y_k = +1 \quad w^T x_k + b \leq -1, \quad if \ y_k = -1$$

In the preceding equations $w^T x_k$ is just the multiplication of input vector x_k with transposed weight vector w^T and b here is the bias term and y_k for the k_{th} point in the given dataset; this can be combined into one equation like this:

$$y_k [w^T x_k + b] \geq 1, \ k = 1, \dots, N$$

Here, we see the final form of the SVM classifier; keep in mind that this is for perfect linear classification. But now comes the question of how to get this w-weight matrix.

Primal Form

There are two types of optimizations generally, constrained and unconstrained. Here's an example of both:

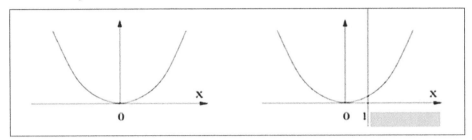

Figure 5.17: *Unconstrained (left) and Constrained (right) optimization*

Let's consider this simple quadratic function and try to find optimization, in this case, minimum on this curve.

For **unconstrained** optimization problem (solution: x=0)

$$min_x \; x^2$$

For **constrained** optimization problem (active constraint)

$$min_x \; x^2 \; such \; that \; x \geq 1$$

Let's write **optimization for SVM.**

$$min_{w,b} \frac{1}{2} w^T w \; s.t. \; y_k [w^T x_k + b] \geq 1, \; k = 1, \dots, N$$

There is another way to write the preceding equation in a way that combines the constraint as well; it's called **Lagrangian**. The following equation is what we solve to optimize SVM.

$$L(w, b; a) = \frac{1}{2} w^T w - \sum_{K=1}^{N} a_k \left\{ y_k \left[w^T x_k + b \right] - 1 \right\}$$

$$a_k \geq 0 \; are \; called \; lagrange \; multipliers \; for \; k = 1, \dots, N$$

Let's talk about the preceding optimization problem; it's an optimization problem where we are trying to minimize (weights and biases) such that are maximized. It's a **MIN(MAX)** problem where we are trying to minimize the product of W(transpose) and W such that $Y_k [W^T X_k + b] >= 1$.

Now it's time to define **support vectors**. All those data points for which the value is greater than 0 are called support vectors. Support vectors are those data points close to the decision margin and set the orientation of the separating hyperplane.

Our preceding equation has two unsolved variables: weight matrix W and α. For calculating , we use a technique called **Sequential Minimal Optimization (SMO) [18]**; this algorithm is based on the Coordinate ascent algorithm (kind of similar to gradient descent, but it minimizes the function in a step-wise shape). What SMO does is, it take pairs of and optimize them to reach the global minima.

The solution of the preceding equation is given by the saddle point of Lagrangian:

$$f(x) = \begin{cases} \dfrac{\partial L}{\partial w} = 0 \ yields \rightarrow \ w = \sum_{k=1}^{N} a_k y_k x_k \quad \dfrac{\partial L}{\partial b} = 0 \ yields \ \rightarrow \ \sum_{k=1}^{N} a_k y_k \geq 0 \end{cases}$$

Resulting classifier:

$$y(x) = sign[\sum_{k=1}^{N} a_k y_{k_k}^{T} x + b]$$

Once α's are calculated, we solve the Lagrangian by taking the partial derivative of the Lagrangian function with respect to weight and bias. The partial derivatives show that Weight matrix W is the product of the Lagrangian multiplier, class_ label, and the data point. And the second differential tells us that the linear combination of Lagrangian multiplier * class_label should always be 0.

The Lagrangian equation shows that it will be awful for high dimensional data as we have to multiply every data point with the entire weight matrix. And also, for applying kernel, as it needs to be first applied on each datapoint X, those points will be put into the Lagrangian. Using Even 5-order polynomials will lead to 5! features for every single data point, which will lead to colossal time complexity. We will have all the possible combinations of $X^5 + X^4 + X^5 X^4 X^3 + \ldots$, which in our case will be huge.

Don't worry if you don't understand the maths behind SVM; the goal here is not to make it a maths book but rather to give you a taste of how even something simple like SVM looks.

Dual form

Now, let's look at the same optimization in Dual Form. Here's the equation for SVM dual form:

$$max_{\smile a}Q(\alpha) = -\frac{1}{2}\sum_{k,l=1}^{N} y_k y_l x_k^T x\, \alpha_k \alpha_l + \sum_{k,=1}^{N} \alpha_k$$

Such that:

$$\{\sum_{k,=1}^{N} \alpha_k y_k = 0\, \alpha_k \geq 0, \qquad k = 1, ..., N$$

The preceding equation is a **maximization (MAX)** problem; there is no term of weights or even margin; then how come these two solve the same problem? This optimization looks completely different from the Primal form. Now how to make sure that both optimizations solve the same problem? For that, we have to satisfy something called **KKT** conditions. Satisfying these conditions makes sure that **MAX(MIN) = MIN(MAX)**; without satisfying KKT, we have **MAX(MIN) <= MIN(MAX)**. How do we satisfy the KKT condition in our case? The constraints we obtain hereafter take the partial derivative to satisfy the KKT condition for this optimization problem.

Let's understand the preceding Lagrangian equation; it's a product of each data point with all other data points, followed by their respective Lagrangian and their class_label. For the preceding equations, we take the partial derivative with respect to weights and biases and get two conditions first, a linear combination of Lagrangian multiplier() * class label() is 0, and secondly, all Lagrangian multipliers are either 0 or greater than 0. We can see why this is unsuitable for large datasets as we have to do N*(N-1) multiplication to solve the preceding optimization problem. After solving this optimization, we will get the same solution as in the primal form.

In the dual form, we can easily apply the kernel; there is a reason it is called the kernel trick, not the kernel method, which can be understood from the following equations. We don't calculate the high-order mappings; we compute the dot product and then do the high-order mapping of that particular point.

The kernel trick is a method used in machine learning to convert a non-linear problem into a linear problem. It's particularly useful in algorithms such as Support Vector Machines (SVMs), which can be more effective in higher-dimensional space. The key idea of the kernel trick is to implicitly map input data into a higher-dimensional space where it becomes linearly separable without actually performing the computationally expensive transformation.

To illustrate the concept of the kernel trick, we first need to explain what a kernel function is. In simple terms, a kernel is a function that computes a dot product in a high-dimensional space without explicitly creating the mapping, without actually going to that high-dimensional space.

Let's understand this concept with an example:

$$\varphi(a)' \cdot \varphi(b) = (a_1^2 \ \sqrt{2}\,a_1 a_2 \ a_2^2)(b_1^2 \ \sqrt{2}\,b_1 b_2 \ b_2^2) = a_1^2 b_1^2 + 2a_1 b_1 a_2 b_2 + a_2^2 b_2^2$$

We see that in the preceding equation, the final form looks like simple $(a+b)^2$. So, we can define a quadratic kernel and get the same results without calculating terms like $a_1^2, b_1^2, \sqrt{2}\,a_1 a_2, \sqrt{2}\,b_1 b_2$, and so on.

$$(a_1 b_1 + a_2 b_2)^2 = \left(\begin{pmatrix} a_1 \\ a_2 \end{pmatrix}' \cdot \begin{pmatrix} b_1 \\ b_2 \end{pmatrix} \right)^2 = \mathbf{(a' \cdot b)}$$

Now we can see that we get the same result as the preceding equation with much fewer calculations, and that's the beauty of the kernel trick.

Note: SVM Dual form can work with different types of Kernels like RBF, Polynomial, and so on. Here's an example from Scikit-Learn's official documentation showcasing SVM dual form using different kernels and giving different decision boundaries.

```python
import matplotlib.pyplot as plt
from sklearn import svm, datasets
from sklearn.inspection import DecisionBoundaryDisplay


# import some data to play with
iris = datasets.load_iris()
# Take the first two features. We could avoid this by using a two-dim
dataset
X = iris.data[:, :2]
y = iris.target


# we create an instance of SVM and fit out data. We do not scale our
# data since we want to plot the support vectors
```

```python
C = 1.0  # SVM regularization parameter
models = (
    svm.SVC(kernel="linear", C=C),
    svm.LinearSVC(C=C, max_iter=10000),
    svm.SVC(kernel="rbf", gamma=0.7, C=C),
    svm.SVC(kernel="poly", degree=3, gamma="auto", C=C),
)
models = (clf.fit(X, y) for clf in models)

# title for the plots
titles = (
    "SVC with linear kernel",
    "LinearSVC (linear kernel)",
    "SVC with RBF kernel",
    "SVC with polynomial (degree 3) kernel",
)

# Set-up 2x2 grid for plotting.
fig, sub = plt.subplots(2, 2)
plt.subplots_adjust(wspace=0.4, hspace=0.4)

X0, X1 = X[:, 0], X[:, 1]
for clf, title, ax in zip(models, titles, sub.flatten()):
    disp = DecisionBoundaryDisplay.from_estimator(
        clf,
        X,
        response_method="predict",
        cmap=plt.cm.coolwarm,
        alpha=0.8,
        ax=ax,
        xlabel=iris.feature_names[0],
```

```
        ylabel=iris.feature_names[1],
    )
    ax.scatter(X0, X1, c=y, cmap=plt.cm.coolwarm, s=20, edgecolors="k")
    ax.set_xticks(())
    ax.set_yticks(())
    ax.set_title(title)


plt.show()
```

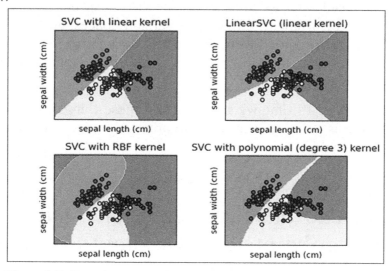

Figure 5.18: *SVM showing its decision boundaries with different Kernels*

Note that there are many other optimizations that you should be aware of, Optimization of Logistic regression is pretty interesting, but we are not going to cover all of them here.

Logistic regression optimization: **https://medium.com/aiguys/beautiful-maths-behind-logistic-regression-optimization-6cefd3ec1c91 [19]**

Conclusion

This chapter serves as the foundational pillar, encompassing all the essential mathematical concepts required to construct a comprehensive understanding of AI. It commences by exploring dimensionality reduction, where three key algorithms—PCA, T-SNE, and Auto-Encoders—are examined. Moving forward, the focus shifts to unsupervised learning, elucidating clustering algorithms such as

K-Means, Hierarchical Clustering, and DBSCAN. This is followed by an extensive discussion on semi-supervised learning methods and a brief introduction to self-supervised learning approaches. The chapter further delves into the theory of Version Spaces, providing a comprehensive definition of the concept learning process. Lastly, the chapter concludes by delving into the mathematical foundations of optimization, illustrated through the SVM Primal form.

In summary, this chapter establishes the cornerstone for comprehending the mathematical principles vital to constructing a holistic framework of AI. It covers dimensionality reduction techniques, unsupervised learning with clustering algorithms, detailed insights into semi-supervised learning, an introduction to self-supervised learning, the theory of Version Spaces, and an exploration of optimization mathematics through the SVM Primal form. By assimilating these concepts, readers will gain a solid grasp of the fundamental mathematical aspects underpinning AI.

Enough with maths; it's time we start building these things from scratch. So, the next chapter is going to deal with the practical implementation of Neural Network components.

"The question is not whether intelligent machines can have any emotions, but whether machines can be intelligent without any emotions."
- Marvin Minsky

https://github.com/OrangeAVA/Ultimate-Neural-Network-Programming-with-Python

## CHAPTER 6

Building Deep Neural Networks from Scratch

Enough with the chit-chat about neural networks (NN) theory; it's time to move from theory to practice and understand the real-life complexity of building even a simple neural network from scratch. In this chapter, we will build everything from scratch to understand better how all the nuts and bolts of a neural network work. Implementing neural networks from scratch will have a deep impact in terms of understanding and modifying state-of-the-art architectures.

Structure

This chapter covers the following topics:

- Coding neurons and simple neuron layers without any libraries
- Understanding tensors, array, lists, matrices, and their operations
- Writing simple neural network using NumPy
- Adding loss functions and calculating accuracy

Coding neurons

In the previous chapters, we have already defined a neuron; let's start by building it in Python from scratch.

A single neuron

Let's start simple and understand the behavior of a single neuron; for example, we'll take a neuron with three inputs. When initializing parameters within neural networks, we typically start with randomly assigned weights and biases set at zero. The rationale behind this approach will become evident as we progress. Inputs for the network may come from actual training data or neuron outputs from the prior layer in the network.

These inputs each require an associated weight. The inputs represent the data fed into our model in order to generate the expected outputs, and the weights are the variables that we adjust later to achieve these results. Weights and biases are values within the model that alter during the training phase (though for the time being, we maintain the biases at 1). The values of weights and biases are "trained", meaning they are adjusted through iterative processes, influencing whether the model operates correctly. Initially, we'll assign arbitrary values to the weights.

Let's assume that the first input (indexed at 0), a 1, is assigned a weight of 0.2, the second input a weight of 0.8, and the third input a weight of -0.5. Our lists of inputs and weights should now reflect these values.

```
inputs = [1, 2, 3]
weights = [0.2, 0.8, -0.5]
bias = 1
```

Our single neuron sums each input multiplied by that input's weight, then adds the bias. All the neuron does is take the fractions of inputs, where these fractions (weights) are the adjustable parameters, and adds another adjustable parameter – the bias – then outputs the result.

```
output = (inputs[0]*weights[0] + inputs[1]*weights[1] + inputs[2]*-
weights[2] + bias)
print(output)

#Output: 1.3
```

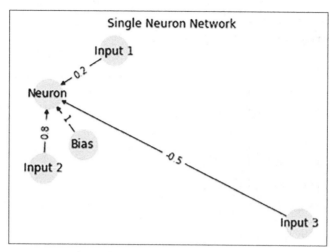

Figure 6.1: *Single Neuron*

Layer of neurons

A single neuron is pretty useless. Let's now consider a layer of neurons. In a proper neural network, you will see several of these layers; the number of layers can easily cross 100. Let's say we have a scenario with three neurons in a layer and four inputs:

```
inputs = [1, 2, 4, 2.5]
```

```
weights1 = [0.1, 0.8, -0.5, 1.1]
weights2 = [0.5, -0.1, 0.6, -0.5]
weights3 = [-0.46, -0.27, 0.17, 0.8]
bias1 = 1
bias2 = 2
bias3 = 0.5
outputs = [
        # Neuron 1:
        inputs[0]*weights1[0] +
        inputs[1]*weights1[1] +
        inputs[2]*weights1[2] +
        inputs[3]*weights1[3] + bias1,
```

```
# Neuron 2:
inputs[0]*weights2[0] +
inputs[1]*weights2[1] +
inputs[2]*weights2[2] +
inputs[3]*weights2[3] + bias2,
# Neuron 3:
inputs[0]*weights3[0] +
inputs[1]*weights3[1] +
inputs[2]*weights3[2] +
inputs[3]*weights3[3] + bias3
]


print(outputs)


# Output: [3.45, 3.4499999999999997, 2.18]
```

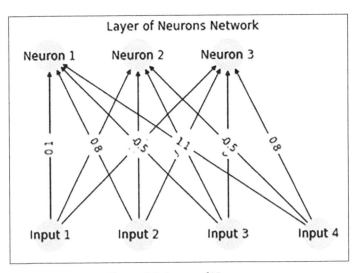

Figure 6.2: Layer of Neuron

In the preceding code, three neurons are defined by three sets of weights and biases. Each neuron is connected to the same inputs, but each applies different weights and biases to the input. This architecture is a **fully connected neural network**, where every neuron in the current layer is connected to every neuron in the previous layer. While this is a common type of neural network, it's important to note that not all connections need to be fully connected.

We have shown code for a single layer with few neurons. However, if we were to code multiple layers with more neurons, it would become challenging using our current methods. Instead, we can use a loop to handle dynamically sized inputs and layers. By transforming the separate weight variables into a list, we can iterate over them and replace the hardcoded operations with loops for more flexibility in our code.

Let's use the power of a for loop:

```python
inputs = [1, 2, 4, 2.5]


weights = [[0.1, 0.8, -0.5, 1.1], [0.5, -0.1, 0.6, -0.5], [-0.46, -0.27, 0.17, 0.8]]
biases = [1, 2, 0.5]


# Output of current layer
layer_out = []
# For each neuron
for neuron_weights, neuron_bias in zip(weights, biases):
    # Zeroed output of given neuron
    neuron_output = 0
    # For each input and weight to the neuron
    for n_input, weight in zip(inputs, neuron_weights):
        # Multiply this input by the associated weight
        # and add to the neuron's output variable
        neuron_output += n_input*weight
    # Adding bias term
    neuron_output += neuron_bias
    # Putting neuron's result in the layer's output list
    layer_out.append(neuron_output)
print(layer_out)
```

```
print(layer_out[-1])
```

```
# Output: [3.45, 3.4499999999999997, 2.18]
```

This section introduces a dynamic approach; I suggest using **print()** to get more clarity on each step. The **zip()** function helps iterate over multiple lists simultaneously. The goal remains unchanged: multiply inputs with associated weights, accumulate the results, add a bias, and append the neuron's output. The presence of three sets of weights and biases indicates three neurons. When creating your network, you decide the number of neurons per layer. Starting with a few neurons aids in understanding neural network fundamentals.

Understanding lists, arrays, tensors, and their operations

When working with actual Neural Networks, we often encounter terms like tensors, vectors, and arrays. What exactly are these? Tensors are closely related to arrays. People usually interchange tensor/array/matrix when it comes to machine learning. However, there are subtle differences, primarily the context or attributes of the tensor object.

List in Python: [1,0,6,34]

List of list: [[[1,5,9,2], [3,2,1,1]],

[[5,9,1,2], [6,4]]]

The difference between **arrays** and **lists** is that an array needs to be homologous, meaning it should have the same number of elements in every row and column. So, for example, the preceding list is not an array as the last element of the second list only has two elements; if it had four elements, this would become an array.

You will also encounter another term called **matrix**. It's a rectangular array and has both columns and rows, making it two- dimensional. So, a matrix can be considered an array (a 2D array). Can all arrays be matrices? No. An array can even have four dimensions, ten dimensions, and more.

We also need to learn one more notion – a **vector**. A vector in math is a list in Python or a one-dimensional array in NumPy.

What's a tensor? A tensor is an object that can be represented as an array. In the context of AI, we treat tensors as arrays, and that's all the thought we have to put into it.

All tensors are not arrays

No (in physics, they mean something else), but for AI purposes, they are represented as arrays. So, to us, they're only arrays, which is why there's so much argument and confusion.

Dot product and vector addition

Vector multiplication is an essential operation in neural networks. Instead of element-wise multiplication, we can use dot products to achieve the same outcome. We can refer to these vectors as tensors or containers. The mysticism around neural networks stems from perceiving them as complex objects in a multi-dimensional vector space. However, we can think of vectors as simple arrays, with a one-dimensional array being a vector (or a list in Python).

We can model intricate and non-linear relationships using non-linear activation functions with the dot product. It simplifies the necessary calculations without adding complexity. The dot product results in a scalar, while a cross product produces a vector.

```
# Performing dot product
a = [1,2,3]
b = [6,5,4]


dot_product = a[0]*b[0] + a[1]*b[1] + a[2]*b[2]
print(dot_product)


# Output: 28
```

If you remember our previous section, we performed a dot product between our weights and inputs. Another thing that you will often come across is vector addition. Here's how to do it in code:

```
# Performing vector addition
```

```
a = [1,2,3]
b = [6,5,4]


vector_add = a[0]+b[0] + a[1]+b[1] + a[2]+b[2]
print(vector_add)


# Output: [7, 7, 7]
```

Remember that we still get a vector in vector addition but a single number in the dot product.

Cross-product, transpose, and order

When you start reading the maths behind all the AI algorithms, you will come across the concept of transpose, a simple matrix operation. Transposition modifies a matrix in a way that its rows become columns and columns become rows:

$$1\ 2\ 3\ 4\ 6\ 1\ 2\ 3\ 2 \qquad 2\ 3\ 4\ 5\ 6\ 7 \qquad 1\ 0\ 1 \rightarrow 1\ 0\ 1$$

The preceding matrices have an order or shape of 3x3, 2x3. The last two matrices are transposed from 1x3 to 3x1, moving from left to right. This order is essential for the cross-product.

Suppose we have two matrices, A and B, with the following dimensions:

Matrix A: 3 x 2

```
A = [[1, 2],
     [3, 4],
     [5, 6]]
```

Matrix B: 2 x 4

```
B = [[7, 8, 9, 10],
     [11, 12, 13, 14]]
```

To perform matrix multiplication, the number of columns in the first matrix (A) should match the number of rows in the second matrix (B). In this case, A has two columns, and B has two rows, satisfying this requirement.

However, if we reverse the order and attempt to multiply B by A, we encounter an issue:

Matrix C = B * A

Matrix B (2 x 4) multiplied by Matrix A (3 x 2) is not possible because the number of columns in B (4) does not match the number of rows in A (3).

Hence, the order of the matrices is essential in matrix multiplication. Swapping the order can result in incompatible dimensions, making the multiplication operation invalid.

Understanding neural networks through NumPy

As discussed in *Chapter 3: Python Libraries for Data Scientists*, in later sections, we will discuss one of the most famous libraries for numerical computation, NumPy. But first, let's understand the use of NumPy in creating our neural networks.

To install NumPy: **pip install numpy**

Neural networks using NumPy

Let's write a single neuron using the NumPy library this time:

```python
# A single neuron using NumPy
import numpy as np


inputs = [1.0, 2.0, 3.0]
weights = [0.2, 0.8, -0.5]
bias = 1.0
outputs = np.dot(weights, inputs) + bias
print(outputs)


# Output: 1.3
```

We can see that NumPy makes our code much cleaner and shorter. Also, it's faster than standard Python-implemented functions. NumPy uses C++ in the backend, making it pretty quick and efficient.

Now let's write our previous neural network layer using NumPy this time:

```python
# A single Neuron layer using NumPy
import numpy as np


inputs = [1, 2, 4, 2.5]
weights = [[0.1, 0.8, -0.5, 1.1], [0.5, -0.1, 0.6, -0.5], [-0.46, -0.27, 0.17, 0.8]]
biases = [1, 2, 0.5]
layer_out = np.dot(weights, inputs) + biases
print(layer_out)


#Output: [3.45 3.45 2.18]
```

Again look at how small our code becomes; **np.dot()** is much faster than running a loop.

Processing batch of data

In real life, we never deal with one example; we always need several hundreds and thousands of examples, sometimes even millions, to train our neural networks. We should understand how to feed this data in chunks or batches in such cases.

```python
# Processing batch of data through 3 neurons layers
import numpy as np


inputs = [[1, 2, 4, 2.5], [1, 0, 0, 1], [1, 3, 8, 6]]
weights = [[0.1, 0.8, -0.5, 1.1], [0.5, -0.1, 0.6, -0.5], [-0.46, -0.27, 0.17, 0.8]]
biases = [1, 2, 0.5]
layer_out = np.dot(inputs, np.array(weights).T) + biases
print(layer_out)
```

```
#Output: [[3.45 3.45 2.18]
#          [2.2  2.   0.84]
#          [6.1  4.   5.39]]
```

As observed, our neural network accepts a collection of samples (inputs) and produces a set of predictions. Suppose you have experience with deep-learning libraries. In that case, you might have noticed that you pass in a list of inputs (even if it's a single feature set) and receive a list of predictions in return, even if it consists of only one. Additionally, we utilize the transpose operation (.T) in the dot product between our weight matrix and input matrix. Omitting this operation would result in an error in the code execution.

```
# Transposing a matrix

import numpy as np


inputs = [[1, 2, 4, 2.5], [1, 0, 0, 1], [1, 3, 8, 6]]
b = np.array(inputs).T
print(b)


#Output: [[1.  1.  1. ]
#          [2.  0.  3. ]
#          [4.  0.  8. ]
#          [2.5 1.  6. ]]
```

Creating a multi-layer network

As we've already discussed in the previous chapters, neural networks are often multi-layered, and they are considered "deep" when they have two or more hidden layers. Currently, our network only has one layer, which serves as the output layer. The importance of incorporating multiple hidden layers will be explained later. For now, our network lacks these hidden layers, which are located between the input and output layers. These hidden layers contain values the scientist doesn't directly work with, hence the name "hidden." However, it's important to note that these values can still be accessed and are often used for troubleshooting or improving the neural network's performance. To explore this concept further, let's add another layer to our network, treating it as a hidden layer for now, considering that we haven't implemented the output layer yet.

To expand the neural network by adding another layer, it is crucial to ensure compatibility between the input expected by the new layer and the output of the previous layer. The number of neurons in a layer is determined by the number of weight sets and biases assigned to it. In the present case, the weight sets of the current layer are influenced by the previous layer, necessitating a distinct weight for each input. This means that each neuron in the previous layer (or each feature in the input) corresponds to a separate weight. Considering that the previous layer has three weight sets and three biases, we can conclude that it consists of three neurons. Consequently, for the next layer, the number of weight sets can be chosen arbitrarily (representing the number of neurons in the new layer), but each of these weight sets will comprise three individual weights.

Let's look at our updated code:

```python
# Processing batch of data through 3 neurons layers
import numpy as np


inputs = [[1, 2, 4, 2.5], [1, 0, 0, 1], [1, 3, 8, 6]]
weights = [[0.1, 0.8, -0.5, 1.1], [0.5, -0.1, 0.6, -0.5], [-0.46, -0.27,
0.17, 0.8]]
biases = [1, 2, 0.5]


weights2 = [[0.11, 0.18, -0.15], [0.5, -0.7, 0.9], [-0.4, -0.7, 0.19]]
biases2 = [-1, 2, 0.2]


# Layer 1 output
layer1_out = np.dot(inputs, np.array(weights).T) + biases


# Layer 2 output
layer2_out = np.dot(layer1_out, np.array(weights2).T) + biases2
```

```
print(layer2_out)


#Output: [[-0.3265   3.272   -3.1808]
#          [-0.524    2.456   -1.9204]
#          [-0.4175   7.101   -4.0159]]
```

We added a single hidden layer between the input and output layers in the preceding code. So, the rest of everything is similar to what we previously had with single-layer networks.

Dense layers

Until now, we've created all our data by manually creating tensors; that's not ideal. We should have some way to load more realistic data. One way to get a sense of more realistic data is to use a sample dataset from sklearn.

To install Matplotlib: **pip install matplotlib**

To install sklearn: **pip install -U scikit-learn**

```
from sklearn.datasets import make_classification
import numpy as np
import matplotlib.pyplot as plt


# Generate dataset
X, y = make_classification(
    n_samples=1000,
    n_features=2,
    n_informative=2,
    n_redundant=0,
    n_clusters_per_class=1,
    class_sep=0.8,
    random_state=42
)
```

```
# Plot the spiral dataset
plt.scatter(X[:, 0], X[:, 1], c=y)
plt.xlabel('Feature 1')
plt.ylabel('Feature 2')
plt.title('Spiral Dataset')
plt.show()
```

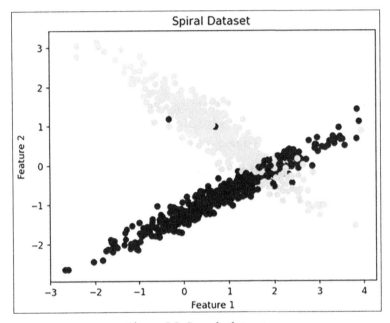

Figure 6.3: *Sample dataset*

In the preceding code, we used the **scikit-learn** (also called sklearn) library to create a new dataset. We also used another library called **matplotlib**, primarily used to draw simple charts and diagrams.

With the convenience of not having to input our data manually, it's time to create analogous structures for our different types of neural network layers. Until now, we have exclusively worked with a type known as a **dense** or **fully connected layer**. These layers are commonly denoted as **dense** in research papers, literature, and code. However, you may also encounter them being referred to as fully connected or abbreviated as **fc** in code.

Weights in a model are commonly initialized randomly, although there are exceptions. For example, if you want to use a pre-trained model, you would initialize the parameters according to the values it already has. Additionally, even for a new model, you might have alternative initialization rules instead of random initialization. However, for now, we will stick with random initialization.

Moving on to the forward method involves passing data through a model from start to finish, known as a **forward pass**. While this is the typical approach, it's important to note that there are other ways to handle data, such as looping it back or exploring alternative techniques. We'll follow the standard practice and perform a regular forward pass for now.

To kickstart our **Dense_layer** class, we will commence with the implementation of two methods.

Let's look at the full code up to this point:

```python
import numpy as np
from sklearn.datasets import make_classification


class Layer_Dense:
    def __init__(self, n_inputs, n_neurons):
        """
        Initialize the Layer_Dense class with given number of input and
output neurons.
        Initialize weights with random values and biases with zeros.
        """
        self.weights = 0.01 * np.random.randn(n_inputs, n_neurons)
        self.biases = np.zeros((1, n_neurons))


    def forward(self, inputs):
        """
        Perform a forward pass through the layer by multiplying the
inputs with weights,
        adding biases, and storing the result in the ‹output› attribute.
        """
        self.output = np.dot(inputs, self.weights) + self.biases


# Generate dataset
```

```
X, y = make_classification(
    n_samples=1000,
    n_features=2,
    n_informative=2,
    n_redundant=0,
    n_clusters_per_class=1,
    class_sep=0.8,
    random_state=42
)


# Create Dense layer with 2 input features and 3 output neurons
dense1 = Layer_Dense(2, 3)


# Perform a forward pass of our training data through this layer
dense1.forward(X)


# Print the output of the first five samples
print(dense1.output[:5])


# Output: [[ 0.00552081 -0.00414039 -0.01683566]
#          [ 0.01143134  0.00287461  0.00670816]
#          [ 0.02203819  0.00209274  0.00040819]
#          [ 0.0523194  -0.00180273 -0.02361715]
#          [ 0.00929377 -0.00188396 -0.00987335]]
```

The preceding code snippet demonstrates the implementation of a neural network layer using the **Layer_Dense** class. Here's a breakdown of the code:

- The **Layer_Dense** class represents a dense or fully connected layer in a neural network. It is initialized with the number of input neurons (**n_inputs**) and output neurons (**n_neurons**).
- The **__init__** method initializes the weights with random values scaled by 0.01 using **np.random.randn**. Then, the biases are set to zeros.

- The forward method performs a forward pass through the layer by multiplying the inputs with the weights, adding the biases, and storing the result in the output attribute.

- A dataset is generated using **make_classification** from sklearn. This generates a binary classification dataset with 1000 samples, two informative features, and a separation of 0.8 between the classes.

- An instance of **Layer_Dense** named **dense1** is created with two input features and   three output neurons.

- The training data (**X**) is passed through the layer using the forward method, and the resulting output is stored in **dense1.output**.

- The output of the first five samples is printed to inspect the results.

Activation functions

Earlier, we touched upon the concept of activation functions. However, our current implementation has not incorporated any activation functions. This means the information flows through the network without any neuron activation. To facilitate learning, we need to activate certain neurons while deactivating others. It is through the activation function that a neural network learns to discern and model complex decision boundaries.

In general, neural networks employ two types of activation functions. The first type is used in the hidden layers, while the second type is used in the output layer. Typically, the same activation function is applied to all hidden neurons, although there is flexibility in choosing different activation functions for each neuron if desired.

Let's expand our code by adding one of the most used activation functions, **ReLU** and **SoftMax**. All the different types of activation functions were already discussed *in Chapter 4: Foundational Concepts for Effective Neural Network Training*.

Let's apply the activation function to a sinusoidal wave and see how it is transformed through these activation functions:

```
import numpy as np
import matplotlib.pyplot as plt


# ReLU activation
class Activation_ReLU:
```

```python
    # Forward pass
    def forward(self, inputs):
        # Calculate output values from input
        self.output = np.maximum(0, inputs)
        return self.output


# Softmax activation
class Activation_Softmax:
    # Forward pass
    def forward(self, inputs):
        # Get unnormalized probabilities
        exp_values = np.exp(inputs - np.max(inputs))
        # Normalize them for each sample
        probabilities = exp_values / np.sum(exp_values)
        self.output = probabilities
        return self.output


# Generate input data
x = np.linspace(0, 2*np.pi, 100)  # Input values
y = np.sin(x)  # Target values


# Apply ReLU activation to input data
relu_activation = Activation_ReLU()
relu_output = relu_activation.forward(y)


# Apply Softmax activation to input data
softmax_activation = Activation_Softmax()
softmax_output = softmax_activation.forward(y)


# Plotting the outputs
plt.figure(figsize=(12, 6))
```

```
plt.subplot(1, 2, 1)
plt.plot(x, y, label='Input')
plt.plot(x, relu_output, label='ReLU Output')
plt.title('ReLU Activation')
plt.legend()

plt.subplot(1, 2, 2)
plt.plot(x, y, label='Input')
plt.plot(x, softmax_output, label='Softmax Output')
plt.title('Softmax Activation')
plt.legend()

plt.show()
```

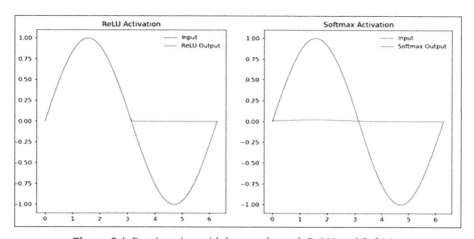

Figure 6.4: *Passing sinusoidal wave through ReLU and SoftMax*

Let's understand what these two activation functions are doing. These two functions implement activation functions commonly used in neural networks: ReLU (Rectified Linear Unit) and SoftMax.

ReLU activation (Rectified Linear Unit)

The ReLU activation function is $f(x) = \max(0, x)$, where x is the input. It returns the maximum of 0 and the input value.

The class **Activation_ReLU** in the preceding code represents the ReLU activation.

It has a forward method that takes an input array and applies the ReLU activation function element-wise to the input. The output is calculated as the maximum of **0**, and the input values using the NumPy maximum **np.max()** function. Finally, the output values are stored in the **self.output** variable and returned.

SoftMax activation

The SoftMax activation function is commonly used in the output layer of a neural network for multiclass classification problems. It takes an input array and converts it into a probability distribution over multiple classes.

The class **Activation_Softmax** in the preceding code represents the SoftMax activation. The **forward** method takes an input array and performs the following steps:

1. Subtracting the maximum value from the input array to avoid numerical instability.

2. Applying the exponential function **np.exp(`)** element-wise to the adjusted input values.

3. Normalizing the exponential values by dividing them by the sum of all exponential values, ensuring that the resulting values sum up to 1.

The output values, which represent the probabilities for each class, are stored in the **self.output** variable and returned.

If you look at the preceding graphs, we see that for all the negative values in the sinusoidal waves, the output becomes 0, and for SoftMax, that's not the case.

Let's apply all the activation functions to the simple neural networks we defined in the previous section   :

```python
import numpy as np
from sklearn.datasets import make_classification


# ReLU activation function
class Activation_ReLU:
    def forward(self, inputs):
        # Apply ReLU function: replace negative values with zero
        self.output = np.maximum(0, inputs)
        return self.output
```

```python
# Softmax activation function
class Activation_Softmax:
    def forward(self, inputs):
        # Apply Softmax function to normalize the inputs into probabilities
        # Subtracting the maximum value for numerical stability
        exp_values = np.exp(inputs - np.max(inputs, axis=1, keepdims=True))
        probabilities = exp_values / np.sum(exp_values, axis=1, keepdims=True)
        self.output = probabilities
        return self.output


# Dense layer
class Layer_Dense:
    def __init__(self, n_inputs, n_neurons):
        # Initialize weights with random values and biases with zeros
        self.weights = 0.01 * np.random.randn(n_inputs, n_neurons)
        self.biases = np.zeros((1, n_neurons))

    def forward(self, inputs):
        # Perform a forward pass through the layer by multiplying the
inputs with weights,
        # adding biases, and storing the result in the 'output' attribute.
        self.output = np.dot(inputs, self.weights) + self.biases
        return self.output


# Generate dataset
X, y = make_classification(
    n_samples=1000,
    n_features=2,
    n_informative=2,
    n_redundant=0,
    n_clusters_per_class=1,
```

```
        class_sep=0.8,
        random_state=42
)


# Create Dense layer with 2 input features and 3 output neurons
dense1 = Layer_Dense(2, 3)


# Apply ReLU activation to the output of the first dense layer
relu_activation = Activation_ReLU()
dense1_output_relu = relu_activation.forward(dense1.forward(X))


# Apply Softmax activation to the output of the ReLU activation
softmax_activation = Activation_Softmax()
dense1_output_softmax = softmax_activation.forward(dense1_output_relu)


# Print the output of the first five samples
print(dense1_output_softmax[:5])


# Output: [[0.32989978 0.34020044 0.32989978]
#          [0.33973738 0.33009912 0.3301635 ]
#          [0.33761584 0.33119208 0.33119208]
#          [0.32925581 0.34148837 0.32925581]
#          [0.33142489 0.33715022 0.33142489]]
```

Let's recap what we've done till this point.

The preceding code implements a simple neural network with a ReLU activation function followed by a SoftMax activation function. Here's a brief explanation of each part:

1. **Import necessary libraries**: NumPy for numerical operations and `make_classification` from `sklearn.dataset` to generate a synthetic classification dataset.

2. **Define the ReLU activation function**: The `Activation_ReLU` class

implements the ReLU activation function, which sets negative values to zero and leaves positive values unchanged.

3. **Define the SoftMax activation function:** The `Activation_Softmax` class implements the SoftMax activation function, normalizing the inputs into probabilities. It subtracts the maximum value for numerical stability and applies the exponential function followed by division to obtain probabilities.

4. **Define the dense layer:** The `Layer_Dense` class represents a dense (fully connected) layer in the neural network. It initializes weights with random values and biases with zeros. The **forward** method performs a forward pass by multiplying the inputs with weights, adding biases, and storing the result in the **output** attribute.

5. **Generate the dataset:** The `make_classification` function creates a synthetic classification dataset with two features, two informative features, and one cluster per class.

6. **Create the first dense layer:** An instance of `Layer_Dense` is created with two input features and three output neurons.

7. **Apply ReLU activation:** The ReLU activation function is applied to the output of the first dense layer by calling the **forward** method of `Activation_ReLU` on the `dense1` layer's output.

8. **Apply SoftMax activation:** The SoftMax activation function is applied to the output of the ReLU activation by calling the **forward** method of `Activation_Softmax` on `dense1_output_relu`.

9. **Print the output:** The first five samples' output is printed, representing the probabilities of each class obtained after passing through the ReLU and SoftMax activation functions.

The code demonstrates the basic flow of information through a neural network, starting with input data, passing through layers with activation functions, and obtaining the final output.

Calculating loss through categorical cross-entropy loss

In training a neural network, we aim to update the model's weights and biases to enhance its accuracy and confidence. This involves minimizing the error or "loss" of the model. The loss function, sometimes referred to as the cost function, is the mechanism that quantifies the model's level of incorrectness. The lower the loss, the better the model's performance.

The model is initially initialized with random values or more sophisticated initialization approaches during training. Then, we iteratively adjust the weights and biases as the training progresses to minimize the loss. Finally, we calculate the loss by analyzing the error between the model's predictions and the actual target values.

The loss value represents how far off the model's predictions are from the desired output. Ultimately, we aim to minimize this loss and drive it towards zero. Achieving a loss value of zero would indicate that the model is perfectly accurate in its predictions.

Categorical cross-entropy loss is a commonly used loss function in machine learning tasks involving multiclass classification. It quantifies the difference between the predicted probability distribution and the true probability distribution of the classes. Let's break down the mathematical equations and explain them in detail.

Given:

Predicted probabilities: $P = [p_1, p_2, ..., p_k]$, where p_i represents the predicted probability for class i.

True probabilities (one-hot encoded): $T = [t_1, t_2, ..., t_k]$, where $t_i = 1$ if the sample belongs to class i and $t_i = 0$ otherwise.

The categorical cross-entropy loss can be computed as follows:

$$L = -\sum (t \log (p))$$

Where the summation is taken over all classes, t represents the true probabilities, and p represents the predicted probabilities.

In more explicit terms, the loss for a single sample can be calculated as follows:

$$L = -\sum_i t_i \log (p_i)$$

Where t_i is the corresponding class's true probability and p_i is that class's predicted probability.

The logarithm in the equation serves two purposes: (1) it penalizes large differences between predicted and true probabilities, and (2) it amplifies the impact of misclassifications by assigning higher loss values.

To understand the intuition behind the equation, consider the following scenarios:

- **Correct prediction:** If the predicted probability for the true class is high, the loss for that class will be low (close to zero). This indicates that the model's prediction aligns well with the ground truth.

- **Incorrect prediction:** If the predicted probability for the true class is low, the loss for that class will be high (approaching infinity). This indicates a significant discrepancy between the model's prediction and the actual class.

By summing up the losses across all classes, the categorical cross-entropy loss measures how well the model performs correctly in classifying the input data.

During training, the goal is to minimize this loss by adjusting the model's weights and biases through optimization algorithms like gradient descent. Then, iteratively updating the model's parameters aims to find the optimal values that minimize the loss function and improve the accuracy of the model's predictions.

Remember that Categorical Cross-Entropy loss is not the only loss function; we have many other loss functions that are used depending on the task at hand.

Here is a list of some common loss functions and their typical use cases in machine learning:

Mean squared error (MSE) loss:

- It is used in regression problems where the output is a continuous variable.
- It measures the average squared difference between predicted and true values.
- It is robust to outliers.

Binary cross-entropy loss:

- It is used in binary classification problems, where the output is a binary label (0 or 1).
- It measures the dissimilarity between predicted and true binary labels.
- It is well-suited for problems with imbalanced classes.

Categorical cross-entropy loss:

- It is used in multiclass classification problems where the output involves multiple classes.
- It measures the difference between predicted and true class probabilities.

- It works well when classes are mutually exclusive.

Sparse categorical cross-entropy loss:

- It is used in multiclass classification problems with sparse labels.
- It handles cases where the true labels are provided as class indices rather than one-hot encoded vectors.

Kullback-Leibler divergence (KL divergence) loss:

- It is used in scenarios involving probability distributions.
- It measures the difference between predicted and true probability distributions.
- It is commonly used in tasks like generative modeling and variational autoencoders.

Hinge loss:

- It is used in support vector machines (SVMs) and binary classification problems.
- It encourages correct classification by enforcing a margin between classes.
- It is particularly suitable for classification tasks with large margins.

Triplet loss:

- It is used in metric learning and Siamese networks.
- It encourages similarity between samples from the same class and dissimilarity between samples from different classes.
- It is commonly used in face recognition and similarity-based tasks.

It's important to note that the choice of loss function depends on the specific problem and the nature of the data. Furthermore, different loss functions capture different aspects of the problem and can lead to different training behaviors and model performances. Therefore, selecting the appropriate loss function based on the problem at hand is crucial.

Let's understand the concept of Categorical Cross-Entropy loss by actually implementing it. But before implementing it in a class structure and combining it with the rest of the code, let's see the output on random input.

```
import math
```

```
# An example output from the output layer of the neural network
```

```
softmax_output = [0.5, 0.02, 0.3]
# Ground truth
target_output = [1, 0, 1]


loss = -(math.log(softmax_output[0])*target_output[0] +
math.log(softmax_output[1])*target_output[1] +
math.log(softmax_output[2])*target_output[2])


print(loss)


# Output: 1.8971199848858813
```

Currently, the loss value of our network is 1.89. As we proceed with training, we aim to decrease this loss value significantly. However, we are working with static weights at this stage, meaning the model has yet to learn from the data.

Let's calculate the loss on our network; the full code up to this point:

```
import numpy as np
from sklearn.datasets import make_classification


# Cross-entropy loss
class Loss_CategoricalCrossentropy:
    # Forward pass
    def forward(self, y_pred, y_true):
        # Number of samples in a batch
        samples = len(y_pred)
        # Clip data to prevent division by 0
        y_pred_clipped = np.clip(y_pred, 1e-7, 1 - 1e-7)
        # Probabilities for target values
        if len(y_true.shape) == 1:
            correct_confidences = y_pred_clipped[range(samples), y_true]
        # Mask values for one-hot encoded labels
        elif len(y_true.shape) == 2:
```

```python
        correct_confidences = np.sum(y_pred_clipped * y_true, axis=1)

        # Losses
        negative_log_likelihoods = -np.log(correct_confidences)

        return negative_log_likelihoods


# ReLU activation function
class Activation_ReLU:
    def forward(self, inputs):
        self.output = np.maximum(0, inputs)
        return self.output


# Softmax activation function
class Activation_Softmax:
    def forward(self, inputs):
        exp_values = np.exp(inputs - np.max(inputs, axis=1, keep-
dims=True))
        probabilities = exp_values / np.sum(exp_values, axis=1, keep-
dims=True)
        self.output = probabilities
        return self.output


# Dense layer
class Layer_Dense:
    def __init__(self, n_inputs, n_neurons):
        self.weights = 0.01 * np.random.randn(n_inputs, n_neurons)
        self.biases = np.zeros((1, n_neurons))

    def forward(self, inputs):
        self.output = np.dot(inputs, self.weights) + self.biases
        return self.output


# Generate dataset
```

```python
X, y = make_classification(
    n_samples=1000,
    n_features=2,
    n_informative=2,
    n_redundant=0,
    n_clusters_per_class=1,
    class_sep=0.8,
    random_state=42
)


# Create Dense layer with 2 input features and 3 output neurons
dense1 = Layer_Dense(2, 3)


# Apply ReLU activation to the output of the first dense layer
relu_activation = Activation_ReLU()
dense1_output_relu = relu_activation.forward(dense1.forward(X))


# Apply Softmax activation to the output of the ReLU activation
softmax_activation = Activation_Softmax()
dense1_output_softmax = softmax_activation.forward(dense1_output_relu)


# Create loss instance
loss = Loss_CategoricalCrossentropy()


# Calculate the loss
loss_value = np.mean(loss.forward(dense1_output_softmax, y))


# Print the loss value
print("Loss:", loss_value)


#Output: Loss: 1.0992215725349792
```

In the preceding code of Categorical Cross-Entropy, there are two important things to understand:

Clipping: We introduced clipping to prevent extreme probabilities during the loss calculation. Extreme values can cause numerical instability in logarithmic calculations. By constraining the predicted probabilities within a valid range, we ensure numerical stability and avoid issues in the loss calculation.

One-hot encoded labels: We handle one-hot encoded labels separately because they require a different calculation approach. One-hot encoded labels represent the true class as a vector with a single non-zero value (1) and the rest as zeros. We use the dot product between the predicted probabilities and the one-hot encoded labels to extract the probabilities of the correct classes. This multiplication effectively retrieves the chances of the correct classes, allowing us to calculate the loss accurately.

By introducing clipping and handling one-hot encoded labels separately, we ensure the robustness and accuracy of the loss calculation in scenarios where extreme probabilities and different label encodings are involved.

The next chapter will delve into the weight updation algorithm, an essential part of the training process. It involves adjusting the model's weights and biases iteratively to minimize the loss function.

Calculating accuracy

Before discussing weight updation, it is important to understand the concept of accuracy. While loss values provide a general indication of how well the model performs, they need to provide more information to compare the two models. For instance, if we train two networks on slightly different datasets, comparing their loss values alone won't reliably determine which model is more likely to perform better on unseen data.

Accuracy is a metric that complements loss values and provides a more comprehensive assessment of model performance. It measures the proportion of correctly classified samples out of the total samples. We better understand a model's predictive capabilities by considering accuracy and loss values.

It is a common practice to analyze loss values and accuracy (or other evaluation metrics) during model evaluation to assess the model's overall performance. This combination of metrics allows us to make more informed comparisons between different models and choose the one that is more likely to perform well on unseen data.

Here's the sample code to calculate accuracy:

```python
import numpy as np

# Probabilities of 3 samples
softmax_outputs = np.array([[0.7, 0.2, 0.1],
                            [0.5, 0.1, 0.4],
                            [0.02, 0.9, 0.08]])

# Target (ground-truth) labels for 3 samples
class_targets = np.array([0, 1, 1])

# Calculate values along the second axis (axis of index 1)
predictions = np.argmax(softmax_outputs, axis=1)

# If targets are one-hot encoded - convert them
if len(class_targets.shape) == 2:
    class_targets = np.argmax(class_targets, axis=1)

# True evaluates to 1; False to 0
accuracy = np.mean(predictions == class_targets)
print('acc:', accuracy)

#Output: acc: 0.6666666666666666


# Calculate accuracy from output of activation2 and targets
# Calculate values along the first axis
activation2_output = np.array([[0.1, 0.2, 0.7],
                               [0.9, 0.1, 0.0],
                               [0.3, 0.4, 0.3]])
```

```python
y = np.array([[1, 0, 0],
              [0, 0, 1],
              [0, 1, 0]])


predictions = np.argmax(activation2_output, axis=1)


if len(y.shape) == 2:
    y = np.argmax(y, axis=1)


accuracy = np.mean(predictions == y)


# Print accuracy
print('acc:', accuracy)


#Output: acc: 0.3333333333333333
```

The preceding code calculates the accuracy of predicted classes by comparing them with the true class labels. The **softmax_outputs** array contains the predicted probabilities for three samples, while the **class_targets** array holds the corresponding true class labels. Using **np.argmax()**, the predicted classes are obtained by selecting the class with the highest probability from each row of **softmax_outputs**. If the **class_targets** are one-hot encoded, they are converted to class indices using **np.argmax()**. The accuracy is then calculated by comparing the predicted classes with the true class labels and taking the mean of the comparison results. Finally, the calculated accuracy is printed.

There is a great resource from TensorFlow that lets us visualize how neural network (NN) is trained and how decision boundaries are formed; we highly recommend checking this tool out in the following link:

https://playground.tensorflow.org/#activation=tanh&batchSize=10 &dataset=circle&regDataset=reg-plane&learningRate=0.03& regularizationRate=0&noise=0&networkShape=4,2&seed=0.19712&show TestData=false&discretize=false&percTrainData=50&x=true&y=true& xTimesY=false&xSquared=false&ySquared=false&cosX=false&sinX=false&

cosY=false&sinY=false&collectStats=false&problem=classification& initZero=false&hideText=false [20]

Here's a screenshot of TensorFlow's Neural Network Playground:

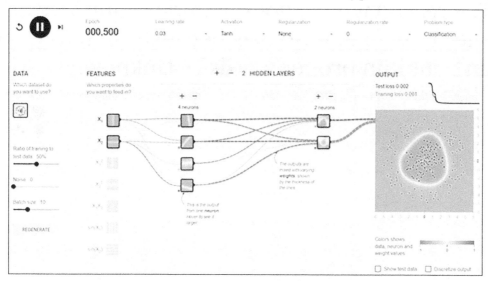

Figure 6.5: *Neural Network Playground*

Conclusion

This chapter serves as the foundation for understanding Neural Networks. We dove headfirst into programming our neurons and layers, eschewing the use of libraries to comprehend the underlying mechanics truly. Following this, we transitioned to applying the same principles with the aid of the NumPy libraries, using the class structure for implementation. As part of this exercise, we successfully implemented a rudimentary version of the Multi-layer Perceptron algorithm.

Thereafter, we proceeded to generate a sample dataset with the help of the sklearn library, further bolstering our knowledge with the practical application of SoftMax and ReLU activation functions. As we concluded this enlightening chapter, we solidified our understanding of Neural Networks by implementing Categorical Cross-Entropy and Accuracy metrics, integral elements in the field of machine learning. This journey from a basic understanding to the application of complex algorithms and functions embodies the essence of this educational endeavor.

The next chapter is an extension of this chapter only, where we start coding Stochastic Gradient Descent and Backpropagation and train our networks using these algorithms.

"The reason why AI doesn't understand love and other human emotions is because we ourselves can't put it in proper words" – Unknown

https://github.com/OrangeAVA/Ultimate-Neural-Network-Programming-with-Python

## CHAPTER 7

Derivatives, Backpropagation, and Optimizers

It is time for us to make our neural network from scratch trainable. Without further ado, let's get straight into the chapter. In this chapter, we are going to essentially cover the mathematical functions and techniques that build the backbone of a neural network. This includes understanding derivatives, optimizations, loss functions, and algorithms such as Backpropagation, Adam, and more.

Structure

This chapter covers the following topics:

- Weights Optimization, Derivatives, and Partial Derivatives
- Implementing Backpropagation
- Understanding Optimizers like SGD and Adam
- Adding loss functions and calculating accuracy

Weights Optimization

In the previous chapter, we covered various neural network components, such as accuracy and loss function for our Multi-Layer Perceptron Network. While the code we've written up so far works fine, the problem is that our network is not learning anything. Our accuracy is not increasing and loss is not decreasing at all. So, in this section, we will focus on reducing our loss and increasing our accuracy.

Let's write the full code and randomly update the weights. You will see that our loss is reduced to a certain level for some random iteration. We want to achieve a decrease in loss and an increase in accuracy with some level of stochasticity:

```python
import numpy as np
from sklearn.datasets import make_classification


# Cross-entropy loss
class Loss_CategoricalCrossentropy:
    # Forward pass
    def forward(self, y_pred, y_true):
        # Number of samples in a batch
        samples = len(y_pred)
        # Clip data to prevent division by 0
        y_pred_clipped = np.clip(y_pred, 1e-7, 1 - 1e-7)
        # Probabilities for target values
        if len(y_true.shape) == 1:
            correct_confidences = y_pred_clipped[range(samples), y_true]
        # Mask values for one-hot encoded labels
        elif len(y_true.shape) == 2:
            correct_confidences = np.sum(y_pred_clipped * y_true, axis=1)
        # Losses
        negative_log_likelihoods = -np.log(correct_confidences)
        return negative_log_likelihoods


# ReLU activation function
class Activation_ReLU:
```

```python
    def forward(self, inputs):
        self.output = np.maximum(0, inputs)
        return self.output


# Softmax activation function
class Activation_Softmax:
    def forward(self, inputs):
        exp_values = np.exp(inputs - np.max(inputs, axis=1, keep-
dims=True))
        probabilities = exp_values / np.sum(exp_values, axis=1, keep-
dims=True)
        self.output = probabilities
        return self.output


# Dense layer
class Layer_Dense:
    def __init__(self, n_inputs, n_neurons):
        self.weights = 0.01 * np.random.randn(n_inputs, n_neurons)
        self.biases = np.zeros((1, n_neurons))

    def forward(self, inputs):
        self.output = np.dot(inputs, self.weights) + self.biases
        return self.output


# Generate dataset
X, y = make_classification(n_samples=1000, n_features=2, n_informative=2,
    n_redundant=0, n_clusters_per_class=1, class_sep=0.8, random_
state=42)


# Model building
dense1 = Layer_Dense(2, 3)
relu_activation = Activation_ReLU()
```

```python
dense2 = Layer_Dense(3, 3)
softmax_activation = Activation_Softmax()

# Create loss instance
loss = Loss_CategoricalCrossentropy()


lowest_loss = 999


best_dense1_wt = dense1.weights.copy()
best_dense1_b = dense1.biases.copy()
best_dense2_wt = dense2.weights.copy()
best_dense2_b = dense2.biases.copy()


for iteration in range(10000):
    dense1.weights += 0.05*np.random.randn(2,3)
    dense1.biases += 0.05*np.random.randn(1,3)
    dense2.weights += 0.05*np.random.randn(3,3)
    dense2.weights += 0.05*np.random.randn(1,3)

    dense1.forward(X)
    relu_activation.forward(dense1.output)
    dense2.forward(relu_activation.output)
    softmax_activation.forward(dense2.output)

    loss_iteration = np.mean(loss.forward(softmax_activation.output, y))

    predictions = np.argmax(softmax_activation.output, axis=1)
    accuracy = np.mean(predictions == y)

    if loss_iteration < lowest_loss:
        print('New set of weights found, iteration:', iteration,
```

```
        'loss:', loss_iteration, 'acc:', accuracy)
        best_dense1_wt = dense1.weights.copy()
        best_dense1_b = dense1.biases.copy()
        best_dense2_wt = dense2.weights.copy()
        best_dense2_b = dense2.biases.copy()
        lowest_loss = loss_iteration


# New set of weights found, iteration: 4 loss: 1.0989542339208993 acc:
0.559

# New set of weights found, iteration: 56 loss: 1.0854732062933512 acc:
0.366

# New set of weights found, iteration: 57 loss: 1.0730188743817546 acc:
0.355

# New set of weights found, iteration: 61 loss: 1.0065003834858366 acc:
0.331

# New set of weights found, iteration: 62 loss: 1.003041528442615 acc:
0.324

# New set of weights found, iteration: 67 loss: 0.9765760773254446 acc:
0.483

# New set of weights found, iteration: 75 loss: 0.9662196849212262 acc:
0.462

# New set of weights found, iteration: 82 loss: 0.9512302053632272 acc:
0.484

# New set of weights found, iteration: 103 loss: 0.94220636792505 acc:
0.394

# New set of weights found, iteration: 149 loss: 0.8938921395678174 acc:
0.5

# New set of weights found, iteration: 150 loss: 0.8711507416623178 acc:
0.5

# New set of weights found, iteration: 153 loss: 0.8584587223100946 acc:
0.495

# New set of weights found, iteration: 155 loss: 0.816362827555145 acc:
0.533

# New set of weights found, iteration: 156 loss: 0.8118560067782634 acc:
0.563
```

```
# New set of weights found, iteration: 4503 loss: 0.8064469416139644
acc: 0.629
# New set of weights found, iteration: 4506 loss: 0.7532695225933412
acc: 0.633
# New set of weights found, iteration: 4512 loss: 0.7423221321738089
acc: 0.642
# New set of weights found, iteration: 4531 loss: 0.7149267325758331
acc: 0.61
# New set of weights found, iteration: 4534 loss: 0.7086429871378375
acc: 0.607
# New set of weights found, iteration: 4536 loss: 0.695993496159264 acc:
0.613
# New set of weights found, iteration: 4541 loss: 0.6907492939463712
acc: 0.621
# New set of weights found, iteration: 4909 loss: 0.6902437508407053
acc: 0.653
# New set of weights found, iteration: 5045 loss: 0.60933738954957 acc:
0.717
# New set of weights found, iteration: 5047 loss: 0.5880086956924404
acc: 0.72
# New set of weights found, iteration: 5382 loss: 0.5404574448921126
acc: 0.767
```

In the preceding output, we see that accuracy reached above 0.72. However, the current code can't be trusted because of the random nature of weight updation. We want to use the concept of derivates to identify how much we want to change our weights.

Derivatives

In the context of neural networks, the concept of derivatives is crucial for optimizing the model's parameters during training. Let's break it down.

The derivative measures the rate at which a function changes with respect to its input. In the context of neural networks, we use derivatives to determine how the loss function (a measure of the model's performance) changes with respect to the network's parameters (weights and biases). By calculating the derivative, we can update the parameters to minimize the loss function, thereby improving the model's performance.

The most commonly used optimization algorithm in neural networks is called stochastic gradient descent (SGD). It relies on the loss function's derivative (or gradient) with respect to the model parameters. The gradient points toward the steepest ascent, so to minimize the loss, we move in the opposite direction of the gradient. We gradually converge toward the optimal values that minimize the loss function by iteratively updating the parameters using the gradient.

We can imagine loss as a surface in N-dimensional space, and our goal is to find the lowest point in that N-dimensional surface. The following example shows how to find the lowest point using the derivative idea:

```python
import numpy as np
import matplotlib.pyplot as plt
from mpl_toolkits.mplot3d import Axes3D


# Define the complex function
def complex_function(x, y):
    return np.sin(x) + np.cos(y)


# Define the partial derivatives of the complex function
def partial_derivative_x(x, y):
    return np.cos(x)


def partial_derivative_y(x, y):
    return -np.sin(y)


# Define the range of x and y values
x = np.linspace(-5, 5, 100)
y = np.linspace(-5, 5, 100)


# Create a grid of x and y values
X, Y = np.meshgrid(x, y)
```

```
# Calculate the corresponding z values using the complex function
Z = complex_function(X, Y)


# Find the lowest point using the partial derivatives
lowest_point_indices = np.unravel_index(np.argmin(Z), Z.shape)
lowest_point_x = X[lowest_point_indices]
lowest_point_y = Y[lowest_point_indices]
lowest_point_z = Z[lowest_point_indices]


# Plot the complex function and the lowest point in 3D
fig = plt.figure()
ax = fig.add_subplot(111, projection='3d')
ax.plot_surface(X, Y, Z, cmap='viridis')
ax.scatter(lowest_point_x, lowest_point_y, lowest_point_z, color='red',
s=50, label='Lowest Point')
ax.set_xlabel('X')
ax.set_ylabel('Y')
ax.set_zlabel('Z')
ax.set_title('Complex Function and Lowest Point')
ax.legend()
plt.show()
```

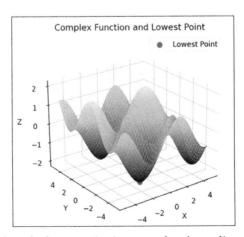

Figure 7.1: *Finding the lowest point in a complex three-dimensional surface*

The aforementioned example demonstrated the application of derivatives in finding the global minima. However, applying derivatives directly to neural networks is not straightforward due to the N-dimensional decision boundaries they form, which are not continuous graphs. To address this, we employ an approximate derivative. When considering derivatives in the context of neural networks, we encounter the concept of the **Chain Rule**. Let's delve into how the Chain Rule works.

Consider a simple neural network with two layers, where the output is the composition of two functions, $f(g(x))$. We want to calculate the derivative of the output with respect to the input x:

$$x \rightarrow g(x) \rightarrow f(g(x)) \rightarrow Output$$

According to the Chain Rule, the derivative of the composition of functions $f(g(x))$ with respect to x can be calculated as the product of two derivatives:

$$\frac{d(f(g(x)))}{dx} = \frac{d(f(g(x)))}{dg} * \frac{d(g(x))}{dx}$$

Here, $d(f(g(x)))/dg$ represents the derivative of f with respect to g, and $dg(x)/dx$ represents the derivative of g with respect to x.

To obtain the derivative of $f(g(x))$ with respect to g, we differentiate $f(g)$ with respect to g, treating g as the independent variable. Similarly, we differentiate $g(x)$ to find the derivative of $g(x)$ with respect to x.

Using the Chain Rule, we can calculate the derivative of the output with respect to the input x, even in complex neural networks with multiple layers and non-linear activation functions.

In summary, the Chain Rule allows us to approximate derivatives in neural networks by decomposing complex functions into smaller components and applying the derivative rules sequentially. This facilitates the optimization of neural network parameters during training, enabling the model to learn and adapt to the given task.

Let's look at some examples of how to apply the Chain Rule to some real examples. Let's consider the following composite function:

$$f(x) = (2x^2 + 3x)^3 = g(x)^3$$

Step 1: Identify the inner function and its derivative.

The inner function here is $g(x) = 2x^2 + 3x$. Let's find its derivative with respect to x: $g'(x) = d/dx\ (2x^2 + 3x) = 4x + 3$

Step 2: Identify the outer function and its derivative with respect to its argument.

The outer function is $f(g) = g^3$. Let's find its derivative with respect to g: $f'(g) = d/dg\,(g^3) = 3g^2$

Step 3: Apply the Chain Rule to obtain the derivative of the composite function.

Using the Chain Rule, we multiply the derivatives obtained in Steps 1 and 2: $df(g(x))\,/\,dx = f'(g) * g'(x) = 3(2x^2 + 3x)^2 * (4x + 3)$

Simplifying further, we get the final derivative: $df(g(x))\,/\,dx = 12x(2x^2 + 3x)^2 + 9(2x^2 + 3x)^2$

Following the preceding steps, you can apply the Chain Rule to differentiate composite functions. It involves identifying the inner and outer functions, finding their respective derivatives, and multiplying them together to obtain the derivative of the composite function. This rule becomes especially useful when dealing with more complex functions in calculus and the context of neural networks.

Partial Derivatives

Partial derivatives are closely related to neural networks, especially in the context of training and optimization. Let's explore how partial derivatives are used in neural networks.

As we already know, neural networks consist of interconnected layers of artificial neurons that process and transform input data to produce the desired output. The network's performance is determined by its parameters, such as weights and biases, which must be optimized during training. Partial derivatives play a crucial role in this optimization.

The goal of training a neural network is to find the optimal set of parameters that minimize a loss function, which quantifies the discrepancy between the predicted output of the network and the true output. This optimization process involves updating the parameters iteratively to reduce the loss.

Partial derivatives come into play when calculating the gradients of the loss function with respect to the parameters. The gradient is a vector of partial derivatives, representing the rate of change of the loss function with respect to each parameter. It provides information on how adjusting a parameter affects the loss.

Using the gradient, specifically the negative gradient (opposite direction of steepest ascent), the parameters are updated to minimize the loss. This process typically uses optimization algorithms like SGD or its variants.

During each iteration of the training process, the partial derivatives of the loss function with respect to the parameters are computed using techniques like backpropagation. Backpropagation involves propagating the error backward through the network, and calculating the derivatives layer by layer. These derivatives guide the updates to the parameters, effectively adjusting the network's weights and biases.

The neural network gradually converges toward an optimal solution that minimizes the loss function by iteratively updating the parameters based on the partial derivatives. This allows the network to learn patterns and relationships in the data and make accurate predictions.

In summary, partial derivatives play a vital role in optimizing neural networks. They are used to compute the gradients of the loss function with respect to the network's parameters, enabling efficient updates and improving the network's performance through training. Partial derivatives help the neural network learn from data, make adjustments, and ultimately achieve better predictions and generalization capabilities.

Let's understand partial derivatives using a simple example:

$$f(x,y) = x^2 + 2xy + y^2$$

To find the partial derivative with respect to x, we treat y as a constant and differentiate the function with respect to x: $\partial f / \partial x = d/dx \, (x^2 + 2xy + y^2) = 2x + 2y$

To find the partial derivative with respect to y, we treat x as a constant and differentiate the function with respect to y: $\partial f / \partial y = d/dy \, (x^2 + 2xy + y^2) = 2x + 2y$

As you can see, both partial derivatives have the same value of 2x + 2y. The partial derivatives represent the rate at which the function changes with respect to each variable, considering all other variables as constants.

These partial derivatives provide valuable insights into the behavior of functions with multiple variables. They allow us to understand how the function changes as each variable is varied while the other variables are fixed. Partial derivatives are widely used in multivariable calculus and optimization problems involving functions with multiple variables.

In summary, partial derivatives are derivatives taken with respect to one variable while holding all other variables constant. They provide valuable information about the sensitivity of a function to changes in specific variables, enabling us to understand and optimize complex functions in various mathematical and scientific contexts.

Backpropagation

Now with the knowledge of derivative and partial derivatives, we are ready to look into the most important algorithm of AI called Backpropagation. Let's try to break it down in a few simple steps.

Step 1: Forward Propagation

During forward propagation, the neural network passes input through each layer, applying weights and activation functions to produce an output. The input data flows forward through the network, layer by layer until the final output is generated.

Step 2: Calculation of Error

After obtaining the output, we compare it with the desired output and calculate the error. The error measures how far off the network's prediction is from the true output. It quantifies the discrepancy between the predicted and expected outputs using a loss function, such as mean squared error (MSE) or cross-entropy.

Step 3: Backward Propagation

Backward propagation is where the actual learning occurs. It involves propagating the error backward through the network to update each neuron's parameters (weights and biases). This process allows the network to adjust its parameters based on the calculated error.

In backward propagation, we compute the gradient of the loss function with respect to the parameters using the Chain Rule. The gradient indicates the direction and magnitude of the steepest ascent in the loss function's landscape. By moving in the opposite direction of the gradient, we can update the parameters to reduce the error and improve the network's performance.

Step 4: Update Parameters

Using the gradients calculated during backward propagation, we update the parameters of the network. This is typically done using an optimization algorithm like SGD or its variants. The algorithm adjusts the parameters to minimize the loss function, gradually improving the network's ability to make accurate predictions.

The process of forward propagation, error calculation, backward propagation, and parameter updates is repeated iteratively for a given number of epochs or until the network reaches a desired level of performance.

By repeatedly adjusting the parameters based on the gradients calculated during backpropagation, the neural network learns from the data, captures patterns, and improves its predictions over time.

In summary, backpropagation is a mechanism for training neural networks. It involves propagating the error backward through the network, calculating gradients using the Chain Rule, and updating the parameters to minimize the error. The network learns from data through this iterative process and improves its ability to make accurate predictions.

Here's a beautiful video on the same topic of Backpropagation from 3Blue1Brown:

https://www.youtube.com/watch?v=Ilg3gGewQ5U&ab_channel=3Blue1Brown [21]

We've already covered the code sections discussed in the previous sections till Step 2 of Backpropagation. Let's now implement the remaining steps of this beautiful algorithm.

Let's start with what we updated in our previous code sections. In the class **Layer_Dense()**, we added a **backward** function and a few things in the class initialization:

```python
# Dense layer
class Layer_Dense:
    def __init__(self, n_inputs, n_neurons):
        # Initialize weights with random values scaled by 0.01
        self.weights = 0.01 * np.random.randn(n_inputs, n_neurons)
        # Initialize biases as zeros
        self.biases = np.zeros((1, n_neurons))
        # Initialize gradient variables as None
        self.dweights = None
        self.dbiases = None


    def forward(self, inputs):
        # Save the inputs for later use in backward propagation
```

```
        self.inputs = inputs
        # Perform the dot product of inputs and weights, and add biases
        self.output = np.dot(inputs, self.weights) + self.biases
        return self.output


        # added backward method for Dense layer
def backward(self, dvalues):
        # Calculate the gradients of weights, biases, and inputs
        self.dweights = np.dot(self.inputs.T, dvalues)
        self.dbiases = np.sum(dvalues, axis=0, keepdims=True)
        self.dinputs = np.dot(dvalues, self.weights.T)
```

Given a dense layer with **inputs X, weights W, biases B**, and output gradients **dvalues**:

Gradients on Parameters

The gradient of the loss function with respect to the layer's weights is calculated as the dot product of the transpose of the input values X^T and the gradient of the loss function with respect to the output values **dvalues**.

Mathematically, it can be represented as: $dW = X^T * dvalues$

The gradient of the loss function with respect to the layer's biases is computed by summing the gradient values along the rows (axis 0) of **dvalues**.

Mathematically, it can be represented as: $dB = sum(dvalues)$

Gradient on Values

The gradient of the loss function with respect to the inputs of the layer is calculated as the dot product of the gradient of the loss function with respect to the output values **dvalues** and the transpose of the layer's weights W^T.

Mathematically, it can be represented as: $dX = dvalues * W^T$

In summary, the backward pass equations of a dense layer involve calculating the gradients of the loss function with respect to the parameters (**dW** and **dB**) and the **inputs (dX)**. These gradients are crucial for updating the parameters during training, allowing the neural network to learn and improve its performance.

Let's now look at the updated **Activation_ReLU()** class ; here also, we added the
backward() method:

```python
# ReLU activation function
class Activation_ReLU:
    def forward(self, inputs):
        # Save the inputs for later use in backward propagation
        self.inputs = inputs
        # Apply the ReLU activation function element-wise
        self.output = np.maximum(0, inputs)
        return self.output



    # backward method for ReLU activation function
    def backward(self, dvalues):
        # Create a copy of the gradients of the outputs
        self.dinputs = dvalues.copy()
        # Set gradients of the inputs corresponding to the negative in-
put values to 0
        self.dinputs[self.inputs <= 0] = 0
```

The derivative of ReLU is really easy, we make the values 0 when the input is
negative, and for the inputs>0, we keep the derivative equal to the input value.

Let's now look at the class **Activation_softmax()**; here also, we added the
backward() method:

```python
# Softmax activation function
class Activation_Softmax:
    def forward(self, inputs):
        # Calculate exponential values of inputs while normalizing them
```

```
        exp_values = np.exp(inputs - np.max(inputs, axis=1,
keepdims=True))
        # Calculate probabilities by dividing each exponential value by
the sum of all exponential values
        probabilities = exp_values / np.sum(exp_values, axis=1,
keepdims=True)
        # Save the output for later use in backward propagation
        self.output = probabilities
        return self.output


# Added backward method for softmax activation
    def backward(self, dvalues):
        # Create an array to store the gradients of the inputs
        self.dinputs = np.empty_like(dvalues)
        for index, (single_output, single_dvalues) in enumerate(zip
(self.output, dvalues)):
            # Reshape the single_output array into a column vector
            single_output = single_output.reshape(-1, 1)
            # Calculate the Jacobian matrix for the softmax function
            jacobian_matrix = np.diagflat(single_output) - np.dot
(single_output, single_output.T)
            # Calculate the gradient of the inputs using the Jacobian
matrix and the gradients of the outputs
            self.dinputs[index] = np.dot(jacobian_matrix, single_
dvalues)
```

1. Let **dvalues** be the input gradients, outputs be the outputs of the layer, and **dinputs** be the resulting gradients.

2. Create an uninitialized array **dinputs** with the same shape as **dvalues**.

3. For each sample **index**, do the following:

   a. Let output represent the output of the layer for the current sample.

   b. Flatten the output array output into a column vector: **output = output. reshape(-1, 1)**.

   c. Calculate the Jacobian matrix: **jacobian_matrix = diag(output)**

- output * output^T, where diag(output) represents the diagonal matrix with the output elements on the diagonal, and output^T is the transpose of output.

d. Calculate the sample-wise gradient: dinputs[index] = jacobian_ matrix * dvalue, where dinputs[index] represents the gradient for the current sample.

Let's now look at the updated class **Loss_CategoricalCrossentropy()**:

```python
# Cross-entropy loss
class Loss_CategoricalCrossentropy:
    def forward(self, y_pred, y_true):
        samples = len(y_pred)
        y_pred_clipped = np.clip(y_pred, 1e-7, 1 - 1e-7)


        if len(y_true.shape) == 1:
            # For sparse label format, extract the correct confidence
scores
            correct_confidences = y_pred_clipped[range(samples), y_true]
        elif len(y_true.shape) == 2:
            # For one-hot encoded label format, calculate the dot product
of probabilities and labels
            correct_confidences = np.sum(y_pred_clipped * y_true, axis=1)


        # Calculate negative log-likelihood loss
        negative_log_likelihoods = -np.log(correct_confidences)
        return negative_log_likelihoods



# Added backward method for categorical cross-entropy
    def backward(self, dvalues, y_true):
        samples = len(dvalues)
        labels = len(dvalues[0])
```

```
            if len(y_true.shape) == 1:
                # For sparse label format, convert y_true to one-hot encoded
format
                y_true = np.eye(labels)[y_true]

            # Calculate gradient of the loss with respect to the inputs
            self.dinputs = -y_true / dvalues
            self.dinputs = self.dinputs / samples
```

1. Let **dvalues** represent the input gradients, **y_true** represent the true labels, and **self.dinputs** represent the resulting gradients.

2. Determine the number of samples: **samples = len(dvalues)**.

3. Determine the number of labels in each sample: **labels = len(dvalues[0])**.

4. If the labels are in sparse form, convert them into one-hot vectors: **if len(y_true.shape) == 1: y_true = np.eye(labels)[y_true]**.

5. Calculate the gradient: **self.dinputs = -y_true / dvalues**.

6. Normalize the gradient: **self.dinputs = self.dinputs / samples**.

The full code up to this point is as follows:

```python
import numpy as np
from sklearn.datasets import make_classification

# Dense layer
class Layer_Dense:
    def __init__(self, n_inputs, n_neurons):
        # Initialize weights with random values scaled by 0.01
        self.weights = 0.01 * np.random.randn(n_inputs, n_neurons)
        # Initialize biases as zeros
        self.biases = np.zeros((1, n_neurons))
        # Initialize gradient variables as None
```

```python
        self.dweights = None
        self.dbiases = None


    def forward(self, inputs):
        # Save the inputs for later use in backward propagation
        self.inputs = inputs
        # Perform the dot product of inputs and weights, and add biases
        self.output = np.dot(inputs, self.weights) + self.biases
        return self.output


    def backward(self, dvalues):
        # Calculate the gradients of weights, biases, and inputs
        self.dweights = np.dot(self.inputs.T, dvalues)
        self.dbiases = np.sum(dvalues, axis=0, keepdims=True)
        self.dinputs = np.dot(dvalues, self.weights.T)


# ReLU activation function
class Activation_ReLU:
    def forward(self, inputs):
        # Save the inputs for later use in backward propagation
        self.inputs = inputs
        # Apply the ReLU activation function element-wise
        self.output = np.maximum(0, inputs)
        return self.output


    def backward(self, dvalues):
        # Create a copy of the gradients of the outputs
        self.dinputs = dvalues.copy()
        # Set gradients of the inputs corresponding to the negative input
values to 0
        self.dinputs[self.inputs <= 0] = 0
```

```python
# Softmax activation function
class Activation_Softmax:
    def forward(self, inputs):
        # Calculate exponential values of inputs while normalizing them
        exp_values = np.exp(inputs - np.max(inputs, axis=1, keep-
dims=True))
        # Calculate probabilities by dividing each exponential value by
the sum of all exponential values
        probabilities = exp_values / np.sum(exp_values, axis=1,
keepdims=True)
        # Save the output for later use in backward propagation
        self.output = probabilities
        return self.output


    def backward(self, dvalues):
        # Create an array to store the gradients of the inputs
        self.dinputs = np.empty_like(dvalues)
        for index, (single_output, single_dvalues) in enumerate(zip
(self.output, dvalues)):
            # Reshape the single_output array into a column vector
            single_output = single_output.reshape(-1, 1)
            # Calculate the Jacobian matrix for the softmax function
            jacobian_matrix = np.diagflat(single_output) - np.dot(single_
output, single_output.T)
            # Calculate the gradient of the inputs using the Jacobian
matrix and the gradients of the outputs
            self.dinputs[index] = np.dot(jacobian_matrix, single_dvalues)

# Cross-entropy loss
class Loss_CategoricalCrossentropy:
    def forward(self, y_pred, y_true):
        samples = len(y_pred)
        y_pred_clipped = np.clip(y_pred, 1e-7, 1 - 1e-7)
```

```python
        if len(y_true.shape) == 1:
            # For sparse label format, extract the correct confidence
scores
            correct_confidences = y_pred_clipped[range(samples), y_true]
        elif len(y_true.shape) == 2:
            # For one-hot encoded label format, calculate the dot product
of probabilities and labels
            correct_confidences = np.sum(y_pred_clipped * y_true, axis=1)

        # Calculate negative log-likelihood loss
        negative_log_likelihoods = -np.log(correct_confidences)
        return negative_log_likelihoods


    def backward(self, dvalues, y_true):
        samples = len(dvalues)
        labels = len(dvalues[0])

        if len(y_true.shape) == 1:
            # For sparse label format, convert y_true to one-hot encoded
format
            y_true = np.eye(labels)[y_true]

        # Calculate gradient of the loss with respect to the inputs
        self.dinputs = -y_true / dvalues
        self.dinputs = self.dinputs / samples


# Generate dataset
X, y = make_classification(n_samples=1000, n_features=2, n_informative=2,
                           n_redundant=0, n_clusters_per_class=1,
class_sep=0.8, random_state=42)
```

```python
# Forward pass
dense1 = Layer_Dense(2, 3)
relu_activation = Activation_ReLU()

dense2 = Layer_Dense(3, 3)
softmax_activation = Activation_Softmax()

dense1_output = dense1.forward(X)
relu_activation_output = relu_activation.forward(dense1_output)

dense2_output = dense2.forward(relu_activation_output)
softmax_activation_output = softmax_activation.forward(dense2_output)

# Create loss instance
loss = Loss_CategoricalCrossentropy()

loss_iteration = np.mean(loss.forward(softmax_activation_output, y))
predictions = np.argmax(softmax_activation_output, axis=1)
accuracy = np.mean(predictions == y)
print("Accuracy: ", accuracy)

# Backward pass
loss.backward(softmax_activation_output, y)
softmax_activation.backward(loss.dinputs)
dense2.backward(softmax_activation.dinputs)
relu_activation.backward(dense2.dinputs)
dense1.backward(relu_activation.dinputs)

# Print gradients
print(dense1.dweights, "\n")
print(dense1.dbiases, "\n")
```

```
print(dense2.dweights, "\n")
print(dense2.dbiases)
```

```
# Accuracy:  0.501
# [[-7.91311439e-04  9.10036274e-05 -3.62927206e-03]
#  [-2.42775242e-03  1.08710225e-03  2.21541699e-03]]


# [[-0.00209153  0.00073589 -0.00212986]]


# [[ 0.00141515 -0.00286223  0.00144708]
#  [ 0.00043136 -0.00086976  0.0004384 ]
#  [-0.001922   -0.0027196   0.0046416 ]]


# [[-0.16761353 -0.16567281  0.33328634]]
```

If you see the output of the preceding code, what it basically tells you is how much all the weights and biases need to change; this is the rudimentary way of implementing backpropagation. In real life, we train our network like SGD or Adam optimizer.

Optimizers: SGD, Adam, and so on

In the previous section, we see how to calculate the optimum amount of change we need to make to update our weights. In this section, let's understand how we use optimizers to train neural networks over hundreds of iterations to finally achieve the weights that actually work for the unseen data, giving our models enough generalization to perform in the real world. There are several types of Optimizers, and let's look at all of them one by one before we start implementing and integrating it without our full custom neural network from scratch pipeline.

Gradient-based optimization

In the world of machine learning, gradient-based optimizers are the powerhouses behind training neural networks. These algorithms iteratively adjust the parameters of our model, such as the weights and biases in a neural network, to minimize the error or loss function. Gradient-based optimizers do this by leveraging information about the gradient of the loss function with respect to the parameters. One such very famous optimizer is called **SGD** or **Stochastic Gradient Descent**.

SGD is the simplest and most fundamental optimizer ; it is called SGD because it uses the gradient of the loss function and stochastically (randomly) updates the model's parameters in the direction of the negative gradient. Stochastic Gradient Descent historically refers to an optimizer that fits a single sample at a time. The second type of SGD is called **Batch Gradient Descent**, this one fits the whole dataset at once. And the third variation is called **Mini-batch Gradient Descent**, this one fits slices or batches of the given dataset.

The SGD algorithm operates by first initializing the parameters randomly, then iteratively adjusting them proportionally to the negative gradient of the error function with respect to the parameters. This process is mathematically expressed as:

$$\theta = \theta - \eta * \nabla J(\theta)$$

Here, θ represents the parameters of our model, η is the learning rate (a tuning parameter determining the step size at each iteration), and $\nabla J(\theta)$ is the gradient of the loss function J at θ.

One major advantage of SGD is its simplicity and ease of implementation. It handles large datasets well because it only requires a single sample (or a mini-batch) to compute the gradient and update the parameters at each iteration.

However, SGD also has notable drawbacks. It's sensitive to the learning rate selection. A very small learning rate makes the model converge slowly, while a large learning rate can lead the model to overshoot the minimum or even diverge. It also needs help navigating ravines, areas where the surface curves much more steeply in one direction than in another, which are common around local optima.

Note: There can be a huge difference between the performance of different variations of SGD. For instance, in most cases, fitting the entire data in the RAM in one go is not possible, and also, running SGD with one sample at a time is quite slow and sometimes gives suboptimal minima. Changing the size of the batch can have a significant impact on training time and the minimum loss value reached.

Momentum-based optimization

Momentum is a method designed to accelerate SGD in the relevant direction and dampen oscillations. It does this by adding a fraction γ of the update vector of the past time step to the current update vector:

$$v = \gamma v - \eta \nabla J(\theta)$$

$$\theta = \theta + v$$

Here **v** is the parameters' velocity (direction and speed), which is set to the gradient at initialization. The momentum term γ is usually set to 0.9 or a similar value.

When using momentum, we add a fraction of the previous update to the current one. When the gradient keeps pointing in the same direction, this will increase the size of the steps taken toward the minimum.

RMSProp

RMSProp (Root Mean Square Propagation) is another optimization algorithm that tries to resolve some of the issues of SGD. The central idea behind RMSProp is to adjust the learning rate adaptively for each weight in the neural network: larger updates for infrequent and small updates for frequent parameters.

RMSProp updates parameters in the following way:

$$E[g^2]_t = 0.9 * E[g^2]_{t-1} + 0.1 * g_t^2$$

$$\theta = \theta - \eta \frac{g_t}{\sqrt{[g^2]_{t-1} + \varepsilon}}$$

Here g_t is the gradient at time step t, $E[g^2]_t$ is the running average of the square of the gradients, and ε is a small number added to increase numerical stability. RMSProp essentially uses a moving average of squared gradients to normalize the gradient itself. That means the learning rate gets adapted as we progress with the training.

Adam

Adam (Adaptive Moment Estimation) combines the best properties of the previously discussed methods: the adaptive learning rate of RMSProp and the momentum acceleration from Momentum SGD.

Adam calculates an exponential moving average of the gradient and the squared gradient, and the parameters β_1 and β_2 control the decay rates of these moving averages.

The updated rules in Adam are as follows:

$$m_t = \beta_1 * m_{t-1} + (1 - \beta_1) * g_t$$

$$v_t = \beta_2 * v_{t-1} + (1 - \beta_2) * g_t^2$$

$$\widehat{m}_t = \frac{m_t}{(1 - \beta_1{}^t)}$$

$$\hat{v}_t = \frac{v_t}{(1 - \beta_2{}^t)}$$

$$\theta = \theta - \eta * \frac{\widehat{m}_t}{\sqrt{\hat{v}} + \varepsilon}$$

Here, m_t and v_t are estimates of the first moment (the mean) and the second moment (the uncentered variance) of the gradients, respectively, hence, the name of the method. As m_t and v_t are initialized as vectors of 0's, the authors of Adam observe that they are biased towards zero, especially during the initial time steps, and especially when the decay rates are small (that is, β_1 and β_2 are close to 1).

Adam is generally fairly robust to the choice of hyperparameters, though the learning rate sometimes needs to be changed from the suggested default.

Optimization is crucial to training neural networks and other machine learning models. Understanding how different optimizers work, their strengths, weaknesses, and their underlying mathematical principles is crucial for effective training models. There are several other optimization algorithms, such as **Adagrad, Adadelta, Adamax, Nadam**, and more, each with its strengths and weaknesses. The selection of the right optimizer depends on the specific problem at hand. There is no one-size-fits-all optimizer; the choice is often made empirically, based on what works best on the validation data.

For our case, we will try to optimize/train our neural network with **SGD** and **Adam** and compare their performance in terms of accuracy and loss.

Here's how our **SGD** Class looks like:

```
class Optimizer_SGD:
```

```
# Initialize optimizer - set settings,
# learning rate of 1. Is default for this optimizer
def __init__(self, learning_rate=1.0):
    self.learning_rate = learning_rate
    # Update parameters
def update_params(self, layer):
    layer.weights += -self.learning_rate * layer.dweights
    layer.biases += -self.learning_rate * layer.dbiases
```

- **class Optimizer_SGD**: This line declares a new class named **Optimizer_SGD**.

- **def __init__(self, learning_rate=1.0):** This line defines the initializer method of the class, which gets called when you create a new instance of the class. It takes an optional parameter **learning_rate** with a default value of 1.0. The learning rate is a hyperparameter that determines the step size at each iteration while moving towards the minimum of a loss function. It decides how quickly the algorithm should update the parameters.

- **self.learning_rate = learning_rate**: This line assigns the value of **learning_rate** to an instance variable **self.learning_rate**. Instance variables in Python are variables that are unique to each instance of a class.

- **def update_params(self, layer):** This line defines a method called **update_params**. This method is used to update the parameters of the given layer object. The layer object is supposed to have weights and biases attributes that represent the parameters of that layer of the neural network, and **dweights** and **dbiases** that represent their gradients with respect to the loss function.

- **layer.weights += -self.learning_rate * layer.dweights**: This line updates the weights of the layer by subtracting the product of the learning rate and the gradients of the weights **layer.dweights**. This is based on the SGD formula mentioned earlier.

- **layer.biases += -self.learning_rate * layer.dbiases**: This line updates the biases of the layer in a similar manner.

Here's how the full code looks after integrating the SGD Optimizer:

```
import numpy as np
from sklearn.datasets import make_classification
```

```python
import matplotlib.pyplot as plt


# Dense layer
class Layer_Dense:
    def __init__(self, n_inputs, n_neurons):
        # Initialize weights with random values scaled by 0.01
        self.weights = 0.01 * np.random.randn(n_inputs, n_neurons)
        # Initialize biases as zeros
        self.biases = np.zeros((1, n_neurons))
        # Initialize gradient variables as None
        self.dweights = None
        self.dbiases = None


    def forward(self, inputs):
        # Save the inputs for later use in backward propagation
        self.inputs = inputs
        # Perform the dot product of inputs and weights, and add biases
        self.output = np.dot(inputs, self.weights) + self.biases
        return self.output


    def backward(self, dvalues):
        # Calculate the gradients of weights, biases, and inputs
        self.dweights = np.dot(self.inputs.T, dvalues)
        self.dbiases = np.sum(dvalues, axis=0, keepdims=True)
        self.dinputs = np.dot(dvalues, self.weights.T)


# ReLU activation function
```

```python
class Activation_ReLU:
    def forward(self, inputs):
        # Save the inputs for later use in backward propagation
        self.inputs = inputs
        # Apply the ReLU activation function element-wise
        self.output = np.maximum(0, inputs)
        return self.output



    def backward(self, dvalues):
        # Create a copy of the gradients of the outputs
        self.dinputs = dvalues.copy()
        # Set gradients of the inputs corresponding to the negative input
values to 0
        self.dinputs[self.inputs <= 0] = 0



# Softmax activation function
class Activation_Softmax:
    def forward(self, inputs):
        # Calculate exponential values of inputs while normalizing them
        exp_values = np.exp(inputs - np.max(inputs, axis=1, keepdims=True))
        # Calculate probabilities by dividing each exponential value by
the sum of all exponential values
        probabilities = exp_values / np.sum(exp_values, axis=1, keep-
dims=True)
        # Save the output for later use in backward propagation
        self.output = probabilities
        return self.output



    def backward(self, dvalues):
```

```python
        # Create an array to store the gradients of the inputs
        self.dinputs = np.empty_like(dvalues)
    for index, (single_output, single_dvalues) in enumerate(zip(self.
output, dvalues)):
            # Reshape the single_output array into a column vector
            single_output = single_output.reshape(-1, 1)
            # Calculate the Jacobian matrix for the softmax function
                jacobian_matrix = np.diagflat(single_output) - np.dot
(single_output, single_output.T)
                # Calculate the gradient of the inputs using the Jacobian
matrix and the gradients of the outputs
            self.dinputs[index] = np.dot(jacobian_matrix, single_dvalues)



# Cross-entropy loss
class Loss_CategoricalCrossentropy:
    def forward(self, y_pred, y_true):
        samples = len(y_pred)
        y_pred_clipped = np.clip(y_pred, 1e-7, 1 - 1e-7)


        if len(y_true.shape) == 1:
          # For sparse label format, extract the correct confidence scores
            correct_confidences = y_pred_clipped[range(samples), y_true]
        elif len(y_true.shape) == 2:
            # For one-hot encoded label format, calculate the dot product
of probabilities and labels
            correct_confidences = np.sum(y_pred_clipped * y_true, axis=1)


        # Calculate negative log-likelihood loss
        negative_log_likelihoods = -np.log(correct_confidences)
        return negative_log_likelihoods
```

```python
    def backward(self, dvalues, y_true):
        samples = len(dvalues)
        labels = len(dvalues[0])

        if len(y_true.shape) == 1:
            # For sparse label format, convert y_true to one-hot encoded
format
            y_true = np.eye(labels)[y_true]
        # Calculate gradient of the loss with respect to the inputs
        self.dinputs = -y_true / dvalues
        self.dinputs = self.dinputs / samples


class Optimizer_SGD:
    # Initialize optimizer - set settings,
    # learning rate of 1. Is default for this optimizer
    def __init__(self, learning_rate=1.0):
        self.learning_rate = learning_rate
        # Update parameters
    def update_params(self, layer):
        layer.weights += -self.learning_rate * layer.dweights
        layer.biases += -self.learning_rate * layer.dbiases


# Generate dataset
X, y = make_classification(n_samples=1000, n_features=2, n_informative=2,
                           n_redundant=0, n_clusters_per_class=1, class_
sep=0.8, random_state=42)

# Create layers
dense1 = Layer_Dense(2, 3)
```

```python
relu_activation = Activation_ReLU()
dense2 = Layer_Dense(3, 3)
softmax_activation = Activation_Softmax()


# Create loss function
loss_function = Loss_CategoricalCrossentropy()



# Create optimizer
optimizer = Optimizer_SGD(learning_rate=0.1)


# Training loop
losses = []
accuracies = []
for epoch in range(500):
    # Forward pass
    dense1_output = dense1.forward(X)
    relu_activation_output = relu_activation.forward(dense1_output)
    dense2_output = dense2.forward(relu_activation_output)
    softmax_activation_output = softmax_activation.forward(dense2_output)


    # Calculate loss
    loss = np.mean(loss_function.forward(softmax_activation_output, y))
    losses.append(loss)
    predictions = np.argmax(softmax_activation_output, axis=1)
    accuracy = np.mean(predictions == y)
    # Append the accuracy to accuracies list
    accuracies.append(accuracy)
    print(f'Epoch: {epoch}, Accuracy: {accuracy:.3f}, Loss: {loss:.3f}')
```

```
    # Backward pass
    loss_function.backward(softmax_activation_output, y)
    softmax_activation.backward(loss_function.dinputs)
    dense2.backward(softmax_activation.dinputs)
    relu_activation.backward(dense2.dinputs)
    dense1.backward(relu_activation.dinputs)

    # Update weights and biases
    optimizer.update_params(dense1)
    optimizer.update_params(dense2)


plt.figure()
plt.xlabel('Epoch')


# Create twin axes that share the same x-axis
ax1 = plt.gca()
ax2 = ax1.twinx()


# Plot loss (on y-axis of ax1)
ax1.plot(losses, color='blue', label='Loss')
ax1.set_ylabel('Loss', color='blue')
ax1.tick_params('y', colors='blue')


# Plot accuracy (on y-axis of ax2)
ax2.plot(accuracies, color='red', label='Accuracy')
ax2.set_ylabel('Accuracy', color='red')
ax2.tick_params('y', colors='red')


plt.title('Loss and Accuracy over epochs')
```

```
plt.show()
```

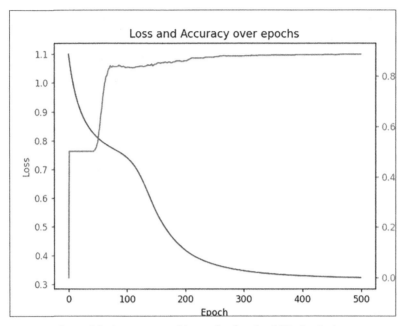

Figure 7.2: *Accuracy and Loss plot for the SGD Optimizer*

The preceding graph shows that our neural network is finally training, and we see our loss decreasing to ~~0.3 and accuracy rising above 0.8. It's important to note that these curves are not smooth, and, after a certain point, both curves start to plateau.

Now, let's look at the same code with **Adam Optimizer**:

```python
import numpy as np

from sklearn.datasets import make_classification

import matplotlib.pyplot as plt


# Dense layer

class Layer_Dense:

    def __init__(self, n_inputs, n_neurons):

        # Initialize weights with random values scaled by 0.01

        self.weights = 0.01 * np.random.randn(n_inputs, n_neurons)
```

```python
        # Initialize biases as zeros
        self.biases = np.zeros((1, n_neurons))
        # Initialize gradient variables as None
        self.dweights = None
        self.dbiases = None

    def forward(self, inputs):
        # Save the inputs for later use in backward propagation
        self.inputs = inputs
        # Perform the dot product of inputs and weights, and add biases
        self.output = np.dot(inputs, self.weights) + self.biases
        return self.output

    def backward(self, dvalues):
        # Calculate the gradients of weights, biases, and inputs
        self.dweights = np.dot(self.inputs.T, dvalues)
        self.dbiases = np.sum(dvalues, axis=0, keepdims=True)
        self.dinputs = np.dot(dvalues, self.weights.T)


# ReLU activation function
class Activation_ReLU:
    def forward(self, inputs):
        # Save the inputs for later use in backward propagation
        self.inputs = inputs
        # Apply the ReLU activation function element-wise
        self.output = np.maximum(0, inputs)
        return self.output

    def backward(self, dvalues):
        # Create a copy of the gradients of the outputs
        self.dinputs = dvalues.copy()
```

```
        # Set gradients of the inputs corresponding to the negative input
values to 0
        self.dinputs[self.inputs <= 0] = 0


# Softmax activation function
class Activation_Softmax:
    def forward(self, inputs):
        # Calculate exponential values of inputs while normalizing them
        exp_values = np.exp(inputs - np.max(inputs, axis=1, keepdims=True))
        # Calculate probabilities by dividing each exponential value by
the sum of all exponential values
        probabilities = exp_values / np.sum(exp_values, axis=1, keep-
dims=True)
        # Save the output for later use in backward propagation
        self.output = probabilities
        return self.output


    def backward(self, dvalues):
        # Create an array to store the gradients of the inputs
        self.dinputs = np.empty_like(dvalues)
        for index, (single_output, single_dvalues) in enumerate(zip(self.
output, dvalues)):
            # Reshape the single_output array into a column vector
            single_output = single_output.reshape(-1, 1)
            # Calculate the Jacobian matrix for the softmax function
            jacobian_matrix = np.diagflat(single_output) - np.dot
(single_output, single_output.T)
            # Calculate the gradient of the inputs using the Jacobian
matrix and the gradients of the outputs
            self.dinputs[index] = np.dot(jacobian_matrix, single_dvalues)


# Cross-entropy loss
class Loss_CategoricalCrossentropy:
```

```python
def forward(self, y_pred, y_true):
    samples = len(y_pred)
    y_pred_clipped = np.clip(y_pred, 1e-7, 1 - 1e-7)

    if len(y_true.shape) == 1:
        # For sparse label format, extract the correct confidence scores
        correct_confidences = y_pred_clipped[range(samples), y_true]
    elif len(y_true.shape) == 2:
        # For one-hot encoded label format, calculate the dot
product of probabilities and labels
        correct_confidences = np.sum(y_pred_clipped * y_true, axis=1)

    # Calculate negative log-likelihood loss
    negative_log_likelihoods = -np.log(correct_confidences)
    return negative_log_likelihoods

def backward(self, dvalues, y_true):
    samples = len(dvalues)
    labels = len(dvalues[0])

    if len(y_true.shape) == 1:
        # For sparse label format, convert y_true to one-hot encoded
format
        y_true = np.eye(labels)[y_true]

    # Calculate gradient of the loss with respect to the inputs
    self.dinputs = -y_true / dvalues
    self.dinputs = self.dinputs / samples

class Optimizer_Adam:
    # Initialize optimizer - set settings
    def __init__(self, learning_rate=0.001, decay=0., epsilon=1e-7,
```

```
beta_1=0.9, beta_2=0.999):
        # Learning rate of 0.001 is default for this optimizer
        self.learning_rate = learning_rate
        self.current_learning_rate = learning_rate
        # Decay rate for the learning rate
        self.decay = decay
        # Number of steps taken so far
        self.iterations = 0
        # Small number to prevent division by zero
        self.epsilon = epsilon
        # Coefficients used for computing running averages of gradient and
its square
        self.beta_1 = beta_1
        self.beta_2 = beta_2


    # Call just before the update step, update learning rate if decay is
set
    def pre_update_params(self):
        if self.decay:
            self.current_learning_rate = self.learning_rate * (1. / (1. +
self.decay * self.iterations))


    # Update parameters
    def update_params(self, layer):
        # If layer does not contain cache arrays, create them
        # filled with zeros
        if not hasattr(layer, 'weight_cache'):
            layer.weight_momentums = np.zeros_like(layer.weights)
            layer.weight_cache = np.zeros_like(layer.weights)
            layer.bias_momentums = np.zeros_like(layer.biases)
            layer.bias_cache = np.zeros_like(layer.biases)
```

```python
        # Update momentum with current gradients
        layer.weight_momentums = self.beta_1 * layer.weight_momentums +
(1 - self.beta_1) * layer.dweights
        layer.bias_momentums = self.beta_1 * layer.bias_momentums +
(1 - self.beta_1) * layer.dbiases


        # Get corrected momentum
        # self.iteration is 0 at first pass and we need to start with 1 here
        weight_momentums_corrected = layer.weight_momentums / (1 - self.
beta_1 ** (self.iterations + 1))
        bias_momentums_corrected = layer.bias_momentums / (1 - self.beta_1
** (self.iterations + 1))


        # Update cache with squared current gradients
        layer.weight_cache = self.beta_2 * layer.weight_cache + (1 - self.
beta_2) * layer.dweights**2
        layer.bias_cache = self.beta_2 * layer.bias_cache + (1 - self.
beta_2) * layer.dbiases**2


        # Get corrected cache
        weight_cache_corrected = layer.weight_cache / (1 - self.beta_2 **
(self.iterations + 1))
        bias_cache_corrected = layer.bias_cache / (1 - self.beta_2 **
(self.iterations + 1))


        # Vanilla SGD parameter update + normalization with square rooted
cache
        layer.weights += -self.current_learning_rate * weight_momentums_
corrected / (np.sqrt(weight_cache_corrected) + self.epsilon)
        layer.biases += -self.current_learning_rate * bias_momentums_
corrected / (np.sqrt(bias_cache_corrected) + self.epsilon)


    # Call after any parameter updates
    def post_update_params(self):
```

```python
        self.iterations += 1


# Generate dataset
X, y = make_classification(n_samples=1000, n_features=2, n_informative=2,
                           n_redundant=0, n_clusters_per_class=1, class_
sep=0.8, random_state=42)


# Create layers
dense1 = Layer_Dense(2, 3)
relu_activation = Activation_ReLU()
dense2 = Layer_Dense(3, 3)
softmax_activation = Activation_Softmax()


# Create loss function
loss_function = Loss_CategoricalCrossentropy()


# Create optimizer
#optimizer = Optimizer_SGD(learning_rate=0.1)
optimizer = Optimizer_Adam(learning_rate=0.01)


# Training loop
losses = []
accuracies = []
for epoch in range(500):

    # Call pre_update_params at the start of each epoch
    optimizer.pre_update_params()

    # Forward pass
    dense1_output = dense1.forward(X)
    relu_activation_output = relu_activation.forward(dense1_output)
```

```python
    dense2_output = dense2.forward(relu_activation_output)
    softmax_activation_output = softmax_activation.forward(dense2_output)


    # Calculate loss
    loss = np.mean(loss_function.forward(softmax_activation_output, y))
    losses.append(loss)
    predictions = np.argmax(softmax_activation_output, axis=1)
    accuracy = np.mean(predictions == y)
    # Append the accuracy to accuracies list
    accuracies.append(accuracy)
    print(f'Epoch: {epoch}, Accuracy: {accuracy:.3f}, Loss: {loss:.3f}')


    # Backward pass
    loss_function.backward(softmax_activation_output, y)
    softmax_activation.backward(loss_function.dinputs)
    dense2.backward(softmax_activation.dinputs)
    relu_activation.backward(dense2.dinputs)
    dense1.backward(relu_activation.dinputs)


    # Update weights and biases
    optimizer.update_params(dense1)
    optimizer.update_params(dense2)


    # Call post_update_params at the end of each epoch
    optimizer.post_update_params()

plt.figure()
plt.xlabel('Epoch')

# Create twin axes that share the same x-axis
ax1 = plt.gca()
```

```
ax2 = ax1.twinx()

# Plot loss (on y-axis of ax1)
ax1.plot(losses, color='blue', label='Loss')
ax1.set_ylabel('Loss', color='blue')
ax1.tick_params('y', colors='blue')

# Plot accuracy (on y-axis of ax2)
ax2.plot(accuracies, color='red', label='Accuracy')
ax2.set_ylabel('Accuracy', color='red')
ax2.tick_params('y', colors='red')

plt.title('Loss and Accuracy over epochs')
plt.show()
```

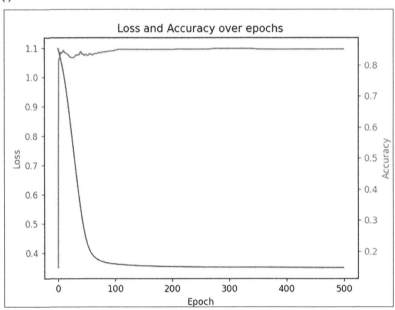

Figure 7.3: *Accuracy and Loss plot for the Adam Optimizer*

Now, here's some interesting thing to note: if you observe the loss-accuracy-epcoh graph for Adam vs. SGD, you will find out that SGD takes more epochs to reach the same level of accuracy. Adam is significantly faster and less likely to get stuck in local minima.

Note: SGD can get stuck in a position called saddle point, where both the local minima and maxima are at the same point. The following diagram Figure 7.4 shows displays the saddle point for SGD. On the other hand, due to momentum, Optimizers like Adam can always come out of such situations.

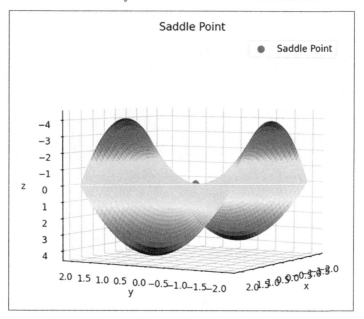

Figure 7.4: *SGD can get stuck in a saddle point (local minima and maxima at the same point)*

Let's also look at the decision boundaries of our trained neural networks. Here's a small code snippet that can be added after the training loop to visualize the decision boundaries of our trained neural network:

```
# Generate a meshgrid of points covering the input space
x_min, x_max = X[:, 0].min() - 0.5, X[:, 0].max() + 0.5
y_min, y_max = X[:, 1].min() - 0.5, X[:, 1].max() + 0.5
xx, yy = np.meshgrid(np.arange(x_min, x_max, 0.02),
                     np.arange(y_min, y_max, 0.02))


# Flatten the meshgrid points and pass them through the trained network
mesh_inputs = np.c_[xx.ravel(), yy.ravel()]
dense1_output = dense1.forward(mesh_inputs)
relu_activation_output = relu_activation.forward(dense1_output)
```

```python
dense2_output = dense2.forward(relu_activation_output)
softmax_activation_output = softmax_activation.forward(dense2_output)


# Get the predicted classes
predictions = np.argmax(softmax_activation_output, axis=1)
predictions = predictions.reshape(xx.shape)


# Plot the decision boundaries
plt.figure(figsize=(8, 6))
plt.contourf(xx, yy, predictions, alpha=0.8)
plt.scatter(X[:, 0], X[:, 1], c=y, edgecolors='k')
plt.xlabel('X1')
plt.ylabel('X2')
plt.title('Decision Boundaries')
plt.show()
```

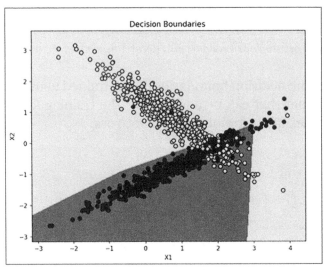

Figure 7.5: *Decision boundary after training our neural network using Adam Optimizer*

This covers the training of our end-to-end neural networks from scratch. Remember, there are still many more things that go into real- world neural networks. There are so many ideas like weight decays, early stopping, and caching that go into a real-world AI pipeline. We'll see all those ideas when we start using the high- level library of TensorFlow and work on a significantly more complex dataset.

Conclusion

In this chapter, we begin by integrating the components discussed in the previous chapter, laying the foundation for further exploration of weight updation. We delve into the concept of random weight updation, which serves as a starting point for our journey. Furthermore, we explore the intricacies of partial derivatives and the Chain Rule, two crucial mathematical concepts employed in the Backpropagation algorithm. With NumPy's aid, we implement the full backpropagation algorithm, allowing us to update our neural network weights efficiently.

Finally, we focus on different Optimizers such as Stochastic Gradient Descent (SGD) and Adam. We train our network using these Optimizers on our dataset, striving to achieve an accuracy exceeding 80%. Additionally, we take the opportunity to compare the performance of SGD and Adam, gaining valuable insights into their respective strengths and weaknesses. Along this path, we also understand the concept of a Saddle point, which further enriches our knowledge of optimization landscapes in neural networks.

The next chapter deals with the concept of CNN and different types of CNN-based networks that helps us deal with image and video data.

" *"The real question is, when will we achieve human-level AI? I would be surprised if this does not happen within the next decade." - Demis Hassabis, CEO of DeepMind"*

https://github.com/OrangeAVA/Ultimate-Neural-Network-Programming-with-Python

## CHAPTER 8

Understanding Convolution and CNN Architectures

We can't develop a comprehensive understanding of AI without delving deeper into the convolution neural networks. These types of networks play major roles in Image Processing and computer vision and have been at the forefront of AI development for a long time. This chapter will deal with different operations related to CNN, and later on, how these concepts have been used to invent new CNN architectures over the years.

Structure

This chapter covers the following topics:

- Understanding bits and pieces of CNN like padding, pooling, and more
- CNN evolution: Skip connections and Inception module
- Understanding the scaling of Conv Network through Efficient Net
- Different types of Convolutions

In the realm of deep learning, Convolutional Neural Networks (CNNs or ConvNets) reign supreme when it comes to analyzing visual imagery. These specialized artificial neural networks, called shift invariant or space invariant neural networks (SIANN), possess a shared-weight convolution kernel or filter architecture. These filters slide along input features, generating translation equivariant responses called feature maps. This chapter explores the workings of CNNs, shedding light on their ability to capture local patterns, exploit translation invariance, and build spatial hierarchies for visual concept extraction.

Intricacies of CNN

Convolution is one key operation in the field of signal processing, but the same operation can be modified to work with image signals. Convolution models are called Convolution Neural Networks because of the Conv layer in their network architecture. There are many intricacies behind convolution; it is important to understand those to build better and more optimized neural network architectures.

Local Patterns and Global Patterns

One key distinction between densely connected and convolutional layers is their learning capabilities. Dense layers excel at discerning global patterns within the input feature space. In the context of image analysis, this involves recognizing patterns involving all pixels in an image, such as the shape of a dog's body, as shown in *Figure 8.1*. Conversely, convolutional layers specialize in detecting local patterns, focusing on small two-dimensional windows of the input. For instance, these windows can be as compact as 3x3 regions. The advantage of convolutional layers is their ability to learn translation invariant patterns. Once a ConvNet learns a specific pattern, it can identify it anywhere within the image, regardless of its location. On the other hand, a densely connected network would need to relearn the pattern from scratch if it appeared in a new position. This inherent translation invariance makes ConvNets highly data-efficient for image processing tasks, requiring fewer training samples to generalize effectively.

Figure 8.1: *Size, space, and translation invariance properties of CNN. CNN (trained to identify dogs) can identify this dog no matter its position or size in the image*

Spatial Hierarchies and Abstraction

Another remarkable characteristic of convolutional layers is their aptitude for capturing spatial hierarchies of patterns. A stack of convolutional layers learns progressively larger and more complex patterns based on the features learned in previous layers. Starting with small local patterns like edges, subsequent layers build on these foundations, ultimately grasping intricate and abstract visual concepts. This spatial hierarchy learning is crucial for ConvNets to navigate the inherent hierarchical structure of the visual world. By efficiently detecting and combining patterns, ConvNets become adept at understanding visual elements' spatial relationships and arrangements.

In *Figure* 8.2, the first layer of the Convolutional Neural Network (CNN) primarily generates horizontal, vertical, and diagonal lines, essential for edge detection in an image. In the second layer, the CNN aims to provide more detailed information by detecting corners. The CNN independently learns these patterns without explicit instructions to focus on complex objects in deeper layers. This progression is natural when training data is fed into a CNN.

Moving on to the third layer, more intricate patterns, such as eyes and faces, emerge. It is reasonable to assume that these feature maps are obtained from a model trained specifically for detecting human faces. In the fourth layer, the features discovered are related to more complex aspects of faces, such as eyes.

When we reach the fifth layer, the feature map begins to depict specific human faces, car tire patterns, animal faces, and so on. This particular feature map contains the most comprehensive information about the patterns found in the images.

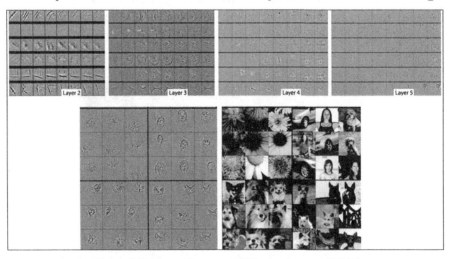

Figure 8.2: *Feature maps at different layers of CNN*

Convolution Operation and Feature Maps

Convolutions are performed on 3D tensors known as feature maps, encompassing two spatial axes (height and width) as well as a depth axis (referred to as the channels axis). In the case of an RGB image, the depth axis has a dimension of 3, representing the red, green, and blue color channels. For grayscale images, the depth is 1, indicating levels of gray. During the convolution operation, patches are extracted from the input feature map, and a consistent transformation is applied to these patches. This process generates an output feature map, maintaining the 3D tensor structure. While the width and height are retained, the depth can vary based on the layer's parameters. In the output feature map, each channel no longer represents specific colors as in RGB input but instead encodes filters that capture distinct aspects of the input data. For instance, a single filter might encapsulate the "presence of a face" concept within the input.

Let's understand the convolution operation.

In *Figure* 8.3, the green matrix is the original image, and the yellow moving matrix is called the **kernel**, which is used to learn the different features of the original image. The kernel first moves horizontally, then shifts down, and again moves horizontally. The sum of the dot product of the image pixel value and kernel pixel value gives the output matrix. Initially, the kernel value initializes randomly, and it's a learning parameter. When we train the networks, it's basically the value of this kernel that we try to optimize. Initially, all the kernels have random weights, but with training finished, all these kernels are filled with specific weights that are responsible for detecting different types of features, such as edges, corners, and more, depending upon the task at hand.

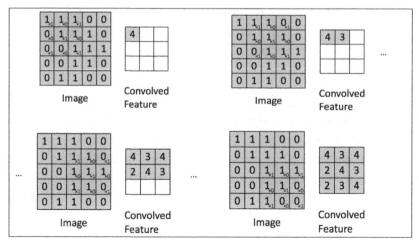

Figure 8.3: *Showing CNN operation for a few step*

For non-trainable kernels or filters, such as the **Sobel filter**, it contain specific pre-set values. In the case of the Sobel filter, the typical values are [[1, 2, 1], [0, 0, 0], [-1, -2, -1]]. This configuration has the advantage of placing additional emphasis on the central row, and, therefore, the central pixel, potentially enhancing the filter's robustness.

Another filter extensively utilized by computer vision researchers is the **Scharr filter**. Instead of the [1, 2, 1] sequence found in the Sobel filter, the Scharr filter uses a [3, 10, 3] sequence, followed by [-3, -10, -3]. This specific pattern confers slightly different properties to the Scharr filter.

One of the key applications of these filters lies in edge detection. For instance, when a Scharr filter is applied in its standard orientation, it serves as a tool for vertical edge detection. However, simply rotating the filter by 90 degrees effectively transforms into a mechanism for horizontal edge detection.

Figure 8.4: *Passing dog image through Sobel filter*

Note: For instance, if a **6x6** matrix convolved with a **3x3** matrix, the output is a **4x4** matrix. To generalize this, if a mxm image convolved with nxn kernel, the output image is of size $(m - n + 1) * (m - n + 1)$.

Pooling

A pooling layer is another building block of a CNN. Its function is to progressively reduce the spatial size of the representation to reduce the network complexity and computational cost. This is performed by decreasing the connections between layers and independently operating on each feature map. Depending upon the method used, there are several types of Pooling operations.

In **Max Pooling**, the largest element is taken from the feature map. **Average Pooling**, on the other hand, calculates the average of the elements in a predefined-sized Image section. The total sum of the elements in the predefined section is computed in Sum Pooling. The Pooling Layer usually serves as a bridge between the Convolutional Layer and the FC Layer.

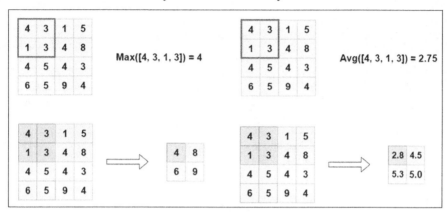

Figure 8.5: *Max Pooling (left) and Average Pooling (right)*

Max Pooling and Average pooling are not the ends of pooling; we have a lot of different types of pooling, such as Mixed pooling, Intermap pooling, multi-scale orderless pooling, Spectral pooling, and more.

Here is a paper on the different types of pooling:
https://arxiv.org/ftp/arxiv/papers/2009/2009.07485.pdf [22]

Padding

Convolution poses two challenges:

Firstly, after each convolution operation, the original image size reduces. As mentioned earlier, a **6x6** image diminished to **4x4**. In image classification tasks that involve multiple convolution layers, this continuous reduction in size becomes undesirable. We aim to prevent the image from shrinking with each convolution operation.

Secondly, when the kernel moves across the original image, it encounters the image edges less frequently and the central region more frequently. This results in overlapping primarily occurring in the middle of the image, neglecting the output's corner features and edge details.

To address these issues, a solution called **padding** is introduced. Padding helps maintain the original image size, resolving the first problem.

Note: If a n x n matrix convolved with an **f x f** matrix with padding **p**, then the size of the output image will be **(n + 2p − f + 1)x (n + 2p − f + 1)**.

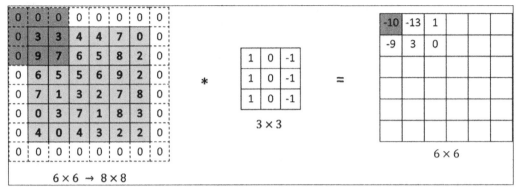

Figure 8.6: *Padding in CNN*

Stride

Stride is the number of pixels that shift over the input matrix. For padding p, filter size **f x f** and input image size **n x n** and stride s, our output image dimension will be [{(n + 2p − f + 1) / s} + 1] ∗ [{(n + 2p − f + 1) / s} + 1]. Stride also determines the feature map's size after a conv operation.

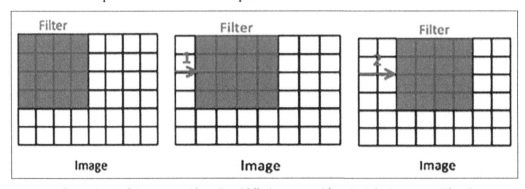

Figure 8.7: *Left image: stride = 0, middle image: stride = 1, right image: stride =2*

Convolutional Neural Networks offer a powerful framework for analyzing visual imagery by leveraging their ability to capture local patterns, exploit translation invariance, and establish spatial hierarchies. These networks revolutionize image analysis tasks and efficiently process large amounts of data, making them indispensable tools in computer vision applications. Understanding the inner workings of convolutional layers and their feature maps enables practitioners to harness the full potential of CNNs, extracting meaningful and abstract visual concepts from raw image data.

Here's the code for implementing the CNN operation:

```python
import numpy as np


def conv2d(input_mat, kernel_mat):
  # Get dimensions
  input_dim = input_mat.shape[0]
  kernel_dim = kernel_mat.shape[0]


  # Check dimensions
  if kernel_dim > input_dim:
    print("Error: Kernel dimension larger than input dimension.")
    return []


  # Compute dimensions of the output feature map
  output_dim = input_dim - kernel_dim + 1


  # Initialize output feature map
  output_mat = np.zeros((output_dim, output_dim))


  # Compute convolution
  for row in range(output_dim):
    for col in range(output_dim):
      # Element-wise multiplication of the kernel and the input
      output_mat[row, col] = np.sum(kernel_mat *
input_mat[row:row+kernel_dim, col:col+kernel_dim])


  return output_mat


# Define 5x5 input matrix
```

```
input_mat = np.array([[1, 2, 3, 4, 5],
            [5, 4, 3, 2, 1],
            [1, 2, 3, 4, 5],
            [5, 4, 3, 2, 1],
            [1, 2, 3, 4, 5]])


# Define 3x3 kernel
kernel_mat = np.array([[0, 1, 0],
            [0, -1, 0],
            [0, 1, 0]])


# Apply 2D convolution
output_mat = conv2d(input_mat, kernel_mat)


print(output_mat)


#Output: [[0. 3. 6.]
#         [6. 3. 0.]
#         [0. 3. 6.]]
```

The preceding code shows the operation with a static kernel. Still, for neural networks to learn meaningful representations, they need to be able to update the kernel weights using the Backpropagation algorithm.

Here's a simplified version of the **conv_2D** layer:

```
import numpy as np


class Conv2D:
    def __init__(self, num_filters, filter_size):
        self.num_filters = num_filters
        self.filter_size = filter_size
```

```
    self.filters = np.random.randn(num_filters, filter_size, filter_size) /
9  # Initialize filters


  def iterate_regions(self, image):
    h, w = image.shape
    for i in range(h - self.filter_size + 1):
      for j in range(w - self.filter_size + 1):
        im_region = image[i:(i + self.filter_size), j:(j +
self.filter_size)]
        yield im_region, i, j


  def forward(self, input):
    self.last_input = input
    h, w = input.shape
    output = np.zeros((h - self.filter_size + 1, w - self.filter_size + 1,
self.num_filters))
    for im_region, i, j in self.iterate_regions(input):
      output[i, j] = np.sum(im_region * self.filters, axis=(1, 2))
    return output


  def backprop(self, d_L_d_out, learning_rate):
    d_L_d_filters = np.zeros(self.filters.shape)
    for im_region, i, j in self.iterate_regions(self.last_input):
      for f in range(self.num_filters):
        d_L_d_filters[f] += d_L_d_out[i, j, f] * im_region
    self.filters -= learning_rate * d_L_d_filters
    return None  # Not necessary but helps to clarify no gradients returned
```

The preceding code is a simplified example of a class representing a Convolutional Layer. It involves initializing weights (filters), forward propagation, backward propagation, and weights updating methods. However, this code needs more features of an actual deep learning framework and needs to be more concise.

Actual TensorFlow implementation of Conv2d layers is quite complex and beyond the book's scope. For instance, the current code lacks many features of a real deep learning framework, such as:

- It does not handle biases or padding.
- It does not support mini-batches.
- It only works with a single channel.
- It only supports one layer.

Here's a video on CNN operations and other details from Stanford: **https://www.youtube.com/watch?v=bNb2fEVKeEo&list=PL3FW7Lu3i5JvHM8ljY j-zLfQRF3EO8sYv&index=5&ab_channel=StanfordUniversitySchoolof Engineering [23]**

Introduction to CNN-based Networks

Yann LeCun, the creator of Convolutional Neural Networks (CNNs), published a seminal paper in the year 1998 titled "LeNet-5." This paper laid the foundation for deep learning and found practical application in the early days of AI, particularly for recognizing zip code digits. To effectively train **LeNet-5**, Bayesian techniques were extensively employed to initialize the weights, ensuring proper convergence.

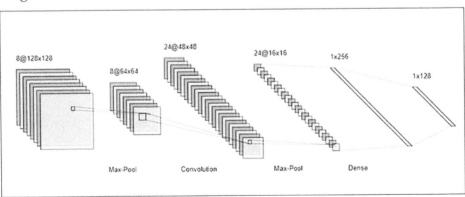

Figure 8.8: *LeNet-5 Architecture*

Subsequently, a groundbreaking paper introduced the architecture known as **AlexNet**, developed by Geoff Hinton's lab and renowned for inventing Backpropagation. AlexNet represented a significant advancement in scale, capable of handling the vast ImageNet dataset. Outperforming other techniques by a substantial margin, this paper sparked extensive research and propelled the widespread exploration of convolutional neural networks.

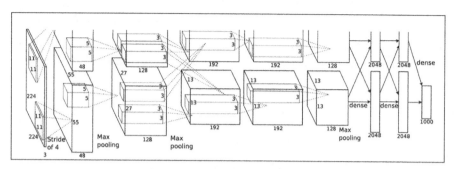

Figure 8.9: *AlexNet Architecture*

Training AlexNet was pretty hard; remember that we're referring to the year 2012, when several modern techniques, such as batch normalization, had not yet been discovered. *Figure* 8.9 illustrates the architecture of Alexnet, which resembles the deep learning architectures commonly used today. One notable distinction between this architecture and contemporary ones is the presence of two streams of layers.

Can you guess the reason for two streams of layers as a design choice?

When this research paper was published, the available memory on a single machine needed to be increased to execute the network. Consequently, the network was devised to run on two parallel clusters. This paper was groundbreaking as it introduced the use of the Rectified Linear Unit (ReLU) activation function, norm layers, and extensive data augmentation techniques like jittering and color manipulation. The training process employed a batch size of 128 and utilized stochastic gradient descent (SGD) with momentum. Additionally, a dropout rate of 0.5 was applied during model training. It is worth noting that the training was conducted on a GTX 580, which possessed a mere 3GB of memory. Upon closer inspection of the diagram, the first convolutional layer yields an output of 55x55x96 divided evenly between the two GPUs, resulting in 55x55x48 per GPU. Furthermore, not every layer in one GPU is connected to the subsequent layer in the other GPU.

Now, let's look at the general architecture of modern deep learning networks. Until now, we have looked at many individual components of DL models, but how do all these things bind together?

Understanding the Complete Flow of CNN-based Network

At its core, a CNN is an image inspector, examining images piece by piece. These dissected elements, known as features, are essentially matrices of pixel values

(MxM matrices with numbers). When a CNN compares two images, it looks for these features in approximately the same positions, thereby outperforming whole-image matching techniques in identifying similarities.

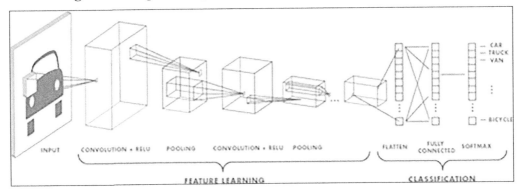

Figure 8.10: *A generalized CNN-based classifier architecture*

When faced with a new image, however, CNN encounters a predicament. It doesn't know where these features might align, so it probes the image relentlessly, trying every possible position to find matches. In doing so, the CNN effectively treats each feature as a filter, applying it across the image through a mathematical operation known as convolution – the concept from which Convolutional Neural Networks derive their name.

This process doesn't stop at one feature. It is repeated for all the features we're looking for in the image, producing one set of filtered images for each filter. We can think of this entire ensemble of convolution operations as a singular step in processing.

Next, we introduce the critical concept of **non-linearity** into our model. This non-linearity enables our model to learn and predict non-linear boundaries. A common method to introduce non-linearity is utilizing a non-linear function such as **ReLU** or **gelu**. ReLU is the most widely used, and it performs a straightforward operation: whenever it encounters a negative number, it replaces it with a zero. This mechanism keeps the CNN mathematically healthy, preventing learned values from stagnating near zero or inflating towards infinity. However, it's important to note that these convolution and ReLU operations may create vast feature maps, hence, necessitating a process to reduce the feature map size while maintaining the identified features.

This brings us to pooling, a technique that takes large images and reduces them while still preserving the most vital information. Pooling involves moving a small window across an image, capturing the maximum value from each step. A typical window size might be 2 or 3 pixels, with a step size of 2 pixels. The pooling layer results from performing this operation on an image or set of images, producing a similar number of images but with fewer pixels – an efficient way to manage the computational load.

After performing a predetermined number of convolution operations (as per the model's design), the process enters the realm of deep learning neural networks to leverage the operations fully carried out thus far. Before doing this, however, we need to flatten the pooled feature maps because a neural network accepts only single-dimension inputs. Imagine stacking them like Lego bricks, turning the raw images into a set of filtered, rectified, and pooled images ready to interface with the neural network.

In the neural network, the fully connected layers take these high-level filtered images (now one-dimensional rectified pooled feature maps) and translate them into votes. These votes are expressed as weights, or connection strengths, between each value and each category. Whenever a new image is presented to the CNN, it percolates through the lower layers until it reaches the fully connected layer at the end. Then, a democratic process takes place: the category with the most votes is declared the winner, the category of the input.

In this way, the intricate machinery of a Deep Convolutional Neural Network operates, transforming the raw data of an image into discernible features and, ultimately, into actionable insights.

Unfortunately, CNN is not a straightforward process. There exists a lengthy checklist of decisions that CNN designers must navigate. For each convolutional layer, several considerations must be made:

- How many features should be employed? What should be the size of each feature in terms of pixels?

- Pooling layers introduce another set of choices: What window size should be used for pooling? What should be the stride value?

- Further decisions arise regarding the activation function: Which function is most suitable for the task at hand? How many epochs should be utilized during training? Should early stopping be employed?

- Additionally, when incorporating additional fully connected layers, questions regarding the number of hidden neurons arise, among other considerations.

Moreover, there are higher-level architectural decisions to address, such as determining the quantity of each layer type to include and their order. Various tweaks can be explored, such as incorporating new layer types or implementing more intricate layer connections. Additionally, options like extending the number of training epochs or altering the activation function can be explored.

In summary, designing a CNN involves grappling with a multitude of decisions, spanning from fine-grained choices at the layer level to broader architectural considerations and experimenting with different adjustments and techniques.

VGG16

Building upon the impressive strides made by AlexNet, which consisted of eight layers, the field of deep learning experienced a revolutionary advancement with the development of significantly more intricate networks like VGG, featuring 16 or 19 layers, and GoogleNet, encompassing 22 layers. Let's delve into the details of VGGNet, also known as Visual Geometry Group Network, and its advancements.

VGG16, one of the most noteworthy variations of VGGNet, stood out with nearly double the number of layers compared to its predecessor, AlexNet. What further distinguished VGG16 was its radical modification in the usage of convolutional filters. Contrary to prior models incorporating various filter sizes, VGG16 uniformly employed 3x3 convolutional filters across all layers. *Figure* 8.11 shows the architecture of VGG16 showcasing all its different layers with output sizes at each layer.

Intriguingly, the VGG researchers found that using a stack of three 3x3 filters in succession produces the same receptive field as deploying a single larger 7x7 filter. This naturally raises the question: why select more layers when a solitary layer could suffice?

The primary motivation behind adopting multiple layers instead of a single, more comprehensive layer lies in the infusion of increased non-linearity in decision boundaries. This approach enhances the network's ability to learn more complex patterns from the data without significantly increasing the computational burden. Specifically, three layers of 3x3 filters require $3\times(3^2\times C^2)$ parameters, while a single layer of 7x7 filters demands much larger $(7^2\times C^2)$ parameters, given the same number of channels, C.

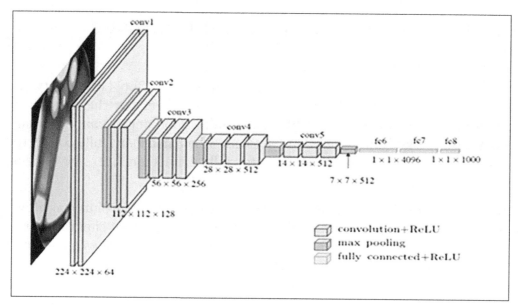

Figure 8.11: *VGG16 Architecture*

This innovative adaptation demonstrated that deeper networks could be trained using fewer parameters without compromising their learning capacity. Moreover, the VGG16 model significantly impacted the machine learning community, becoming a benchmark in the ILSVRC (ImageNet Large Scale Visual Recognition Challenge) 2014 competition, and has been extensively used for transfer learning in various computer vision tasks since then. It is worth noting that VGG's architectural simplicity, efficiency, and effectiveness have played a substantial role in influencing the design of subsequent deep learning models.

Despite reducing the kernel size, to process a single image using VGG16, approximately 100 MB of memory is required. The VGG16 model is equipped with a substantial 138 million parameters, which is a considerable amount even when considering the current computing power available. Additionally, filters increase as we delve deeper into the network. The initial layers possess larger width and height dimensions to maintain a consistent level of information throughout the network. As we progress towards deeper layers with smaller sizes, we compensate for this by increasing the depth of the filters. Another notable aspect of this architecture is the significant number of parameters in the fully connected layers, particularly in the final layer. Of the 138 million parameters, a staggering 102 million are solely attributed to the first fully connected layers. In the subsequent sections, we will explore techniques to reduce the parameter count, facilitating easier model training.

Inception Module: Naïve and Improved Version

The **Inception module** is a key component of the GoogLeNet network, introduced by Google in 2014. It was designed to reduce the number of parameters and memory usage while maintaining good performance in image classification tasks. Unlike the VGG16 network, which had many fully connected layers, GoogLeNet eliminated the need for fully connected layers by utilizing the Inception module.

The Inception module employs a concept called parallel convolutional filters, where multiple filters of different sizes are applied to the input simultaneously. These parallel filters capture information at different spatial scales and extract features of various sizes. The outputs of these filters are then concatenated depth-wise, meaning the channel dimensions are stacked together.

Let's take a closer look at the naïve implementation of the Inception module. Assuming an input size of 28x28x256 (28 pixels width, 28 pixels height, and 256 channels), the module applies convolutional filters of different sizes to the input in parallel. After the convolutional operations, the resulting feature maps from each branch are concatenated along the depth dimension. In *Figure* 8.12, the Inception module's output size would be 28x28x672 (28 pixels width, 28 pixels height, and 672 channels). Applying this naïve inception reduced the number of trainable weights but the number of calculations needed was still huge.

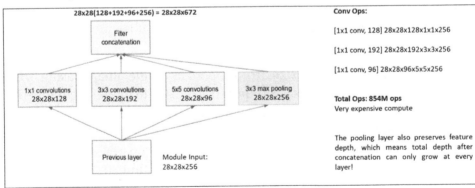

Figure 8.12: *Naïve Inception module*

Naïve implementation of the Inception module involved a significant number of calculations. In fact, the total number of operations reaches **854 million** in just one layer of the Inception module. This can be computationally expensive and may limit the efficiency of the network.

Additionally, as the network progresses through multiple Inception modules, the output depth will continue to increase. This occurs because the pooling operation used in the Inception module preserves depth-wise features. The increased depth allows the network to capture and represent more complex and diverse features as the information flows through subsequent layers.

The Inception module's parallel convolutional filters and depth-wise concatenation strategy help reduce the number of parameters compared to traditional fully connected layers, resulting in memory-efficient networks. While the naïve implementation involves many operations, subsequent improvements and optimizations have been made to the Inception module, leading to more efficient and powerful network architectures.

In order to optimize the Inception module and reduce the number of parameters, 1x1 convolutional filters are introduced before each convolutional layer and after the max pooling layer. This additional use of 1x1 filters helps decrease the dimensionality in the depth dimension. By incorporating these 1x1 filters, the architecture of the Inception module is enhanced, as illustrated in *Figure 8.13*:

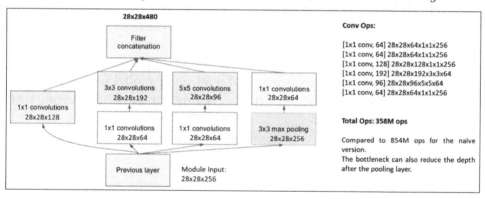

Figure 8.13: *Improved Inception Module*

The inclusion of 1x1 convolutional filters has a significant impact on the computational load. As depicted in the accompanying image, the number of calculations is reduced from **854 million** to **358 million**, resulting in a more than twofold reduction in computation. Furthermore, the use of 1x1 filters assists in managing the depth dimension effectively.

The introduction of the 1x1 convolutional filter not only reduces the number of parameters but also enhances performance compared to the naive implementation. It enables increased non-linearity and diminishes redundancy in the feature maps by combining them linearly. This process aids in achieving better results.

The paper's authors on the Inception module also introduced two auxiliary classifiers. These auxiliary classifiers contribute to discrimination in the lower stages of the classifier, amplify the gradient signal propagation during training, and offer additional regularization. However, the auxiliary networks connected to the auxiliary classifiers are discarded during inference.

Overall, the incorporation of **1x1** convolutional filters, along with the inclusion of auxiliary classifiers, improves the efficiency and effectiveness of the Inception module.

ResNet

ResNet, short for Residual Network, is a deep neural network architecture that introduces skip connections, allowing for the creation of networks with many layers, such as the 152-layer variant. However, the question arises: Can we stack these modules and construct an extremely deep network? The answer is no, as we encounter a challenge known as vanishing or exploding gradients.

To illustrate this issue, consider the following diagram (see *Figure* 8.14), which demonstrates that a 56-layer network performs worse than a 20-layer network on test data. It is important to note that this performance discrepancy is not due to overfitting caused by an excessive number of parameters. If overfitting were the issue, the training accuracy of the 56-layer model would surpass that of the 20-layer model, with the disparity becoming apparent only during testing. However, this is different here.

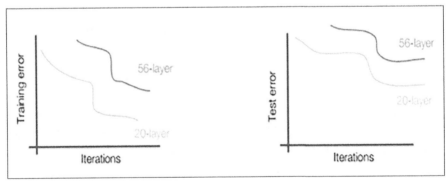

Figure 8.14: *56 layers model performs worse on both train and test error*

So, what is the problem with deeper models?

The hypothesis is that deeper models are more difficult to optimize. As the network depth increases, the gradients used for updating the weights during training tend to either vanish (become extremely small) or explode (become extremely large). This phenomenon makes it challenging for the network to learn effectively, hindering its performance on both training and testing data.

To address the problem of vanishing and exploding gradients, ResNet introduces skip connections, also known as **residual connections**. These connections allow the network to bypass certain layers and retain information from previous layers, aiding in gradient propagation and alleviating the optimization difficulties associated with deep networks. By incorporating skip connections, ResNet enables the successful training of extremely deep models, resulting in improved performance compared to shallower counterparts.

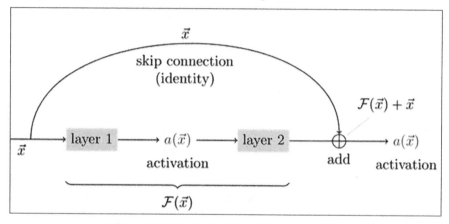

Figure 8.15: *Understanding skip connections*

Let's delve into the architecture of ResNet and its impact on the learning process. As depicted in *Figure 8.15*, a skip connection is introduced in the ResNet architecture after every two Convolutional (Conv) layers. To comprehend the significance of this change in the learning process, we need to understand what each layer aims to learn.

Consider a conventional Conv layer, which endeavors to learn a mapping from one set of features to another. However, with the addition of skip connections, everything changes. The inclusion of a skip connection transforms the learning objective. Instead of learning the actual transformation $F(\bar{x})$, the layer now focuses on learning the delta, or the change required to learn the subsequent mapping. Essentially it is learning the residual, rather than the complete transformation $F(\bar{x})$.

In a neural network without skip connections, each layer learns to transform the input based on the information passed from the previous layer. The final layer, in particular, learns to produce the desired output $F_{new}(\bar{x})$ based solely on the transformed input $F_{old}(\bar{x})$. However, with the inclusion of skip connections, the layer learns not only the transformation but also the delta or residual needed to obtain the desired output.

By adopting this residual learning approach, ResNet allows the network to focus on learning the incremental changes needed to refine the previous layers' representations. This mechanism facilitates the training process and enables the network to effectively capture and model complex patterns and features, ultimately leading to improved performance and the ability to construct extremely deep ResNet architectures.

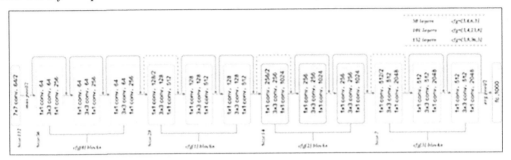

Figure 8.16: *ResNet architectures*

Other Variants of ResNet

ResNet is a popular architecture and has been adopted into various similar networks. The idea of skip connection was a great contribution, thus leading to other ResNet-like architectures such as Resnet50+, Wide ResNet, ResNeXt, and so on.

ResNet-50+ added a 1x1 Conv filter before and after the Conv layer.

A wide residual network is the same network with more filters in each Conv layer. Instead of using F filters, it uses F x k filters in each conv layer.

Another really interesting network is called ResNeXt, it combines properties of both ResNet and Inception modules.

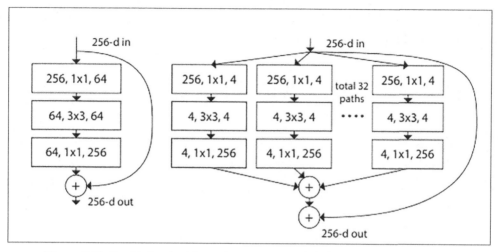

Figure 8.17: *Combining ResNet and Inception module for ResNeXt architecture*

Note: ResNet training is done in the following manner: Batch Normalization after every layer. SGD + Momentum (0.9), learning rate 0.1, divided by 10 when validation error plateaus, Mini batch size of 256, weight decay of 1e-5, and No dropout are used.

FractalNet and DenseNet

FractalNet is a deep neural network architecture that utilizes a fractal-like structure to improve the learning and representational capacity of the network. It was proposed as a way to address the challenges of training very deep networks by introducing fractal-like connections within the layers.

The key idea behind FractalNet is to create recursive connectivity patterns within the network. Instead of having a linear sequence of layers, it introduces skip connections that allow for shorter paths and information flow between different layers. These skip connections create a hierarchical structure resembling fractal patterns.

By incorporating these skip connections, FractalNet promotes information exchange across different levels of abstraction and enables the network to learn both fine-grained and high-level features simultaneously. This architectural design helps alleviate the vanishing gradient problem and enables efficient gradient propagation during training.

FractalNet has demonstrated improved performance in various tasks, including image classification, object recognition, and speech recognition. It allows for the construction of deeper networks while maintaining computational efficiency. By leveraging fractal-like connectivity, FractalNet provides a scalable and powerful framework for deep learning models.

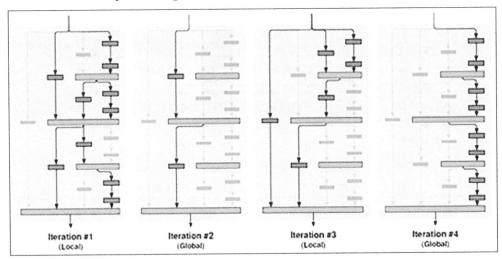

Figure 8.18: *Different portions in FractalNet learning both lower and higher level representations*

DenseNet is a deep neural network architecture that addresses information flow and gradient propagation issues in very deep networks. It introduces dense connections, where each layer is directly connected to every other layer in a feed-forward manner. This dense connectivity significantly improves the flow of information throughout the network and enhances learning capabilities.

In a DenseNet, each layer receives feature maps from all preceding layers and, in turn, passes its own feature maps to all subsequent layers. This densely connected structure promotes feature reuse and allows for better information sharing across the network. It enables each layer to directly access and incorporate the feature maps from earlier layers, resulting in richer representations and more efficient learning.

The dense connections in DenseNet also address the vanishing gradient problem by providing shorter paths for gradients to propagate through the network during training. This gradient flow enhances training and helps capture fine-grained details and complex patterns.

DenseNet architectures have demonstrated impressive performance in various computer vision tasks, such as image classification, object detection, and semantic segmentation. They have achieved state-of-the-art results with fewer parameters and computations than other deep network architectures.

DenseNet's dense connectivity and gradient flow mechanisms make it a powerful and effective deep learning architecture, enabling highly accurate and efficient learning of complex patterns and representations.

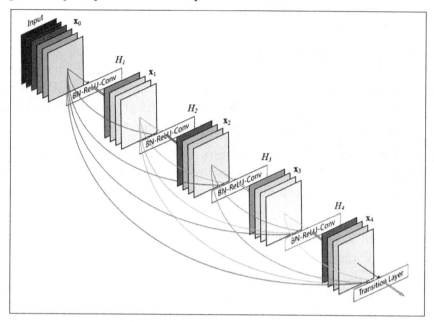

Figure 8.19: *DenseNet Architecture*

Note: What exactly are we trying to achieve with all these new architecture designs? The idea is to make the gradients flow as smoothly as possible. All the new DL architectures basically try to make gradients flow smoother and extract more detailed and abstract representations of the feature maps or input images.

Scaling Conv Networks: Efficient Net Architecture

Despite the fundamental mathematics underpinning neural networks being established since the 90s, it wasn't until more recent years that they truly began to gain traction. The delay was largely due to a need to understand how to scale these networks to manage intricate tasks effectively. For example, **Batchnorm()**, a key technique in training complex networks, didn't emerge until 2014. This absence made the training of robust architectures like VGG16 rather challenging.

If we examine the VGG16 architecture in the preceding section, we notice the pivotal role of scaling in three distinct dimensions: **depth, width, and resolution**. Depth scaling corresponds to the number of layers within the network. Width scaling refers to the dimensions of each Convolutional (Conv) layer (for instance,

112x112 or 56x56), while resolution relates to the depth of each Conv layer (for example, 112x112x128, where 128 represents the resolution).

Why is scaling so important?

Why not maintain uniform size and resolution across all layers for our predictions? Two main reasons discourage this approach: First, consistent layer size drastically increases the number of parameters, escalating memory requirements. Second, we aspire to detect patterns at varied scales in our data stream, which is akin to adjusting the resolution on a microscope.

Therefore, choosing scaling parameters isn't arbitrary; optimal scaling is instrumental to a model's success. Ignoring proper scaling leads to suboptimal performance, underscoring the vital role scaling plays in creating efficient and effective neural networks.

Currently, VGG16 is considered ancient and its scaling is very linear, thus, it fails in complex tasks. Recently, Efficient Net has gained huge popularity because of its dynamic scaling. Efficient Net is considered to be the state-of-the-art developed by Google. It combines a compound scaling methodology to considerably improve accuracy and low computational complexity.

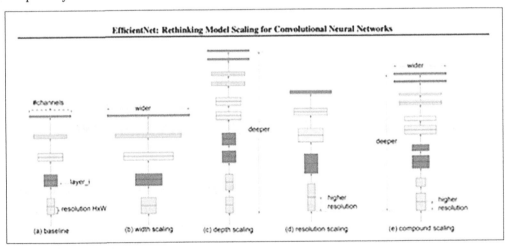

Figure 8.20: *Compound scaling used in Efficient Net*

Compound scaling: The compound scaling method uses a compound coefficient φ to uniformly scale network width, depth, and resolution in a principled way:

$$\text{Depth}: d = \alpha^{\phi}$$

$$\text{Width}: w = \beta^{\phi}$$

Resolution : $r = \gamma^\phi$

such that $\alpha^\phi \beta^\phi \gamma^\phi = 2$ (approx)

given that $\alpha > 1, \beta > 1$ and $\gamma > 1$

Here α, β, γ are constants that can be determined by a small grid search. Intuitively, φ is a user-specified coefficient that controls how many more resources are available for model scaling, while α, β, γ specify how to assign these extra resources to network width, depth, and resolution, respectively. Notably, the FLOPS of a regular convolution op is proportional to d, w^2, r^2, that is, doubling network depth will double FLOPS, but doubling network width or resolution will increase FLOPS by four times. Since convolution ops usually dominate the computation cost in ConvNets, scaling a ConvNet with equation 3 will approximately increase total FLOPS by $(\alpha\beta^2\gamma^2)^\varphi$. In this paper, we constraint $\alpha\beta^2\gamma^2 \approx 2$, such that for any new φ, the total FLOPS will approximately increase by 2^φ.

Note: FLOPS are called floating-point Operations, basically the number of mathematical operations. FLOPS is the common way to represent the computation a neural network requires.

Currently, there are seven different architectures of Efficient Net (B0, B1,...B7), with each modification introducing smaller changes and more layers. However, the core idea remains the same, scaling the Conv layers dynamically.

Here's another resource from Stanford, understanding CNN architectures: **https://www.youtube.com/watch?v=DAOcjicFr1Y&list=PL3FW7Lu3i5JvHM8ljYj-zLfQRF3EO8sYv&index=9&ab_channel=StanfordUniversitySchoolofEngineering** [24]

Different Types of Convolutions

Let's also look into different types of Convolution that we can perform to save some FLOPS and make our network learn different feature sets.

Depth-Separable Convolution

Depth-Separable Convolutions are an efficient alternative to standard convolutions, pioneered partly by Google's MobileNet architecture. They are designed to reduce the computational cost of the operation without significantly compromising the model's performance.

The operation is carried out in two steps: Depth-wise Convolution and Point-wise Convolution.

In Depth-wise convolution, different filters are applied to each channel of the input image (say, Red, Green, or Blue in a color image). This means that instead of learning a single filter that mixes information from all channels, we learn separate filters for each channel.

The Point-wise convolution step involves applying a 1x1 convolution to combine the outputs of the depth-wise step. This step allows the model to learn more complex representations by mixing information from different channels.

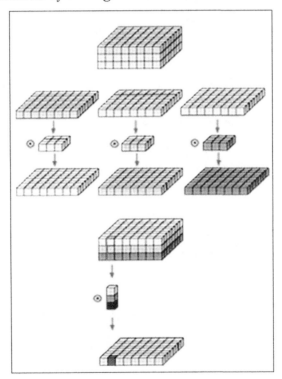

Figure 8.21: Depth Separable Convolution on an RGB image

Dilated Convolution

Dilated Convolutions, also known as atrous convolutions, offer a way to increase the field of view (the area of the input that influences an output pixel) of the filters without increasing the filter size or the computational cost.

In a dilated convolution, the filter is applied to the input not at every location but at intervals determined by a dilation factor. For example, with a dilation factor of 2, the filter skips one pixel at a time. This allows the filter to have a larger field of view and incorporate more global context into the feature map.

These three types of convolution operations offer unique ways of extracting and processing features from an image. Standard Convolutions are simple yet powerful, Depth-Separable Convolutions offer computational efficiency, and Dilated Convolutions expand the field of view without extra computational cost. Understanding these operations is crucial to appreciate the inner workings of CNNs and how they manage to excel in pattern recognition tasks.

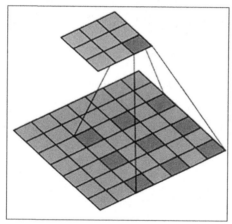

Figure 8.22: *Dilated Convolution using a 3x3 kernel with a dilation rate of 2 and no padding*

Note: There are still more types of convolutions that are used according to different use cases. Here's a list of other types of Convolution: Transposed Convolution (Deconvolution, checkerboard artifacts), Flattened Convolution, Grouped Convolution, Shuffled Grouped Convolution, Pointwise Grouped Convolution, and more.

Conclusion

This chapter focuses on Convolutional Neural Networks (CNNs), which serve as the foundation for various image and video-related tasks. Our exploration begins with a comprehensive understanding of the fundamental operations involved in Convolution, including Pooling, Padding, and Stride. These operations are crucial in extracting meaningful features from images and videos.

Moving forward, we delve into the key architectural concepts of popular CNN models such as VGG16, ResNet, FractalNet, and DenseNet. We explore the theory behind Skip connections and inception modules, which enhance the network's ability to capture and retain important information at different layers. Additionally, we investigate the concept of scaling through Efficient Nets, which allows us to balance the model's complexity and computational requirements efficiently. Finally, we examine different types of Convolutions that are specifically designed for diverse tasks, providing a comprehensive understanding of how CNNs can be tailored to various applications.

In the next chapter, we will start with understanding the fundamentals of the TensorFlow framework, understand its usage, and subsequently build an end-to-end AI pipeline.

"Artificial intelligence is no match for natural stupidity." – Albert Einstein

https://github.com/OrangeAVA/Ultimate-Neural-Network-Programming-with-Python

## CHAPTER 9

Understanding Basics of TensorFlow and Keras

After developing Neural Networks from scratch, it is time to explore the world of TensorFlow and Keras. Both of these are really famous frameworks that make writing neural networks easier and more practical. As we saw in the previous chapter, writing even a simple neural network from scratch is quite challenging. Using these fully developed frameworks helps us spend more time developing new architectures than implementing everything from scratch.

Structure

This chapter covers the following topics:

- A brief look at Keras
- Understanding TensorFlow's working
- TensorFlow components like activations, layers, and loss function
- Multi-input single-output network with custom callback

Keras is a powerful and user-friendly deep-learning library written in Python. Renowned for its simplicity and ease of use, it operates as a high-level neural network API capable of running on top of lower-level deep-learning libraries like

TensorFlow, Theano, and CNTK. The key idea behind Keras is to facilitate fast experimentation with deep neural networks.

A Brief Look at Keras

Keras was developed by François Chollet, a software engineer at Google, to enable fast prototyping and production of neural network models, focusing on user-friendliness, modularity, and extensibility.

The library provides various pre-processed datasets and pre-trained models, such as VGG16, VGG19, ResNet, and InceptionV3, which are immensely useful for model testing or transfer learning. Since Keras integrates seamlessly with the core TensorFlow library, users can leverage all the power of TensorFlow with a simpler interface.

Note: As of TensorFlow version 2.0, Keras is officially incorporated into TensorFlow as its default high-level API.

Why is Keras so popular?

- **User-friendliness**: Keras offers a straightforward, easy-to-understand API, which makes it accessible for newcomers and practical for experts.

- **Modularity:** A Keras model can be considered as a sequence or a graph of fully configurable standalone modules that can be plugged together with very few restrictions.

- **Easy extensibility**: Easy to add new modules in the form of classes and functions, and existing modules provide ample examples.

- **Python integration**: Keras models can be developed with standard Python workflows and inspected with standard Python tools.

Let's build a simple network to analyze the different components of Keras. For this purpose, we will look into the example of the world-famous MNIST dataset and try to train a simple neural network classifier. The goal here is only to introduce the readers to different components of Keras library.

Importing necessary modules

```
import numpy as np
from keras.models import Sequential
from keras.layers import Dense, Flatten
```

```
from keras.datasets import mnist
from keras.utils import to_categorical
```

Loading and pre-processing data

Next, we load the MNIST data, which is conveniently provided by Keras, and pre-process it:

```
# Load MNIST dataset
(train_images, train_labels), (test_images, test_labels) = mnist.load_
data()


# Normalize the images
train_images = train_images / 255.0
test_images = test_images / 255.0


# Convert labels to categorical one-hot encoding
train_labels = to_categorical(train_labels)
test_labels = to_categorical(test_labels)
```

Defining the model

We'll use a simple feedforward neural network (also known as a dense or fully connected network). We will include an input flatten layer (as our data is 2D but we need it in a 1D array for our Dense layer), two hidden layers, and an output layer.

```
# Define the model
model = Sequential()
model.add(Flatten(input_shape=(28, 28)))
model.add(Dense(128, activation='relu'))
model.add(Dense(128, activation='relu'))
model.add(Dense(10, activation='softmax'))  # 10 classes (0-9 digits)
```

Compiling the model

The model needs to be compiled before training. We specify the optimizer, loss function, and metrics to track during training.

```
# Compile the model
model.compile(optimizer='adam',
```

```
        loss='categorical_crossentropy',
        metrics=['accuracy'])
```

Training the model

We can now train the model using the fit function.

```
# Train the model
model.fit(train_images, train_labels, epochs=5, batch_size=32)
```

Evaluating the model

Finally, we can evaluate our trained model's performance on the test dataset.

```
# Evaluate the model
test_loss, test_acc = model.evaluate(test_images, test_labels)
print('Test accuracy:', test_acc)
```

That's it! We've just built and trained a neural network using Keras. This model can now recognize handwritten digits with impressive accuracy.

Let's look at the entire code together and see what kind of accuracy we get.

```
import numpy as np
from keras.models import Sequential
from keras.layers import Dense, Flatten
from keras.datasets import mnist
from keras.utils import to_categorical


# Load MNIST dataset
(train_images, train_labels), (test_images, test_labels) = mnist.load_data()


# Normalize the images
train_images = train_images / 255.0
test_images = test_images / 255.0


# Convert labels to categorical one-hot encoding
train_labels = to_categorical(train_labels)
test_labels = to_categorical(test_labels)
```

```python
# Define the model
model = Sequential()
model.add(Flatten(input_shape=(28, 28)))
model.add(Dense(128, activation='relu'))
model.add(Dense(128, activation='relu'))
model.add(Dense(10, activation='softmax'))  # 10 classes (0-9 digits)

# Compile the model
model.compile(optimizer='adam',
              loss='categorical_crossentropy',
              metrics=['accuracy'])

# Train the model
model.fit(train_images, train_labels, epochs=5, batch_size=32)

# Evaluate the model
test_loss, test_acc = model.evaluate(test_images, test_labels)
print('Test accuracy:', test_acc)

# Output:
# Epoch 1/5
# 1875/1875 [==============================] - 4s 2ms/step - loss: 0.2327
- accuracy: 0.9316
# Epoch 2/5
# 1875/1875 [==============================] - 4s 2ms/step - loss: 0.0966
- accuracy: 0.9703
# Epoch 3/5
# 1875/1875 [==============================] - 4s 2ms/step - loss: 0.0686
- accuracy: 0.9784
# Epoch 4/5
# 1875/1875 [==============================] - 4s 2ms/step - loss: 0.0526
```

```
- accuracy: 0.9831

# Epoch 5/5

# 1875/1875 [==============================] - 4s 2ms/step - loss: 0.0408
- accuracy: 0.9870

# 313/313 [==============================] - 1s 1ms/step - loss: 0.0863
- accuracy: 0.9745

# Test accuracy: 0.9745000004768372
```

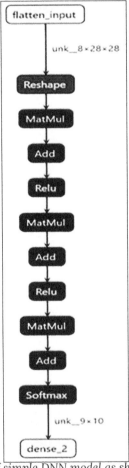

Figure 9.1: *Architecture of simple DNN model as shown in the preceding code*

In *Figure* 9.1, we can observe that we have a very simple linear structure of our model, and we can achieve a test accuracy of 97% quite easily. It's important to note that real-world models are much more complex and require an intensive amount of fine-tuning and experimentation. Real-world data is not easy to clean and pre-process.

With its simplicity and power, Keras has proven to be a go-to library for beginners to start their journey into deep learning and for researchers and experts to prototype and build complex models efficiently. As deep learning continues to evolve, Keras will undoubtedly play a significant role in shaping the field. Understanding Keras, thus, is a critical skill for anyone aiming to leverage the power of deep learning.

Other Keras in-built features are as follows:

- Keras enables identical code execution on the CPU and GPU without trouble.
- With its intuitive and accessible API, Keras simplifies the rapid prototyping of deep learning models.
- It provides innate support for various networks, including convolutional networks for image processing, recurrent networks for sequence handling, and a blend of both.
- Keras endorses diverse network designs, such as models with multiple inputs or outputs, shared layers, and shared models. This versatility makes Keras suitable for constructing virtually any deep learning model, ranging from a generative adversarial network to a neural Turing machine.

Understanding TensorFlow Internals

Let's now take a detailed look at the TensorFlow library and compare it with other popular similar frameworks.

Tensors

As the name suggests, tensors are the fundamental aspect of TensorFlow. These are data structures that you can think of as multi-dimensional arrays. Tensors are represented as n-dimensional arrays of base datatypes such as a string or integer – they provide a way to generalize vectors and matrices to higher dimensions.

The **shape** of a Tensor defines its number of dimensions and the size of each dimension. The **rank** of a Tensor provides the number of dimensions (n-dimensions) – it can be scalar, vector, or matrix.

Let's look at the examples of Tensors directly from TensorFlow's website: **https://www.tensorflow.org/guide/** [25].

```
import tensorflow as tf

# This will be an int32 tensor by default; see "dtypes" below.
rank_0_tensor = tf.constant(4)
print(rank_0_tensor)

# Let's make this a float tensor.
rank_1_tensor = tf.constant([2.0, 3.0, 4.0])
print(rank_1_tensor)

# If you want to be specific, you can set the dtype (see below) at creation
time
rank_2_tensor = tf.constant([[1, 2],
                             [3, 4],
                             [5, 6]], dtype=tf.float16)
print(rank_2_tensor)

# Ouptut:
# tf.Tensor(4, shape=(), dtype=int32)

# tf.Tensor([2. 3. 4.], shape=(3,), dtype=float32)

# tf.Tensor(
# [[1. 2.]
#  [3. 4.]
#  [5. 6.]], shape=(3, 2), dtype=float16)
```

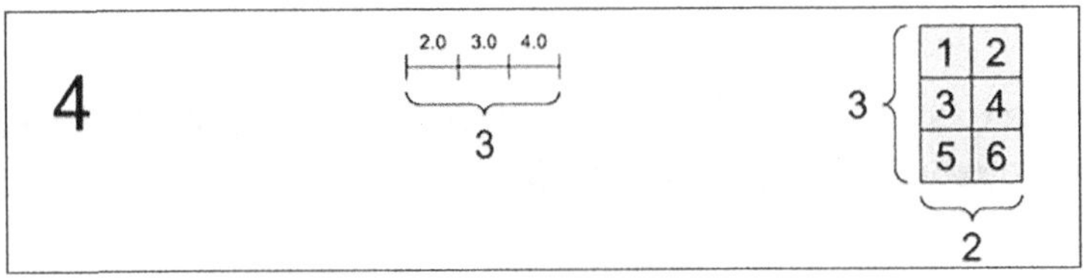

Figure 9.2: A scalar, shape [] (left), a vector shape [3] (center), and a matrix, shape [3, 2] (right)

We can even have four-or five-dimensional tensors. *Figure* 9.3 shows how to read higher-order tensors.

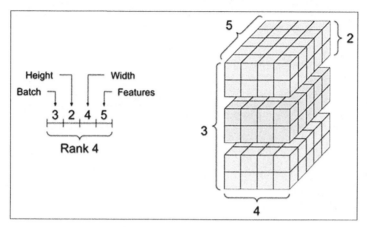

Figure 9.3: *Rank 4 Tensor*

Let's also look at basic tensor operations like multiplication, addition, and more.

```
import tensorflow as tf


a = tf.constant([[1, 2],
                 [3, 4]])
b = tf.constant([[1, 1],
                 [1, 1]]) # Could have also said `tf.ones([2,2])`


print(tf.add(a, b), "\n")
print(tf.multiply(a, b), "\n")
print(tf.matmul(a, b), "\n")


## The above operation can be written in other way as well


print(a + b, "\n") # element-wise addition
print(a * b, "\n") # element-wise multiplication
print(a @ b, "\n") # matrix multiplication
```

```
#Output:
# [[2 3]
#  [4 5]], shape=(2, 2), dtype=int32)

# tf.Tensor(
# [[1 2]
#  [3 4]], shape=(2, 2), dtype=int32)

# tf.Tensor(
# [[3 3]
#  [7 7]], shape=(2, 2), dtype=int32)
```

Few other operations:
```
c = tf.constant([[4.0, 5.0], [10.0, 1.0]])

# Find the largest value
print(tf.reduce_max(c))
# Find the index of the largest value
print(tf.math.argmax(c))
# Compute the softmax
print(tf.nn.softmax(c))

#Output:
# tf.Tensor(10.0, shape=(), dtype=float32)
# tf.Tensor([1 0], shape=(2,), dtype=int64)
# tf.Tensor(
# [[2.6894143e-01 7.3105860e-01]
#  [9.9987662e-01 1.2339458e-04]], shape=(2, 2), dtype=float32)
```

Computational Graphs

Every TensorFlow program involves building a computational graph. This is a series of TensorFlow operations arranged into a graph of nodes, where each node represents an operation that takes in a tensor and outputs a tensor.

The idea behind computational graphs is not to compute operations immediately but to define them all in relation to one another. This is useful because, often, you'll want to compute gradients, and graphs make this process efficient by allowing automatic error backpropagation.

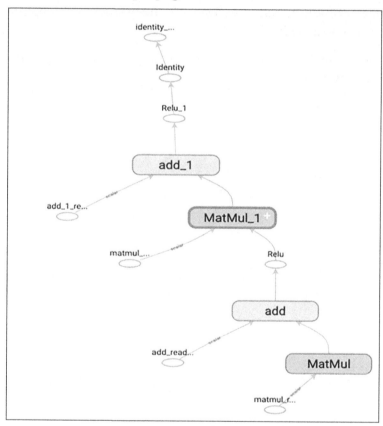

Figure 9.4: *TensorFlow Computational graphs*

Operations (Ops)

Operations or Ops are nodes that perform computation on or with tensors. An operation can be as simple as addition or subtraction and can be as complex as some multivariate equation.

An operation also has a name, which is an identifier for the operation and its output. This name can be given by the user or automatically generated by TensorFlow. These names are essential when exporting models from TensorFlow into other formats. The image shown in the computational graphs sections shows ops.

Automatic Differentiation

Automatic differentiation is a technique for computing the derivative of a function using the Chain Rule. TensorFlow's **tf.GradientTape** API provides for automatic differentiation, that is, computing the gradient of a computation with respect to its input variables.

Here's a basic example of how **tf.GradientTape** can be used to compute the derivative of a simple function:

```python
import tensorflow as tf


# Define a simple function
def f(x):
    return tf.square(x)


# Use tf.GradientTape to compute the derivative
with tf.GradientTape() as t:
    t.watch(tf.constant(3.0))   # Declare the variable you want to
differentiate
    y = f(tf.constant(3.0))


# Compute the gradient
dy_dx = t.gradient(y, tf.constant(3.0))
print(dy_dx)
```

In the preceding code, we first define a simple function, $f(x)$, that returns the square of x. Then, we use **tf.GradientTape** to start recording the operations for automatic differentiation. We declare the variable we want to differentiate with the **watch()** function. Finally, we call our function $f(x)$.

After we 've recorded our operations, we use the **gradient()** function of the **tf.GradientTape** instance to compute the derivative. We pass in the function output y and the variable we want to differentiate. The result will be 6.0, which is the derivative of x^2 at $x=3$.

This mechanism underpins the training process of neural networks, allowing for efficient computation of gradients when updating weights and biases, ultimately leading to more accurate models.

Sessions

A Session object encapsulates the environment in which Operation objects are executed and Tensor objects are evaluated. It allocates resources (on one or more machines) for this purpose and holds the actual values of intermediate results and variables.

However, with the arrival of TensorFlow 2.0, sessions are no longer used because it has eager execution by default, making TensorFlow more user-friendly and efficient.

Variables

Variables in TensorFlow are in-memory buffers that contain tensors. They must be explicitly initialized and can be saved to disk during and after training. You can later restore saved values to exercise or analyze the model.

TensorFlow provides an optimization algorithm for cost minimization. This optimization algorithm adjusts the variables of our model. Most tensor operations usually work on variables as expected, with the exception that variables cannot be reshaped.

```python
import tensorflow as tf


my_tensor = tf.constant([[1.0, 2.0], [3.0, 4.0]])
my_variable = tf.Variable(my_tensor)


# Variables can be all kinds of types, just like tensors
bool_variable = tf.Variable([False, False, False, True])
complex_variable = tf.Variable([5 + 4j, 6 + 1j])


#A variable looks and acts like a tensor, and, in fact, is a data
structure backed by a tf.Tensor.
```

```
# Like tensors, they have a dtype and a shape, and can be exported to
NumPy.
Print(     "Shape:      ", my_variable.shape)         # Shape: (2, 2)
print(     "Dtype:      ", my_variable.dtype)         # Dtype: <dtype:
'float32    '>
print(     "As NumPy:      ", my_variable.numpy())   # As NumPy: [[1. 2.]


# Creating new variables from existing variables duplicates the backing
tensors.
# Two variables will not share the same memory.
A = tf.Variable([2.0, 3.0])
# Create b based on the value of a
b = tf.Variable(a)
a.assign([5, 6])


# a and b are different
print(a.numpy())    # [5. 6.]
print(b.numpy())    # [2. 3.]


# There are other versions of assign
print(a.assign_add([2,3]).numpy())  # [7. 9.]
print(a.assign_sub([7,9]).numpy())  # [0. 0.]



# We can create variable and do operation using both CPU and GPU
with tf.device(     'CPU:0     '):
  a = tf.Variable([[1.0, 2.0, 3.0], [4.0, 5.0, 6.0]])
  b = tf.Variable([[1.0, 2.0, 3.0]])


with tf.device(     'GPU:0     '):
  # Element-wise multiply
```

```
k = a * b
```

```
print(k)
# Output: tf.Tensor(
# [[ 1.   4.   9.]
#  [ 4. 10. 18.]], shape=(2, 3), dtype=float32)
```

Eager Execution

Eager execution is an imperative programming environment that evaluates operations immediately without building graphs. Operations return concrete values instead of constructing a computational graph to run later. This makes it easy to start with TensorFlow and debug models, and it reduces boilerplate as well.

Eager execution is a flexible mach5ine learning platform for research and experimentation, providing an intuitive interface, easy debugging, and natural control flow.

Layers and Models (Keras)

The TensorFlow **tf.keras** API is a high-level API for defining and training models. It includes functionalities for building deep learning models, defining layers, setting up multiple inputs or outputs, and managing complex topologies like inception blocks or residual blocks.

It also includes modules for computing losses, metrics, optimizers, creating and managing datasets, and automatic differentiation and gradient application. We will look at different layers and Models in the later section of this chapter.

TensorFlow's ability to automate the mathematical computations involved in machine learning algorithms and its scalable and flexible nature makes it an excellent choice for both researchers and developers in machine learning and deep learning. By understanding the core components and how they work together, one can leverage the full capabilities of this powerful library.

TensorFlow vs. PyTorch vs. Theano

As the field of machine learning and artificial intelligence expands, several libraries and frameworks have emerged to support researchers and developers.

TensorFlow is amongst the top contenders, but how does it compare with its competitors, like PyTorch, Theano, CNTK, and others? What makes TensorFlow stand out, and where does it fall short?

TensorFlow vs. PyTorch

One of the most significant competitors to TensorFlow is PyTorch, an open-source machine learning library developed by Facebook's AI Research lab.

Advantages of TensorFlow over PyTorch:

- **Deployment:** TensorFlow excels in large-scale deployment and model serving, thanks to TensorFlow Serving and TensorFlow Lite, allowing models to be used on various platforms, including mobile, web, and IoT devices.

- **Visualization:** TensorFlow comes with TensorBoard, a powerful tool for visualization and debugging of the training process. TensorBoard allows developers to monitor metrics, inspect the model architecture, and observe how weights and biases change over time.

- **Google Ecosystem Integration:** Being a product of Google, TensorFlow integrates seamlessly with other Google Cloud services such as Google Cloud AI and DataFlow, making it an excellent choice for developers operating in a Google-centric environment.

- **Performance Optimization:** TensorFlow includes several built-in functionalities to optimize performance at scale. These include XLA (Accelerated Linear Algebra) for tensor computations and mixed precision training, which leverages NVIDIA's Tensor Cores for faster training.

Advantages of PyTorch over TensorFlow:

- **Dynamic Computation Graph:** Unlike TensorFlow's static graph, PyTorch uses a dynamic computation graph, which is more intuitive and allows for more flexibility in building complex architectures.

- **Debugging:** Since PyTorch operates with eager execution, it is considered more pythonic and is typically easier to debug.

- **Research Oriented:** Researchers often favor PyTorch due to its flexibility and ease of use for rapid prototyping.

TensorFlow vs. Theano

Theano is another popular deep-learning library. It has been around for a while but has declined since its development ceased in 2017.

Advantages of TensorFlow over Theano:

- **Active Development:** TensorFlow is under active development by Google, with regular updates that add new features and optimize performance.

- **Ecosystem:** TensorFlow has a more extensive ecosystem with various tools and extensions like TensorBoard, TensorFlow Extended (TFX), and TensorFlow Hub.

- **Community and Support:** TensorFlow has a much larger community and better support, with extensive documentation and resources for learning.

Advantages of Theano over TensorFlow:

- **Simplicity:** Theano is simpler and more straightforward to learn, particularly for beginners.

- **Lower-level Interface:** Theano provides a lower-level interface, offering more control over the model.

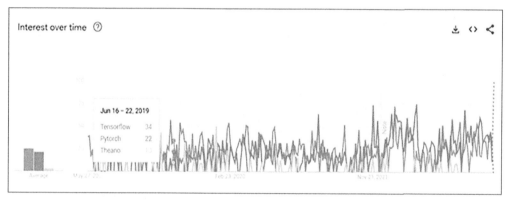

Figure 9.5: Google Trends for TensorFlow, PyTorch, and Theano

PyTorch is rapidly becoming the go-to choice for researchers, while TensorFlow remains more usable for the industry due to its deployment compatibility with Google Cloud solutions.

TensorFlow: Layers, Activations, and More

Let's explore how to call the different layers, activations, and other important things in TensorFlow that we might require in setting up our training pipeline. TensorFlow offers many layers, loss functions, optimizers, weight initialization methods, and more.

Types of Layers

TensorFlow offers a plethora of layers to work with. Let's explore how and when to use these layers. It's important to note that we are showing the most basic usage of each layer, all of them can be initialized with many other arguments, such as **kernel_initializer**, **kernel_regularizer**, and more. We will show all the parameters for the dense layer only, but for the rest, please refer to the official TensorFlow documentation.

Dense Layer (Fully Connected Layer)

The Dense layer is the most basic and commonly used in neural networks. It connects every neuron in the current layer to every neuron in the previous layer. It is generally used in the last section of neural networks right before the output layer.

```python
import tensorflow as tf


model = tf.keras.Sequential([
    tf.keras.layers.Dense(
    units,
    activation=None,
    use_bias=True,
    kernel_initializer='glorot_uniform',
    bias_initializer='zeros',
    kernel_regularizer=None,
    bias_regularizer=None,
    activity_regularizer=None,
    kernel_constraint=None,
    bias_constraint=None,
    input_shape=(input_size,))
])
```

- **units:** Positive integer, dimensionality of the output space.
- **activation:** Activation function to use. If you don't specify anything, no activation is applied (that is, "linear" activation: a(x) = x).

- **use_bias:** Boolean, whether the layer uses a bias vector.
- **kernel_initializer:** Initializer for the kernel weights matrix.
- **bias_initializer:** Initializer for the bias vector.
- **kernel_regularizer:** Regularizer function applied to the kernel weights matrix.
- **bias_regularizer:** Regularizer function applied to the bias vector.
- **activity_regularizer:** Regularizer function applied to the layer's output (its "activation").
- **kernel_constraint:** Constraint function applied to the kernel weights matrix.
- **bias_constraint:** Constraint function applied to the bias vector.
- **input_shape:** Shape of the previous layer.

Convolution Layer

Convolutional layers are primarily used in convolutional neural networks (CNNs) for processing grid-like data such as images. They apply filters to input data to extract features.

```
model = tf.keras.Sequential([
    tf.keras.layers.Conv2D(filters=32, kernel_size=(3, 3), activation='relu',
input_shape=(height, width, channels))
])
```

The **filters** parameter determines the number of filters to use, **kernel_size** specifies the size of the convolutional kernel, and **input_shape** defines the shape of the input data.

Max Pooling Layer

Max pooling layers downsample the input data by selecting the maximum value within a defined window. It is used to decrease the size of the feature matrix.

```
model = tf.keras.Sequential([
    tf.keras.layers.MaxPooling2D(pool_size=(2, 2))
```

```
])
```

The `pool_size` parameter specifies the size of the pooling window. For example, a pool size of 2 will choose one value out of a 2x2 matrix, and depending upon stride, the size of the matrix will be reduced.

Dropout Layer

Dropout layers are used to prevent overfitting by randomly dropping out a fraction of the neurons during training.

```
model = tf.keras.Sequential([
    tf.keras.layers.Dropout(rate=0.2)
])
```

The `rate` parameter defines the fraction of neurons to drop out during training, typically ranging from 0.2 to 0.5.

Recurrent Layer (LSTM)

Recurrent layers, particularly LSTM (Long Short-Term Memory), are used for processing sequential or time-series data. They retain the memory of previous inputs to capture dependencies over time.

```
model = tf.keras.Sequential([
    tf.keras.layers.LSTM(units=64, return_sequences=True, input_shape=
(timesteps, features))
])
```

The `units` parameter determines the number of LSTM cells, `return_sequences=True` specifies returning the full sequence rather than just the last output, and `input_shape` defines the shape of the input sequence.

Embedding Layer

Embedding layers are commonly used in natural language processing (NLP) tasks to convert categorical inputs into continuous representations.

```
model = tf.keras.Sequential([
    tf.keras.layers.Embedding(input_dim=vocab_size, output_dim=embedding_
dim, input_length=max_length)
])
```

The **input_dim** parameter defines the vocabulary size, **output_dim** specifies the dimensionality of the embedding space, and **input_length** defines the length of the input sequences.

Flatten Layer

The Flatten layer converts multidimensional input data into a 1D array. It is often used as a transition between convolutional and fully connected layers.

```
model = tf.keras.Sequential([
    tf.keras.layers.Flatten()
])
```

Batch Normalization Layer

Batch Normalization is a technique used to normalize a neural network's activations, which helps improve training speed and stability.

```
model = tf.keras.Sequential([
    tf.keras.layers.BatchNormalization()
])
```

Global Average Pooling Layer

Global Average Pooling computes the spatial average of each feature map in the input, resulting in a fixed-length output regardless of input size. It is often used instead of fully connected layers to reduce the model's parameters.

```
model = tf.keras.Sequential([
    tf.keras.layers.GlobalAveragePooling2D()
])
```

Upsampling/Transposed Convolution Layer

Upsampling or transposed convolution layers are used in tasks such as image segmentation or generating higher-resolution images from low-resolution inputs.

```
model = tf.keras.Sequential([
    tf.keras.layers.Conv2DTranspose(filters=32, kernel_size=(3, 3),
strides=(2, 2), padding='same')
])
```

The **strides** parameter determines the upsampling factor, and **padding** can be set to either 'same' or 'valid' to control the output size.

These are some of the most commonly used TensorFlow layers. While there may be more, having knowledge of these layers is more than enough to get a good grasp of what's available in TensorFlow.

Activation Functions

We've already explored different activation functions in detail. Here, we will only focus on how to use them in TensorFlow.

```
import tensorflow as tf

# Sample tensor
x = tf.constant([-1.0, 0.0, 1.0, 2.0, 3.0])

# Sigmoid Activation Function
```

```python
def sigmoid_activation(x):
    return tf.nn.sigmoid(x)


# ReLU (Rectified Linear Unit) Activation Function
def relu_activation(x):
    return tf.nn.relu(x)


# Leaky ReLU Activation Function
def leaky_relu_activation(x):
    return tf.nn.leaky_relu(x, alpha=0.2)


# ELU (Exponential Linear Unit) Activation Function
def elu_activation(x):
    return tf.nn.elu(x)


# Softmax Activation Function
def softmax_activation(x):
    return tf.nn.softmax(x)


# Tanh Activation Function
def tanh_activation(x):
    return tf.nn.tanh(x)


# Swish Activation Function
def swish_activation(x):
    return tf.nn.swish(x)


# Softplus Activation Function
def softplus_activation(x):
    return tf.nn.softplus(x)
```

```python
# Apply activation functions to the sample tensor
sigmoid_result = sigmoid_activation(x)
relu_result = relu_activation(x)
leaky_relu_result = leaky_relu_activation(x)
elu_result = elu_activation(x)
softmax_result = softmax_activation(x)
tanh_result = tanh_activation(x)
swish_result = swish_activation(x)
softplus_result = softplus_activation(x)


# Print the results
print("Sample Tensor: ", x)
print("Sigmoid Activation: ", sigmoid_result)
print("ReLU Activation: ", relu_result)
print("Leaky ReLU Activation: ", leaky_relu_result)
print("ELU Activation: ", elu_result)
print("Softmax Activation: ", softmax_result)
print("Tanh Activation: ", tanh_result)
print("Swish Activation: ", swish_result)
print("Softplus Activation: ", softplus_result)


# # Output:
# Sample Tensor:  tf.Tensor([-1.  0.  1.  2.  3.], shape=(5,), dtype
=float32)
# Sigmoid Activation:  tf.Tensor([0.26894143 0.5        0.7310586
0.8807971  0.95257413], shape=(5,), dtype=float32)
# ReLU Activation:  tf.Tensor([0. 0. 1. 2. 3.], shape=(5,), dtype
=float32)
# Leaky ReLU Activation:  tf.Tensor([-0.2 0.   1.   2.   3. ],
shape=(5,), dtype=float32)
# ELU Activation:  tf.Tensor([-0.63212055 0.         1.         2.
3.        ], shape=(5,), dtype=float32)
# Softmax Activation:  tf.Tensor([0.01165623 0.03168492 0.08612854
```

```
0.23412165 0.6364086 ], shape=(5,), dtype=float32)
# Tanh Activation:  tf.Tensor([-0.7615942  0.         0.7615942
0.9640276  0.9950547], shape=(5,), dtype=float32)
# Swish Activation:  tf.Tensor([-0.26894143  0.         0.7310586
1.7615942    2.8577223 ], shape=(5,), dtype=float32)
# Softplus Activation:   tf.Tensor([0.3132617 0.6931472 1.3132616
2.126928   3.0485873], shape=(5,), dtype=float32)
```

Optimizers

Here's how to use the different Optimizers available in TensorFlow:

```
# Define different optimizers
sgd_optimizer = tf.keras.optimizers.SGD(learning_rate=0.01)
rmsprop_optimizer = tf.keras.optimizers.RMSprop(learning_rate=0.001)
adagrad_optimizer = tf.keras.optimizers.Adagrad(learning_rate=0.01)
adadelta_optimizer = tf.keras.optimizers.Adadelta(learning_rate=1.0)
adamax_optimizer = tf.keras.optimizers.Adamax(learning_rate=0.001)
nadam_optimizer = tf.keras.optimizers.Nadam(learning_rate=0.001)


# Compile the model with different optimizers
model.compile(optimizer=<optimizer_name>,
              loss='categorical_crossentropy',
              metrics=['accuracy'])
```

Note: Adam might be the fastest of all, but we can improve the performance of a network by first training it with Adam and then fine-tuning it with SGD. It's advisable not to Don't use SGD from the start, as it can get stuck in local minima and it is significantly slow to converge. This strategy might not always work, but in my practical experience, I've found this hack quite useful.

Weight Initialization

Weight initialization techniques are crucial in deep learning models as they determine the initial values assigned to the neural network's weights. These initial values can significantly impact the convergence speed, training stability, and overall performance of the model.

One common weight initialization technique is random initialization, where the weights are initialized with random values. However, simply using random initialization can lead to issues like vanishing or exploding gradients, where the gradients become extremely small or large, hindering the learning process.

To address these problems, several weight initialization techniques have been developed. One popular technique is the **Xavier** initialization or **Glorot** initialization. It sets the initial weights based on the number of input and output connections to a neuron, ensuring that the variance of the activations and gradients remains consistent throughout the network. This technique is particularly effective for activation functions like sigmoid and tanh.

Another commonly used initialization technique is the **He** initialization. It is specifically designed for activation functions like ReLU (Rectified Linear Unit) and its variants. The He initialization considers the number of input connections to a neuron to adjust the variance of the weights, allowing the network to learn more effectively.

These weight initialization techniques help to overcome challenges such as gradient vanishing or exploding and provide a better starting point for the learning process. By initializing the weights appropriately, these techniques ensure that the neural network can learn more efficiently and converge to better solutions. Proper weight initialization can also lead to faster convergence, reduced training time, and improved model generalization performance.

It is worth noting that the choice of weight initialization technique depends on the specific architecture, activation functions, and problem domain. The following code shows how to initialize weights in dense layers:

```python
import tensorflow as tf


# Define your model architecture
model = tf.keras.Sequential([
    tf.keras.layers.Dense(64, activation='relu', input_shape=(784,),
                          kernel_initializer='glorot_uniform'),
    tf.keras.layers.Dense(64, activation='relu',
```

```
                    kernel_initializer='he_normal'),
    tf.keras.layers.Dense(10, activation='softmax',
                    kernel_initializer='glorot_uniform')
])
```

Loss Functions

Few commonly used loss functions are as follows:

Categorical Crossentropy (categorical_crossentropy):

- Suitable for multi-class classification tasks.
- Calculates the cross-entropy loss between the true labels and predicted probabilities.
- Works well when the target variables are one-hot encoded or in categorical format.

Binary Crossentropy (binary_crossentropy):

- Suitable for binary classification tasks.
- Computes the cross-entropy loss between the true binary labels and predicted probabilities.
- Appropriate when the target variable has two classes or represents a binary decision.

Mean Squared Error (mean_squared_error):

- Used for regression tasks.
- Measures the average squared difference between the true and predicted values.
- Penalizes larger errors more than smaller errors, making them sensitive to outliers.

Mean Absolute Error (mean_absolute_error):

- Another loss function for regression tasks.
- Calculates the average absolute difference between the true and predicted values.
- Treats all errors equally and is less sensitive to outliers than mean squared error.

Sparse Categorical Crossentropy (sparse_categorical_crossentropy):

- Similar to categorical cross-entropy but suitable when the target variable is in integer format instead of one-hot encoded, generally used in classification tasks.

- Computes the cross-entropy loss between the true integer labels and predicted probabilities.

Usage:

```python
model.compile(optimizer='adam',
         loss='<loss function name>',
         metrics=['accuracy'])
```

Multi-Input Single-Output Network with Custom Callbacks

Let's try to combine all the pieces from the preceding sections into a single code. Here, we are designing a multi-input single-output network with a lot of custom parts.

```python
import tensorflow as tf
from tensorflow.keras.models import Model
from tensorflow.keras.layers import Input, Dense, Embedding, Flatten, Concatenate
from tensorflow.keras.callbacks import Callback
import matplotlib.pyplot as plt
from tensorflow.keras.utils import plot_model
import numpy as np


class CustomCallback(Callback):
    def on_train_begin(self, logs=None):
        print("Starting training...")
```

```python
    def on_train_end(self, logs=None):
        print("Finished training.")

    def on_epoch_begin(self, epoch, logs=None):
        print(f"Starting epoch {epoch}")

    def on_epoch_end(self, epoch, logs=None):
        print(f"Finished epoch {epoch}")
        print(f"Train loss: {logs['loss']}")

    def on_train_batch_begin(self, batch, logs=None):
        print(f"Training: Starting batch {batch}")

    def on_train_batch_end(self, batch, logs=None):
        print(f"Training: Finished batch {batch}")
        print(f"Train loss: {logs['loss']}")

    def on_test_begin(self, logs=None):
        print("Starting testing...")

    def on_test_end(self, logs=None):
        print("Finished testing.")

    def on_test_batch_begin(self, batch, logs=None):
        print(f"Testing: Starting batch {batch}")

    def on_test_batch_end(self, batch, logs=None):
        print(f"Testing: Finished batch {batch}")
        print(f"Test loss: {logs['loss']}")

# Custom Loss
```

```python
def custom_loss(y_true, y_pred):
    y_true = tf.cast(y_true, tf.float32)
    return tf.reduce_mean(tf.square(y_true - y_pred))


# Model
inputA = Input(shape=(32,))
inputB = Input(shape=(100,))


# For inputA
x = Embedding(input_dim=10000, output_dim=64)(inputA)
x = Flatten()(x)
x = Dense(16, activation='relu', kernel_initializer='he_normal')(x)
x = Model(inputs=inputA, outputs=x)


# For inputB
y = Dense(64, activation='sigmoid', kernel_initializer='glorot_uniform')
(inputB)
y = Model(inputs=inputB, outputs=y)


combined = Concatenate()([x.output, y.output])


z = Dense(10, activation="linear")(combined)
z = Dense(1, activation="sigmoid")(z)


model = Model(inputs=[x.input, y.input], outputs=z)


model.compile(loss=custom_loss, optimizer="adam")


# Data
num_samples = 1000
inputA_data = np.random.randint(10000, size=(num_samples, 32))
inputB_data = np.random.rand(num_samples, 100)
```

```
labels = np.random.randint(2, size=(num_samples, 1))


# Fit the model

history = model.fit([inputA_data, inputB_data], labels, epochs=50,
callbacks=[CustomCallback()])


#Output:

# Training: Starting batch 31

# Training: Finished batch 31

# Train loss: 6.00976136411191e-06

# Finished epoch 49

# Train loss: 6.00976136411191e-06
```

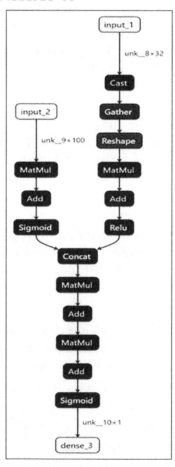

Figure 9.6: *Model architecture for the multi-input single-output network*

The multi-input single-output network shown in the preceding model architecture diagram is not running on particular data but randomly generated datasets. The goal is not to train a real-world model but to showcase how different parts are connected in a complex network:

- **custom_loss:** In the preceding example, we used a custom loss function that calculates the mean squared error. It can be used in cases where the predefined loss functions are insufficient. The goal is to showcase that it is not necessary to use TensorFlow's inbuilt loss functions only.

- **Embedding Layer:** Responsible for learning and embedding the words in the training dataset, starting with random weight initialization. It offers a way to project sparse one-hot representation into a dense lower-dimensional space.

- **Multiple Inputs:** This model receives inputs from two different sources (**inputA** and **inputB**), and processes them separately. Their outputs are then concatenated and processed by a final series of dense layers.

- **Different activation functions:** Activation functions define the output of a node given an input or set of inputs. Here, we use **relu (Rectified Linear Unit)** and sigmoid activation functions. relu is used primarily in the hidden layers, while 'sigmoid' is used in the output layer for binary classification.

- **Weight initialization:** The initial weights of a neural network can play an important role in the convergence of the network. `He_normal` is used when we use 'relu' as an activation function, and `glorot_uniform` (also known as Xavier uniform initialization) is used when 'sigmoid' activation is used.

- **CustomCallback:** In Keras, a callback is a Python class meant to be subclassed to provide specific functionality, with several methods that can be called at various stages of training, testing, and predicting. They are used to get the status of internal states and statistics of the model during training. A custom callback is implemented to print a message at the end of every 5th epoch.

Custom callbacks in TensorFlow/Keras are a very interesting and powerful tool to customize the behavior of a model during training, evaluation, or inference. They allow you to perform specific actions at different stages of model training (such as at the start or end of an epoch, before or after a batch, and more). Following are some use cases of custom callbacks:

- **Flexibility:** You can define exactly what happens and when during training. For example, you could program a callback to send you an email when training finishes or if it encounters an exception.

- **Monitoring:** Custom callbacks are great for monitoring the internal states of a model during training and making real-time modifications. This can be particularly helpful for debugging or optimizing your models.

- **Logging:** You can use callbacks to log extra metrics, visualize layers, or model internals during training.

- **Early Stopping:** You can implement a custom callback to stop training when your model starts overfitting, underfitting, or when it stops improving, based on your own custom criteria.

- **Learning Rate Schedules:** While there are already predefined schedules, sometimes they may need to be more, or you may want to use a custom one. A callback can allow you to modify the learning rate as training progresses.

- **Regularization:** You can add custom regularization strategies beyond those built into Keras or TensorFlow.

- **Saving and Loading Models:** Custom callbacks can be used to save model weights during training at different intervals. This enables you to resume training from the same point in case your training gets interrupted. Or, you can pick the model with the best performance during the training phase.

In summary, custom callbacks in TensorFlow allow you to have granular control and flexibility over the training process of your models, enabling you to perform tasks like custom monitoring, dynamic learning rate adjustments, conditional stopping, and more.

Conclusion

In this chapter, we start by covering the basics of Keras and building a sample model on the MNIST dataset. We then dive into the internal workings of TensorFlow, including concepts like automatic differentiation and eager execution. Additionally, we compare TensorFlow with other frameworks, such as PyTorch and Theano, to understand their unique features.

Next, we explore commonly used layers like Dense, Convolutional, and Pooling, along with various optimizers, activations, and loss functions. This knowledge equips us with the tools to design and fine-tune deep learning models effectively. Finally, we implement a multi-input single-output network, incorporating custom loss functions, callbacks, embedding layers, and He & Glorot weight initialization. This comprehensive approach allows us to leverage the full potential of Keras and TensorFlow for advanced deep-learning applications.

In the next chapter, we will build an end-to-end AI image segmentation pipeline using TensorFlow and other best practices.

" Forget artificial intelligence – in the brave new world of big data, it's artificial idiocy we should be looking out for" - Tom Chatfield

https://github.com/OrangeAVA/Ultimate-Neural-Network-Programming-with-Python

CHAPTER 10

Building End-to-end Image Segmentation Pipeline

After developing a sense of how Neural Network works and how TensorFlow works, it's time to build an end-to-end Image segmentation pipeline and, by doing this, also delve into how to structure real-life AI projects.

Structure

This chapter covers the following topics:

- Structuring DL code, Unit testing, Debugging, Logging, and more
- Understanding UNet and the importance of Attention gate
- Building end-to-end segmentation pipeline
- Testing the trained pipeline and results

Fine-tuning and Interpretability

Fine-tuning is the key to the success of Neural Networks in all the different domains. Let's start by understanding how and why fine-tuning works.

Power of Fine-Tuning in Deep Learning

The primary advantage of deep learning models is their ability to learn hierarchically. They learn from simple to complex features, layer by layer. This leads us to an interesting possibility – could we repurpose these learned features of one problem for another problem? This concept, known as Transfer Learning, is a cornerstone of modern deep learning applications.

When we work with deep learning models, especially Convolutional Neural Networks (CNNs), the initial layers learn to identify simple patterns like edges, colors, and textures. As we progress through the layers, the patterns learned become increasingly complex.

Imagine training a model from scratch for image recognition. The model must learn everything from scratch, from identifying simple edges to complex patterns. This takes significant computational power and time and requires large volumes of training data.

This is where the concept of fine-tuning comes into play. We can use a pre-trained model trained on a large dataset (such as ImageNet) and adjust its final layers to solve our specific problem. This saves computational resources and enables us to work with smaller datasets while achieving high performance.

SHAP - An Intuitive Way to Interpret Machine Learning Models

Deep Learning (DL) models can perform complex tasks accurately, but their decision-making process can be difficult to understand. This interpretability is especially important in fields like healthcare and finance, where incorrect predictions can lead to serious consequences. Understanding why and how a model arrives at its predictions helps in trust, accountability, and model improvement.

SHAP, or **SHapley** Additive exPlanations, is a powerful tool designed to enhance the interpretability of these models. Drawing on principles from cooperative game theory, SHAP treats each feature of the data as a **player** that contributes to the final prediction. Using the Shapley values concept, SHAP quantifies each feature's contribution, thereby providing insights into their relative importance in the model's decision-making process. This allows for a better understanding of the features that have the most influence on the model's predictions.

Let's understand the idea of fine-tuning and interpretability through some code:

```python
import tensorflow as tf
from tensorflow.keras import datasets, layers, models
from tensorflow.keras.applications.vgg16 import VGG16
import shap
import numpy as np


# Load CIFAR-10 Data
(train_images, train_labels), (test_images, test_labels) =
datasets.cifar10.load_data()


# Convert the images to float type and scale to [0, 1]
train_images = train_images.astype(np.float32) / 255.
test_images = test_images.astype(np.float32) / 255.


# Preprocess images in the same way as VGG16 model does
train_images_preprocessed =
tf.keras.applications.vgg16.preprocess_input(train_images * 255)   # The
preprocess_input function expects images in [0, 255]
test_images_preprocessed =
tf.keras.applications.vgg16.preprocess_input(test_images * 255)


# Load Pre-trained VGG16 model
base_model = VGG16(weights='imagenet', include_top=False, input_shape=(32,
32, 3))


# Freeze the layers
for layer in base_model.layers:
    layer.trainable = False


# Create new model on top
inputs = tf.keras.Input(shape=(32, 32, 3))
```

```python
x = base_model(inputs, training=False)

x = tf.keras.layers.GlobalAveragePooling2D()(x)

outputs = tf.keras.layers.Dense(10)(x)

model = tf.keras.Model(inputs, outputs)


# Compile the model
model.compile(optimizer=tf.keras.optimizers.Adam(),
                 loss=tf.keras.losses.SparseCategoricalCrossentropy(from_
logits=True),
                 metrics=['accuracy'])


# Train the model
model.fit(train_images_preprocessed, train_labels, epochs=5)


# Choose the images you want to explain
to_explain = train_images_preprocessed[0:5]


# Create an explainer object
explainer = shap.GradientExplainer(model, train_images_preprocessed[:100])


# Compute SHAP values
shap_values = explainer.shap_values(to_explain)


# Function to reverse the preprocessing function of VGG16 and swap back
to 'RGB' order
def reverse_preprocess_input(im):
    mean = [103.939, 116.779, 123.68]
    im[..., 0] += mean[0]
    im[..., 1] += mean[1]
    im[..., 2] += mean[2]
    im = im[..., ::-1]  # reverse axis bgr->rgb
```

```
    return im / 255.


# Reverse preprocessing for the SHAP image plot

to_explain_unprocessed = reverse_preprocess_input(to_explain.copy())


# Plot the SHAP values

shap.image_plot(shap_values, to_explain_unprocessed)
```

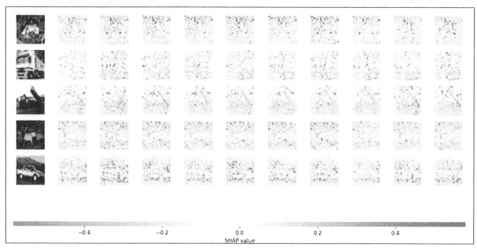

Figure 10.1: *Shapley DL model explainability*

The preceding script leverages the transfer learning concept to create a model for classifying the CIFAR-10 dataset. Transfer learning enables the reuse of a pre-trained model, in this case, VGG16, to take advantage of the features learned from a different task, like ImageNet. The script loads the VGG16 model, freezes its layers to maintain its learned features, and then constructs a new model on top of it with a GlobalAveragePooling2D and a Dense final layer for CIFAR-10 classification. Once the model is compiled and trained on the CIFAR-10 dataset, it is ready to classify CIFAR-10 images, benefiting from the learned features of VGG16.

After training the model, the script employs SHAP (SHapley Additive exPlanations), a game theory approach, to interpret the model's predictions. The explainer object created computes the SHAP values for a given set of images. Each SHAP value quantifies the contribution of each pixel in an image towards the model's output for that particular image. Thus, it helps understand how the model is making its decisions. These SHAP values are plotted as heatmaps with **shap. image_plot**, visually highlighting the contribution of each pixel. To visualize correctly, the preprocessing that was originally done for VGG16 needs to be reversed. This complete process combines the power of transfer learning for effective image classification and SHAP for the interpretability of predictions.

Up to this point, we've covered many concepts and codes behind neural networks. But now it's time to enter the real world, where data is not clean, where testing is important, where logging is required, and many more such things.

For this chapter, we will build an end-to-end image segmentation pipeline using Attention UNet. We will add as many industry practices as possible in this chapter.

Structuring Deep Learning Code

Let's be honest here, most young data scientists write AI code in a way that can't be put into production or even easily understood by other people. For instance, the code written in the preceding section is to explain the concept but not to be put in the real world.

Although Jupyter Notebook is fine for experimentation, writing a complete AI pipeline could be better. Let's define the general structure of any AI pipeline when you have multiple components and people working together on a big AI project.

Project Structure

It's important to set a pre-defined practice while working on AI projects. Here's one suggestion:

```
AI Project Folder
    ---configs
    ---dataloader
    ---evaluation
    ---executor
    ---model
    ---notebooks
    ---ops
```

```
---utils
main.py (this is a file, rest above are folders)
```

Feel free to modify this according to your taste.

Python modules and packages

In the preceding folder structure, each folder is a module that can be easily imported by just writing:

```
import config or import dataloader
```

A quick distinction between the Python module and packages is that a module is just a simple **.py** file, but a package is a directory with sub-packages and modules. For a package to be importable, it should contain an **__init__.py** file (even an empty file works).

Let's understand what goes on in all the preceding folders:

- **configs:** In this module, we define everything that can be configured and changed in the future. Examples of what goes in the config folder are files containing hyperparameters, metrics, folder paths, and model architecture (not always).

- **dataloader:** This folder has a self-explanatory name and contains all the data loading and pre-processing classes.

- **evaluation:** This folder contains the files to evaluate the performance of our models on various metrics or even files for inference.

- **executor:** This folder usually contains the files to train our models. This package is our connection with the outer world, which is what **main. py** usually calls. We can have different scripts for CPU and GPU-based training.

- **model:** This is a directory to write model architectures and save our trained models that are later used for inference. This can save the model in JSON format, hdf5, or any other format.

- **notebooks:** As we already know, building an end-to-end pipeline is tricky, requiring a lot of experimentation. Here, we keep all our experimentation notebooks used during pipeline building.

- **ops:** This one is not always needed and might include operations unrelated to machine learning, such as image manipulation, algebraic transformation, and more.

- **utils:** This function includes all the functions and classes used in multiple places and cannot be put in the aforementioned folders. Your pipeline might have components that don't belong to any deep learning libraries. Real-world pipelines have multiple models running in them, which might share some common post-processing in addition to their individual post-processing.

Documentation

If you want others to understand your code, it's important that your code is properly documented. Let's look at an example to understand how we write proper documentation:

```python
import numpy as np
import tensorflow as tf


def _nomralize_at_kscale(self, input_image: np.array, k: int) -> np.array:
    """"""
    Normalizing image between 0-k
    Args:
        input_image (np.array): input image for processing
        k (int): scaling factor
    Returns:
        scaled_image (np.array): scaled image between 0 and k
    """"""
    # we are assuming we need to give this image to our tensorflow
    pipeline, thus we are casting our numpy array to tf.tensor
    input_image = tf.cast(input_image, tf.float32) / 255.0
    scaled_image = k*input_image


    return scaled_image
```

Observe how docstrings are written for the preceding function. **Docstrings** are text written at the start of every function to give an overview. For simple functions, one can easily understand what it is doing even without reading the code part of it.

The basic structure of docstring has three parts: defining what it is doing, **args:**

what are the inputs or arguments it takes (also their datatypes or dtypes), and **returns:** what it is returning (always mention datatypes).

It's a good practice to write dtypes even in the function argument itself along with docstring. When the code becomes very complex, and we are constantly switching between dtypes, it's important to keep this structure to prevent any data leaks or failures.

Unit testing

Even though we can write check conditions in the main code itself, for larger pipelines, entire sub-packages are written for unit testing. Here's a simple example of writing a unit test for the preceding function using TensorFlow:

```python
import numpy as np
import tensorflow as tf


class TestNormalizeAtKScale(tf.test.TestCase):
    def test_normalize_at_kscale(self):
        # Create test input image
        input_image = np.array([[50, 100, 150], [200, 250, 255]], dtype=np.uint8)


        # Define expected output
        expected_output = np.array([[0.2, 0.4, 0.6], [0.8, 1.0, 1.0]], dtype=np.float32)


        # Call the function to get the actual output
        actual_output = _normalize_at_kscale(input_image, k=1.0)


        # Assert that the actual output matches the expected output
        self.assertAllClose(actual_output, expected_output, rtol=1e-1, atol=1e-1)
```

```
if __name__ == '__main__':
    tf.test.main()
```

- The test class **TestNormalizeAtKScale** is created, inheriting from **tf.test. TestCase**.
- Inside the test class, the **test_normalize_at_kscale** method is defined, which represents a single test case.
- The test case sets up the input image (**input_image**) and the expected output (**expected_output**) that should be returned by the function.
- The function **_normalize_at_kscale** is called with the input image and the scaling factor k=1.0, and the actual output is obtained in **actual_output**.
- The **self.assertAllClose** method is used to compare the actual output with the expected output. It checks if the values are close within a small tolerance.
- Finally, the **tf.test.main()** function is called to run the test cases.

By running the unit test, you can verify if the function **_normalize_at_kscale** is correctly normalizing the input image between 0 and k, and if the TensorFlow operations are working as expected.

Debugging

Let's understand debugging using a simple TensorFlow code; we can use a debugger such as **pdb** (Python's built-in debugger) or an IDE with integrated debugging support like PyCharm. Here's an example of how you can debug TensorFlow code using pdb:

```python
import tensorflow as tf
import pdb


def divide_tensors(a, b):
    result = tf.divide(a, b)
    return result


# Define input tensors
a = tf.constant([1, 2, 3], dtype=tf.float32)
```

```
b = tf.constant([0, 2, 4], dtype=tf.float32)


# Call the function
output = divide_tensors(a, b)


# Create a TensorFlow session
with tf.Session() as sess:
    try:
        # Start the debugger
        pdb.set_trace()

        # Run the session and print the output
        result = sess.run(output)
        print("Result:", result)
    except tf.errors.InvalidArgumentError as e:
        print("Error:", e)
```

In the preceding code, the **pdb.set_trace()** statement is added to set a breakpoint in the code. When the code execution reaches this point, the debugger will be activated, allowing you to inspect the variables and step through the code interactively. Run the preceding code   on your end to better understand the use of Debugger.

Here's how to use **pdb** debugger during execution:

- Run the code: When the execution reaches the **pdb.set_trace()** statement, the debugger will start.
- The debugger prompt ((Pdb)) will appear in the console, indicating that you can enter debugger commands.
- You can use various commands such as **n (next), s (step), c (continue),** and **p (print)** to navigate through the code and inspect variables.
- For example, you can print the values of **a** and **b** by entering **p a** or **p b** at the debugger prompt.
- You can step through the code line by line using the **n command** or into a function call using the s command.

- By examining the variable values and stepping through the code, you can identify any issues or errors and understand the flow of execution.
- To exit the debugger and continue program execution, you can enter **c (continue)** or press **Ctrl + D**.

Using a debugger provides a powerful way to interactively investigate the execution of TensorFlow code, allowing you to inspect variables, step through the code, and identify and resolve any issues or errors.

Logging

Another important concept in developing a real-world AI pipeline is Logging. Logging becomes super important when multiple are experimenting with multiple models simultaneously. Keeping track of all the model's hyperparameters, metrics, and other details becomes very tough. Although TensorFlow has its own logging functionality, we can still write our own Python-based logging capabilities.

When creating AI pipelines, logging is crucial for tracking the progress, identifying errors, and understanding the behavior of the pipeline. Here's an example of logging in the context of an AI pipeline using the Python logging module:

```python
import logging


# Configure the logging settings
logging.basicConfig(level=logging.INFO, format='%(asctime)s - %(levelname)s - %(message)s')


def preprocess_data(data):
    logging.info("Preprocessing data...")
    # Perform data preprocessing steps
    # ...


def train_model(data):
    logging.info("Training model...")
    # Train the model using the preprocessed data
    # ...
```

```
def evaluate_model(model, data):
    logging.info("Evaluating model...")
    # Evaluate the trained model on the test data
    # ...


def main():
    # Load the data
    logging.info("Loading data...")
    data = load_data()

    # Preprocess the data
    preprocess_data(data)

    # Train the model
    train_model(data)

    # Evaluate the model
    evaluate_model(model, data)


if __name__ == '__main__':
    main()
```

This code works in the following way:

- The **logging.basicConfig** function is used to configure the logging settings. In this example, the logging level is set to **INFO**, which means that all log messages with a severity level of **INFO** or higher will be displayed.

- Inside each function of the AI pipeline (**preprocess_data, train_model, evaluate_model**), log messages are added using **logging.info**. These messages provide information about the progress and current stage of the pipeline.

- In the **main** function, log messages are added to indicate the loading of data and the progression through different stages of the pipeline.

- By using the **logging** module, log messages will be printed to the console with a timestamp, severity level, and the specified message format (`'%(asctime)s - %(levelname)s - %(message)s'` in this case).

- Adjusting the logging level can help control the amount of information displayed. For example, setting the level to **DEBUG** will display more detailed log messages, while setting it to **WARNING** will only show messages of warning severity and above.

- Logging can be further customized by adding log handlers to write the log messages to files, sending them to a centralized logging system, or applying different formatting options.

By incorporating logging into our AI pipelines, we can effectively monitor the progress of your pipeline, track potential issues, and gain insights into the execution flow, making it easier to troubleshoot and optimize your pipeline.

Note: Another great way to track logging is using the Weights and Biases or W&B platform. Weights and Biases have recently gained a lot of popularity because of their flexibility and ease of use.

We would highly recommend using W&B for experiment tracking; here's the link to its tutorials: **https://docs.wandb.ai/tutorials [26]**

W&B allows us to organize and compare experiments, enabling us to make data-driven decisions about model performance and optimization. Additionally, W&B provides real-time visualizations and dashboards, giving you a comprehensive view of your experiments and facilitating insights and debugging.

Moreover, W&B integrates seamlessly with popular machine learning libraries, frameworks, and platforms, such as TensorFlow, PyTorch, and Jupyter Notebooks. This integration enables you to log experiments with just a few lines of code, saving you valuable time and effort. Furthermore, W&B supports collaboration by providing features such as project sharing, team collaboration, and experiment versioning.

Overall, Weights and Biases is a robust and user-friendly platform that empowers machine learning practitioners to track, visualize, and manage their experiments effectively. It enhances experiment reproducibility, facilitates collaboration, and enables efficient analysis and optimization of machine learning models.

Building End-to-end Segmentation Pipeline

Let's start with building our end-to-end AI solution for Attention Mechanism-based UNet on the Oxford **iiit pet dataset [27]**. Without further ado, let's jump into our AI pipeline.

Before we start writing our code, let's understand what we are trying to achieve here.

Image segmentation is crucial in various computer vision tasks, allowing us to partition an image into meaningful regions or objects. It enables a more detailed understanding of the visual content by identifying and delineating different objects or regions of interest within an image. Image segmentation finds applications in diverse fields such as medical imaging, autonomous driving, object recognition, semantic scene understanding, and more. It plays a fundamental role in tasks like object detection, instance segmentation, image editing, and image-based measurements, making it an essential component in many computer vision applications.

In the upcoming coding sections, we will achieve Image Segmentation using Attention U-Net. *Figure 10.2* is just a sample of binary and multi-class segmentation.

Figure 10.2: *Image Segmentation*

UNet and Attention Gates

U-Net architecture is a groundbreaking solution tailored for image segmentation. The core objective of U-Net is to generate a segmentation output mask (as shown in the preceding image) that can accurately classify each pixel. To achieve this, U-Net harnesses the power of an encoder-decoder structure. At its heart, the encoder diligently learns to extract crucial features from the input image while progressively reducing the spatial size of the feature blocks. This reduction paves the way for the decoder to generate the desired segmentation mask.

- **Contextual Conundrum**

However, a perplexing issue arises in this intricate dance between encoder and decoder. The decoder layers lack the necessary contextual information to generate precise segmentation masks based solely on the encoder's output. This contextual deficit hampers the decoder's ability to make informed decisions regarding pixel classification, resulting in suboptimal performance.

- **The Rise of Attention Gates**

Driven by the pursuit of context-rich segmentation, a pivotal breakthrough emerged in the form of attention gates. These attention mechanisms infused the U-Net architecture with much-needed contextual awareness. By incorporating attention gates into the decoder, the U-Net model gains a deeper understanding of the relationship between different regions in the image, enhancing the generation of accurate segmentation masks.

- **Unlocking the Context Code**

The genius behind U-Net lies in its innovative use of skip connections. Before each size-reduction step, the encoder's valuable features are preserved through skip connections and concatenated with the decoder's progress. This fusion gives the decoder a holistic image view, giving it the context to generate precise segmentation masks. An intriguing variation of this technique replaces concatenation with addition, giving birth to a network known as LinkNet.

The U-Net architecture, with its encoder-decoder structure and attention gates, stands as a pioneering milestone in the realm of image segmentation. U-Net and its variants, like LinkNet, have opened new horizons for accurate pixel-level classification by addressing the contextual conundrum through skip connections and attention mechanisms. The quest for comprehensive image segmentation continues as researchers and practitioners explore further refinements and innovations. The era of context-rich segmentation has arrived, unveiling the true potential of unraveling the visual world pixel by pixel.

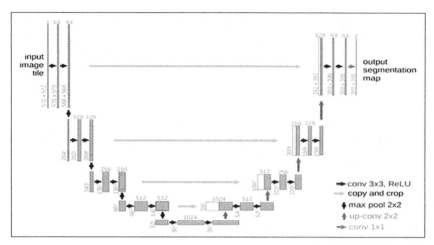

Figure 10.3: *UNet architecture*

Now, let's look at implementing the UNet combined with an attention mechanism. We will follow the same structure as defined earlier and shown in *Figure* 10.4 to create our AI pipeline.

Figure 10.4: *Project structure for our AI pipeline*

First, let's start with downloading the data and putting it in a data folder. If you have curl installed, use the following commands in cmd or copy-paste two links to download the zip files automatically:

```
!curl -O https://thor.robots.ox.ac.uk/~vgg/data/pets/images.tar.gz
!curl -O https://thor.robots.ox.ac.uk/~vgg/data/pets/annotations.tar.gz
```

Unzip in CMD using the following commands or manually unzip by going to where you downloaded the zip files:

```
!tar -xf images.tar.gz
!tar -xf annotations.tar.gz
```

Config

Let's start by defining some basic configurations in our **config.json** file:

```
{
    "data": {
        "image_size": [128, 128]
    },
    "train": {
        "batch_size": 64,
        "epochs": 10,
        "val_samples": 1000
    }
}
```

The preceding configuration file is a JSON format Python file. It has two main components: **data** and **train**.

The **data** part defines the image's size, path to the dataset, and other information related to our dataset.

Whereas the **train** part defines **batch_size** (how many samples will be fed at a time, this is basically the size of the batch in mini-batch gradient descent), **epochs** (number of passes of the entire dataset through our network), **val_samples** (how many samples for validation).

Note: You can even add mode parameters and hyperparameters for tuning here. Also, change the batch and image sizes in the above file if you run across memory errors.

Dataloader

Now it's time to ingest some data in our AI pipeline. For this purpose, we are going to write our own custom data loader in a file called **custom_dataloader. py**:

```python
# -*- coding: utf-8 -*-
"""Data Loader, custom_dataloader.py"""

import numpy as np
from tensorflow.keras.preprocessing.image import load_img, img_to_array
import tensorflow as tf
import random



class OxfordPetsDataLoader(tf.keras.utils.Sequence):
    def __init__(self, batch_size, img_size, input_img_paths, target_img_paths):
        """

        OxfordPetsDataLoader class to load and preprocess image data for
        the Oxford Pets dataset.


        Args:
            batch_size (int): Number of samples per batch.
            img_size (tuple): Tuple representing the target image size in
        the format (height, width).
            input_img_paths (list): List of input image paths.
            target_img_paths (list): List of target image paths.
        """
```

```
        self.batch_size = batch_size
        self.img_size = img_size
        self.input_img_paths = input_img_paths
        self.target_img_paths = target_img_paths

    def __len__(self):
        """
        Returns the number of batches in the Sequence.

        Returns:
            int: Number of batches.
        """
        return len(self.target_img_paths) // self.batch_size

    def __getitem__(self, idx):
        """
        Generates one batch of data.

        Args:
            idx (int): Index of the batch.

        Returns:
            tuple: A tuple containing the input and target image batches.
        """
        i = idx * self.batch_size
        batch_input_img_paths = self.input_img_paths[i: i + self.batch_size]
        batch_target_img_paths = self.target_img_paths[i: i + self.batch_size]

        # Preallocate arrays for input and target images
        x = np.zeros((self.batch_size,) + self.img_size + (3,), dtype=np.
```

```
float32)
        y = np.zeros((self.batch_size,) + self.img_size + (1,), dtype=np.
uint8)


        # Load and preprocess input images
        for j, path in enumerate(batch_input_img_paths):
            img = load_img(path, target_size=self.img_size)
            x[j] = img_to_array(img)


        # Load and preprocess target images
        for j, path in enumerate(batch_target_img_paths):
                img = load_img(path, target_size=self.img_size, color_
mode="grayscale")
            y[j] = np.expand_dims(img_to_array(img)[:, :, 0], axis=2)
            y[j] -= 1


        return x, y


    def on_epoch_end(self):
        """"""
        Method called at the end of each epoch.
        """"""
        # Shuffle the input and target image paths
        random.Random(1337).shuffle(self.input_img_paths)
        random.Random(1337).shuffle(self.target_img_paths)


    def prefetch(self, num_prefetch):
        """"""
        Prefetches the next <num_prefetch> batches of data.


        Args:
            num_prefetch (int): Number of batches to prefetch.
```

```
«»»
for _ in range(num_prefetch):
    self.__getitem__(np.random.randint(0, self.__len__()))
```

The given code defines the **OxfordPetsDataLoader** class, which is responsible for loading and preprocessing image data for the Oxford Pets dataset. It inherits from **tf.keras.utils.Sequence** and implements the necessary methods for generating data batches.

During initialization, the class takes parameters like **batch_size**, **img_size**, **input_img_path**, and **target_img_paths,** representing the batch size, image size, input image paths, and target image paths, respectively.

The **__len__** method returns the number of batches in the sequence, which is calculated based on the length of the target image paths divided by the batch size.

The **__getitem__** method generates one batch of data. It loads and preprocesses the input images by converting them to arrays and storing them in the **x** array. Similarly, it processes the target images by converting them to grayscale arrays, expanding dimensions, and subtracting 1 to adjust the range. The method returns a tuple containing the input and target image batches.

The **on_epoch_end** method is called at the end of each epoch and shuffles the input and target image paths to ensure randomization during training.

Additionally, the **prefetch** method prefetches the next **num_prefetch** batches of data. It calls the **__getitem__** method with randomly selected batch indices to load and preprocess the data for future use.

Overall, the **OxfordPetsDataLoader** class provides a convenient way to load and preprocess image data in batches for training or evaluation purposes, ensuring efficient handling of large datasets.

Model building

This is the most important part of our AI pipeline: building our AI model architecture. Let's take a detailed look at the **attention_unet.py** file.

The first method we define is called **conv_down()**. This method basically creates two layers of **Conv2D** with a **Dropout** in between. This will act as one block of Conv layers in our model's architecture. The code and diagram of this **Conv Block** are given as follows:

```python
def conv_down(self, n_conv, inputs):
    """
    This method creates a down-convolution block with given parameters
    """
    cd = Conv2D(n_conv, self.kernel, activation=self.activation,
                kernel_regularizer=self.reg, padding='same')(inputs)
    cd = Dropout(self.dropout)(cd)
    cd = Conv2D(n_conv, self.kernel, activation=self.activation,
                kernel_regularizer=self.reg, padding='same')(cd)

    return cd
```

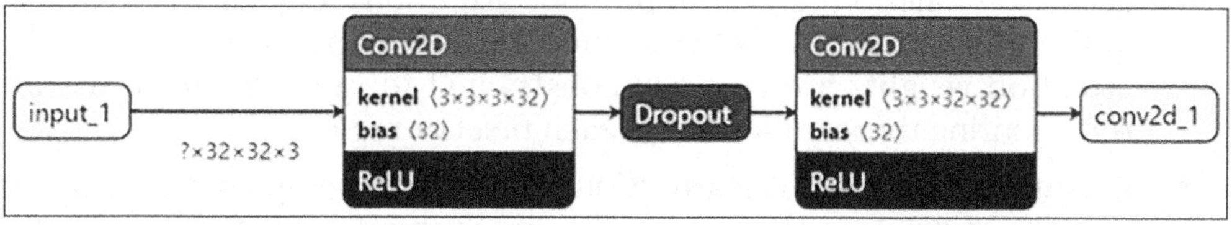

Figure 10.5: *Representation of the conv_down() method*

Next, we will define the Attention Block; this part goes between the skip connections going from encoder to decoder. Attention block is a slightly complex function. Before we write the code for it, let's try to understand it in more detail.

Understanding Attention block

The attention block is a component commonly used in deep learning models, particularly in computer vision tasks, to learn to focus on specific areas or regions of an input image. It aims to enhance the representation of important features and suppress irrelevant or less informative regions.

The concept behind the attention block is inspired by the mechanism of human visual attention. Just as humans tend to focus on salient objects or regions in a scene, the attention block learns to selectively attend to relevant parts of an image, enabling the model to allocate more resources and processing power to those areas.

The attention block typically consists of the following steps:

- **Gating mechanism:** The gating mechanism takes a low-level feature representation (often called **g**) and applies a convolutional operation to reduce its dimensionality. It serves as a way to capture global contextual information about the image.

- **Feature representation:** The input image features (often called **x**) are also passed through a convolutional layer to transform them into a higher-dimensional space.

- **Addition:** The output of the gating mechanism is added element-wise to the output of the feature representation step. This allows the attention block to combine the global contextual information with the local features.

- **Non-linear activation:** An activation function, such as the rectified linear unit (ReLU), is applied to the sum of the gated and transformed input features. This activation helps introduce non-linearity to the attention mechanism.

- **Attention generation:** Another convolutional layer with a sigmoid activation function is used to produce attention weights. These weights indicate the importance or relevance of different parts of the image. The attention weights are typically constrained to range between 0 and 1, representing the significance of each pixel or region.

- **Feature modulation:** The attention weights are multiplied element-wise with the original input features, allowing the model to focus on important regions while attenuating the less relevant areas. This modulation enhances the representation of salient features and suppresses noise or irrelevant information.

Let's now look at implementing **attention_block()** method in our code:

```python
def attention_block(self, g, x, n_intermediate_filters):
    """
    This method creates an attention block, that learns to focus on
    specific areas of the image
    """
    gating = Conv2D(n_intermediate_filters, (1, 1), padding='same')(g)
    # gating mechanism
    x = Conv2D(n_intermediate_filters, (2, 2), padding='same')(x)
    attention = tf.keras.layers.Add()([gating, x])
```

```
attention = Activation('relu')(attention)

attention = Conv2D(1, (1, 1), padding='same', activation='
sigmoid')(attention)

return tf.keras.layers.Multiply()([x, attention])
```

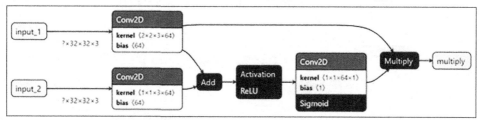

Figure 10.6: *Representation of attention gate*

By incorporating attention blocks into deep learning models, the model can adaptively learn to attend to relevant spatial regions in an input image, emphasizing informative features and reducing the impact of noise or less significant regions. This helps improve the model's ability to capture and utilize important visual cues, leading to better performance in various computer vision tasks such as object recognition, segmentation, and image synthesis. *Figure 10.6* shows the structure of the Attention gate.

Next, we have to integrate the attention block with the rest of the model's architecture. Thus, we define an additional method called **concat()**:

```
def concat(self, n_conv, inputs, skip):
        """

        This method concatenates the input and skip connection with
attention

        """
        con = Conv2DTranspose(n_conv, (2, 2), strides=(2, 2), padding='same')
(inputs)
        con = concatenate([self.attention_block(con, skip, n_conv), con])

        return con
```

The **concat()** method takes input tensor **inputs** and a skip connection tensor **skip** and concatenates them using a transposed convolution operation and an attention block. The input tensor undergoes a transposed convolution to increase its spatial dimensions, and the resulting tensor is combined with the output of the attention block applied to the skip connection tensor. The method returns the final concatenated tensor, combining the input information and skipping connection with attention. *Figure* 10.7 displays the **concat()** method's layout.

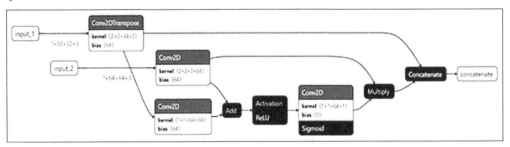

Figure 10.7: Representation of concat() method

Now, let's try to integrate all the pieces to build our Attention UNet model:

```python
# -*- coding: utf-8 -*-
"""Unet model with attention gates"""


import json
import tensorflow as tf
from tensorflow.keras.layers import Conv2D, Dropout, Input, MaxPool2D, Conv2DTranspose, concatenate, Activation
from tensorflow.keras import backend as K



class CNNBlocks:
    """
    A class used to create Convolution Blocks of UNet Model
    """


    def __init__(self, kernel_size: int):
        """
        Initializes the CNNBlocks class with kernel size and other
parameters
```

```
        Args:
            kernel_size (int): The size of the convolution kernel
        «»»
        self.activation = "relu"
        self.reg = tf.keras.regularizers.l1_l2(l1=1e-5, l2=1e-4)
        self.kernel = kernel_size
        self.dropout = 0.1
        self.output_channel = 3


    def conv_down(self, n_conv: int, inputs: tf.Tensor) -> tf.Tensor:
        «»»»
        Creates a down-convolution block with the given parameters
        Args:
            n_conv (int): Number of filters in the convolution layer
            inputs (tf.Tensor): Input tensor
        Returns:
            tf.Tensor: Output tensor
        «»»
        cd = Conv2D(n_conv, self.kernel, activation=self.activation,
                    kernel_regularizer=self.reg, padding='same')(inputs)
        cd = Dropout(self.dropout)(cd)
        cd = Conv2D(n_conv, self.kernel, activation=self.activation,
                    kernel_regularizer=self.reg, padding='same')(cd)


        return cd


    def attention_block(self, g: tf.Tensor, x: tf.Tensor, n_intermediate_
filters: int) -> tf.Tensor:
        «»»»
        Creates an attention block that learns to focus on specific areas
of the image
        Args:
```

```
            g (tf.Tensor): Gating tensor

            x (tf.Tensor): Input tensor

            n_intermediate_filters (int): Number of filters in the
intermediate convolution layer

        Returns:

            tf.Tensor: Output tensor

        «»»

        gating = Conv2D(n_intermediate_filters, (1, 1), padding='same')(g)
# gating mechanism

        x = Conv2D(n_intermediate_filters, (2, 2), padding='same')(x)

        attention = tf.keras.layers.Add()([gating, x])

        attention = Activation('relu')(attention)

        attention = Conv2D(1, (1, 1), padding='same', activation='
sigmoid')(attention)

        return tf.keras.layers.Multiply()([x, attention])


    def concat(self, n_conv: int, inputs: tf.Tensor, skip: tf.Tensor) ->
tf.Tensor:
        «»»»

        Concatenates the input and skip connection with attention

        Args:

            n_conv (int): Number of filters in the transposed convolution
layer

            inputs (tf.Tensor): Input tensor

            skip (tf.Tensor): Skip connection tensor

        Returns:

            tf.Tensor: Output tensor

        «»»

        con = Conv2DTranspose(n_conv, (2, 2), strides=(2, 2),
padding='same')(inputs)

        con = concatenate([self.attention_block(con, skip, n_conv), con])


        return con
```

```python
class Attention_UNet:
    """"""
    Unet Model class with attention gates
    """"""

    def __init__(self, config_path="D:/mine/AISummer/project2/configs/
config.json"): # Give path to your config file
        self.output_channels = 3
        self.config_file = config_path

        # Load the configuration file
        with open(self.config_file, "r") as f:
            config = json.load(f)

        self.img_size = tuple(config["data"]["image_size"])
        self.height = self.img_size[0]
        self.width = self.img_size[1]

    def build(self) -> tf.keras.Model:
        """"""
        Builds the keras model with attention gates
        Returns:
            tf.keras.Model: The built model
        """"""

        inputs = tf.keras.layers.Input(shape=[self.height, self.width, 3])

        conv_block = CNNBlocks(kernel_size=3)

        # Down block
```

```
d1 = conv_block.conv_down(16, inputs)

p1 = MaxPool2D((2, 2))(d1)

d2 = conv_block.conv_down(32, p1)

p2 = MaxPool2D((2, 2))(d2)

d3 = conv_block.conv_down(64, p2)

p3 = MaxPool2D((2, 2))(d3)

d4 = conv_block.conv_down(128, p3)

p4 = MaxPool2D((2, 2))(d4)

d5 = conv_block.conv_down(256, p4)


# Up block

u6 = conv_block.concat(128, d5, d4)

u6 = conv_block.conv_down(128, u6)

u7 = conv_block.concat(64, u6, d3)

u7 = conv_block.conv_down(64, u7)

u8 = conv_block.concat(32, u7, d2)

u8 = conv_block.conv_down(32, u8)

u9 = conv_block.concat(16, u8, d1)

u9 = conv_block.conv_down(16, u9)


outputs = Conv2D(self.output_channels, 3, activation="softmax",
padding="same")(u9)


self.model = tf.keras.Model(inputs=[inputs], outputs=[outputs])


return self.model
```

Let's try to understand the entire code:

The preceding code defines two classes, **CNNBlocks** and **Attention_UNet**, which are used to build an Attention U-Net model.

The **CNNBlocks** class is responsible for creating the convolution blocks of the U-Net model. It has methods such as **conv_down**, which creates a down-convolution block with the given parameters, and **attention_block**, which creates an attention block that learns to focus on specific image areas.

The **Attention_UNet** class represents the Attention U-Net model itself. It has an **__init__** method that sets the number of output channels. The **build** method constructs the actual U-Net model with attention gates.

The U-Net model consists of two blocks: the **down and up blocks**. The input image is progressively downsampled in the down block using convolutional layers and max pooling. The output of each down block is stored in **d1**, **d2**, **d3**, **d4**, and **d5**.

In the **up block**, transposed convolutions **Conv2DTranspose** are used to upsample the feature maps. At each step, the feature map from the corresponding down block is concatenated **concat** with the upsampled feature map. This concatenated feature map is passed through a down-convolution block **conv_down** to refine the features. The resulting feature map from the last up block is passed through a final convolution layer to obtain the model's output.

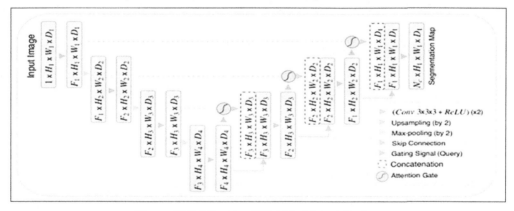

Figure 10.8: *Attention UNet Model Architecture*

Overall, the Attention U-Net model combines the U-Net architecture with attention mechanisms to improve feature representation and focus on relevant image areas during upsampling. *Figure* 10.8 is the representational image of Attention UNet, displaying full architecture is a bit tricky because of too many layers.

Note: In our case, we don't have any files in Notebooks and Ops. So, we are not going to write anything in those folders.

Executor

Let's now look into the executor folder, which contains a **train.py** file. This file basically trains our AI model.

```
import random
import os
import json
import tensorflow as tf


# Internal imports
from model.att_unet import Attention_UNet
from custom_dataloader.dataloader import OxfordPetsDataLoader
from utils.losses import CustomLossAndMetrics


class AttentionUNetTrainer:
    def __init__(self, input_dir: str, target_dir: str, config_path: str =
"D:/mine/AISummer/project2/configs/config.json"): # Give path to you config file
        """"

        AttentionUNetTrainer class to train the Attention UNet model on
the Oxford Pets dataset.


        Args:
            input_dir (str): Directory containing input images.
            target_dir (str): Directory containing target images.
            config_path (str, optional): Path to the configuration file.
Defaults to «D:/mine/AISummer/project2/configs/config.json".
        «»»
        self.input_dir = input_dir
        self.target_dir = target_dir
        self.config_file = config_path
```

```
# Load the configuration file
with open(self.config_file, "r") as f:
    config = json.load(f)


self.img_size = tuple(config["data"]["image_size"])
self.batch_size = config["train"]["batch_size"]
self.val_samples = config["train"]["val_samples"]
self.epochs = config["train"]["epochs"]


self.input_img_paths = sorted(
    [
        os.path.join(input_dir, fname)
        for fname in os.listdir(input_dir)
        if fname.endswith(".jpg")
    ]
)
self.target_img_paths = sorted(
    [
        os.path.join(target_dir, fname)
        for fname in os.listdir(target_dir)
        if fname.endswith(".png") and not fname.startswith(".")
    ]
)


random.Random(1337).shuffle(self.input_img_paths)
random.Random(1337).shuffle(self.target_img_paths)
    self.train_input_img_paths = self.input_img_paths[:-self.val_
samples]
        self.train_target_img_paths = self.target_img_paths[:-self.val_
samples]
            self.val_input_img_paths = self.input_img_paths[-self.val_
samples:]
```

```
            self.val_target_img_paths = self.target_img_paths[-self.val_
samples:]
            self.val_gen = OxfordPetsDataLoader(self.batch_size, self.img_
size, self.val_input_img_paths, self.val_target_img_paths)


    def train(self):
        """"
        Trains the Attention UNet model on the Oxford Pets dataset.
        """"
        model = Attention_UNet().build()
        model.compile(
            optimizer="adam",
            loss=CustomLossAndMetrics.combined_loss,
            metrics=[CustomLossAndMetrics.dice_coeff]
        )


        train_gen = OxfordPetsDataLoader(self.batch_size, self.img_size,
self.train_input_img_paths, self.train_target_img_paths)
        val_gen = OxfordPetsDataLoader(self.batch_size, self.img_size,
self.val_input_img_paths, self.val_target_img_paths)


        callbacks = [
            tf.keras.callbacks.ModelCheckpoint("oxford_segmentation.h5",
save_best_only=True),
            tf.keras.callbacks.EarlyStopping(patience=5),
            tf.keras.callbacks.ReduceLROnPlateau(factor=0.1, patience=3)
        ]


        # Prefetch the next 2 batches for training and validation data
loaders
        train_gen.prefetch(2)
        val_gen.prefetch(2)
```

```
        model.fit(train_gen, epochs=self.epochs, validation_data=val_gen,
callbacks=callbacks)
```

The preceding code demonstrates the training process for the Attention UNet model on the Oxford Pets dataset.

The **AttentionUNetTrainer** class is the central component for training the model. It takes the input directory, target directory, and an optional configuration file path during initialization. The configuration file is loaded to obtain parameters such as image size, batch size, validation samples, and the number of epochs.

The input and target image paths are sorted and stored in **input_img_paths** and **target_img_paths**, respectively. Random shuffling is performed on both sets of paths to ensure randomness during training. The paths are then split into training and validation sets using the specified number of validation samples. A **val_gen** object is created by instantiating the **OxfordPetsDataLoader** class with the validation set paths.

The **train** method handles the training process. It initializes the Attention UNet model, compiling it with the Adam optimizer and the **combined_loss** function, and **dice_coeff** as the evaluation metric. Data loaders (**train_gen** and **val_gen**) are created using the **OxfordPetsDataLoader** class with the corresponding image paths. Callbacks for model checkpointing, early stopping, and reducing the learning rate are defined. Finally, the model is trained using the **fit** method, passing the data loaders, number of epochs, and callbacks.

The code demonstrates a complete training pipeline for the Attention UNet model on the Oxford Pets dataset, including data loading, model initialization, compilation, training, and callbacks for monitoring and optimizing the training process.

Utils

In this section, we will write the custom losses we use in our **train.py** file. Here's our **losses.py** file:

```
# -*- coding: utf-8 -*-
"""Custom loss class, losses.py"""
import tensorflow as tf
from tensorflow.keras import backend as K
```

```python
class CustomLossAndMetrics:
    def __init__(self):
        """"""

        CustomLossAndMetrics class for defining custom loss and metrics
functions.

        """"""
        pass


    @staticmethod
    def dice_coeff(y_true: tf.Tensor, y_pred: tf.Tensor) -> tf.Tensor:
        """"""

        Calculate the Dice coefficient between the true and predicted
segmentation masks.

        Args:
            y_true (tf.Tensor): True segmentation masks.
            y_pred (tf.Tensor): Predicted segmentation masks.

        Returns:
            tf.Tensor: Dice coefficient score.
        """"""
        smooth = 1.


        # Flatten
        y_true_f = tf.reshape(tf.one_hot(tf.cast(y_true, tf.int32), 3),
[-1, 3])
        y_pred_f = tf.reshape(y_pred, [-1, 3])


        intersection = K.sum(y_true_f * y_pred_f)
        score = (2. * intersection + smooth) / (K.sum(y_true_f) + K.
sum(y_pred_f) + smooth)
        return score
```

```python
@staticmethod
def dice_loss(y_true: tf.Tensor, y_pred: tf.Tensor) -> tf.Tensor:
    """
    Calculate the Dice loss between the true and predicted segmentation
    masks.

        Args:
            y_true (tf.Tensor): True segmentation masks.
            y_pred (tf.Tensor): Predicted segmentation masks.


        Returns:
            tf.Tensor: Dice loss.
    """
    loss = 1 - CustomLossAndMetrics.dice_coeff(y_true, y_pred)
    return loss


@staticmethod
def entropy_loss(y_true: tf.Tensor, y_pred: tf.Tensor) -> tf.Tensor:
    """
    Calculate the entropy loss between the true and predicted segmen-
    tation masks.

        Args:
            y_true (tf.Tensor): True segmentation masks.
            y_pred (tf.Tensor): Predicted segmentation masks.


        Returns:
            tf.Tensor: Entropy loss.
    """
        loss = tf.keras.losses.sparse_categorical_crossentropy(y_true,
y_pred)
```

```
        return loss


    @staticmethod
    def combined_loss(y_true: tf.Tensor, y_pred: tf.Tensor) -> tf.Tensor:
        """
```

Calculate the combined loss (entropy loss + dice loss) between the true and predicted segmentation masks.

```
        Args:
            y_true (tf.Tensor): True segmentation masks.
            y_pred (tf.Tensor): Predicted segmentation masks.

        Returns:
            tf.Tensor: Combined loss.
        """
        loss = CustomLossAndMetrics.entropy_loss(y_true, y_pred) + Cus-
tomLossAndMetrics.dice_loss(y_true, y_pred)
        return loss
```

The **CustomLossAndMetrics** class provides custom loss and metrics functions for segmentation tasks. It includes methods like **dice_coeff**, **dice_loss**, **entropy_loss**, and **combined_loss** to calculate evaluation metrics and losses between true and predicted segmentation masks. These functions offer flexibility and modularity for assessing segmentation model performance and optimizing training processes.

Note: Breaking the pipeline using custom loss and metrics is easy. The biggest error people face in this is the number of channels in the predicted output and actual output. Often these functions need to be modified according to the model's architecture. For instance, instead of calculating the dice coefficient on all channels, you might want to calculate it in the foreground only.

Evaluation

Now let's look into how to evaluate our trained model using **eval.py**:

```python
# -*- coding: utf-8 -*-
"""evaluation class, eval.py"""


from IPython.display import Image, display
from tensorflow.keras.preprocessing.image import load_img, img_to_array
from PIL import ImageOps
from utils.losses import CustomLossAndMetrics
import tensorflow as tf
import numpy as np
import matplotlib.pyplot as plt



class Evaluator:
    def __init__(self, trainer):
        """

        Evaluator class to evaluate the model›s predictions on the
validation dataset.


        Args:
            trainer: Instance of the AttentionUNetTrainer class.
        """
        self.trainer = trainer
        self.model = tf.keras.models.load_model('oxford_segmentation.h5',
                                            custom_objects={'combined_
loss': CustomLossAndMetrics.combined_loss,

                                                    'dice_coeff':
CustomLossAndMetrics.dice_coeff})
```

```python
def evaluate(self):
    """"""

    Evaluate the model's predictions on the validation dataset and display
the results.
    """"""
    val_gen = self.trainer.val_gen
    val_preds = self.model.predict(val_gen)


    def display_mask(mask: np.ndarray) -> np.ndarray:
        """"""

        Quick utility to display a model's prediction.

        Args:
            mask (np.ndarray): Predicted segmentation mask.

        Returns:
            np.ndarray: RGB mask for visualization.
        """"""
        color_map = {
            0: np.array([0, 0, 0]),
            1: np.array([0, 120, 120]),
            2: np.array([120, 0, 120]),
        }
        rgb_mask = np.zeros((*mask.shape, 3))
        for k in color_map.keys():
            rgb_mask[mask == k] = color_map[k]
        return rgb_mask


    # Display results for validation image #5
    i = 5


    # Load and display input image
```

```
        input_img = img_to_array(load_img(self.trainer.val_input_img_
paths[i], target_size=self.trainer.img_size))
        predicted_mask = display_mask(np.argmax(val_preds[i], axis=-1))
        target_mask = display_mask(np.squeeze(img_to_array(load_img(self.
trainer.val_target_img_paths[i], target_size=self.trainer.img_size, color_
mode="grayscale")).astype(int)))

        fig, ax = plt.subplots(1, 3, figsize=(20, 20))
        ax[0].imshow(input_img/255.0)
        ax[0].title.set_text('Input Image')
        ax[0].axis('off')

        ax[1].imshow(predicted_mask/255.0)
        ax[1].title.set_text('Predicted Mask')
        ax[1].axis('off')

        ax[2].imshow(target_mask/255.0)
        ax[2].title.set_text('Ground Truth Mask')
        ax[2].axis('off')
        plt.show()
```

The code snippet defines the **Evaluator** class, which evaluates the model's predictions on the validation dataset and displays the results. The class takes an instance of the `AttentionUNetTrainer` class as an argument and loads a pre-trained model from the `oxford_segmentation.h5` file.

The **evaluate** method of the Evaluator class uses the loaded model to make predictions on the validation dataset `val_gen`. It defines a utility function, `display_mask`, to convert the predicted segmentation mask into an RGB mask for visualization. It then selects a specific validation image (index 5) and loads the input image, predicted mask, and ground truth mask. Finally, it plots these images side by side using matplotlib.

To use this code, you would need to instantiate the `AttentionUNetTrainer` class and pass it to an instance of the **Evaluator** class. Calling the **evaluate** method will display the evaluation results.

main

Now, it's time to write our **main.py** and check whether everything is working or not. This file calls the **AttentionUNetTrainer,** which internally builds the model, loads the data, and starts the training. After that, it just plots the output on a sample image using **eval.py**. Modify the evaluation file to get the inference in whatever way you want.

```python
# -*- coding: utf-8 -*-
"""main.py"""

import json
import tensorflow as tf
from executor.train import AttentionUNetTrainer
from evaluation.eval import Evaluator


def main():
    # Change these paths and set your directories here, also change paths
in other files as well
    input_dir = "D:/mine/AISummer/project2/data/images/images"
    target_dir = "D:/mine/AISummer/project2/data/annotations/annotations/
trimaps"
    config_file = "D:/mine/AISummer/project2/configs/config.json"

    trainer = AttentionUNetTrainer(input_dir, target_dir, config_file)
    trainer.train()


    evaluator = Evaluator(trainer)  # Initialize the evaluator with the
trainer
    evaluator.evaluate()  # Evaluate the model


if __name__ == "__main__":
    main()
```

Finally, we are done with building our end-to-end image segmentation pipeline using Attention UNet. I understand that the preceding sections contain a lot of code, and you might need some guidance as well. However, writing production-level code is daunting, and one should really embrace the process of building it in order to become a good AI developer.

Let's recap what we've actually built here:

- Made a **config.json** for setting up training, data, model parameters, and hyper-parameters.
- Wrote a custom **dataloader** that can handle the dataset in batches instead of passing all the data in one go. We also implemented prefetching to make the data-loading process faster.
- Build the Attention UNet module from scratch.
- A training script that loads the models and data and starts training the model while saving the best model automatically.
- And finally, a simple script to see the performance of our trained model on the validation dataset.

After running everything, this is how our AI pipeline directory structure will look:

```
AI Project:
    configs
        --config.json
    custom_dataloader
        --dataloader.py
    evaluation
        --eval.py
    executor
        --train.py
    logs
        (log folders, this will be automatically created)
    model
        --att_net.py
    notebooks
        (put your own testing notebooks here)
```

```
ops
    (empty for now)
utils
    --losses.py
main.py
oxford_segmentation.h5 (this will be created after training is done)
```

Let's take a look at the results here. First of all, don't worry about the color switch in the predicted and actual mask. Nevertheless, the goal here is not to train the best model ever; this model can be further fine-tuned and trained for more epochs. We only trained it for 10 epochs, which is very less. Additionally, we kept the image size relatively small, 128x128. The key reason to implement this pipeline is to show that in real-life scenarios, AI pipelines consist of many components, and it's best to write in a class structure as it becomes much more manageable for larger projects.

```
# Output:
# 99/99 [==============================] - 359s 4s/step - loss: 0.8932 -
dice_coeff: 0.7239 - val_loss: 0.8859 - val_dice_coeff: 0.7305 - lr: 0.0010
# Epoch 7/10
# 99/99 [==============================] - 340s 3s/step - loss: 0.8479 -
dice_coeff: 0.7394 - val_loss: 0.8124 - val_dice_coeff: 0.7512 - lr: 0.0010
# Epoch 8/10
# 99/99 [==============================] - 350s 4s/step - loss: 0.8027 -
dice_coeff: 0.7547 - val_loss: 0.7765 - val_dice_coeff: 0.7625 - lr: 0.0010
# Epoch 9/10
# 99/99 [==============================] - 349s 4s/step - loss: 0.7853 -
dice_coeff: 0.7603 - val_loss: 0.7672 - val_dice_coeff: 0.7619 - lr: 0.0010
# Epoch 10/10
# 99/99 [==============================] - 339s 3s/step - loss: 0.7591 -
dice_coeff: 0.7693 - val_loss: 0.7372 - val_dice_coeff: 0.7775 - lr: 0.0010
```

Just within 10 epochs, we see the dice coefficient of 77.5%, which is a very good number for an image segmentation model. We can surely get better results by training it for longer epochs and adapting the learning rate and other parameters.

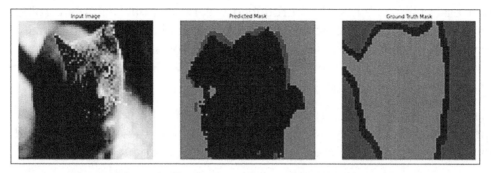

Figure 10.9: *AI pipeline segmentation results on 64x64 sized image with categorical cross-entropy (CCE) loss*

Figure 10.10 displays the results of our segmentation model trained using Categorical cross-entropy combined with Dice loss. Combining loss functions tends to make models more robust against adversarial attacks simultaneously, increasing the accuracy as well but by a small percentage.

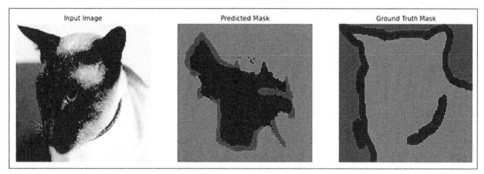

Figure 10.10: *AI pipeline segmentation results on 128x128 sized image with CCE + Dice loss*

Once you are done with building the AI pipeline, there's an entire field to deploy these models. We will not look into model deployment as it will take another book to explain it.

Conclusion

In this chapter, our focus was on developing a production-ready pipeline. We began by delving into the concept of organizing deep learning codes and understanding the importance of structuring them effectively. Moving forward, we delved into the background of Image segmentation and Unet, gaining insights into their significance and applications.

Following that, we embarked on building the various components of our AI Pipeline. We developed the dataloader, models, evaluator, executor, and other essential elements. We introduced several custom features throughout this process, including custom loss functions and metrics. Additionally, we incorporated techniques such as prefetching to optimize the pipeline's speed and efficiency. Leveraging TensorFlow's callbacks, we implemented a mechanism to save the best model during training.

Finally, we unveiled the structure and showcased the results of our trained pipeline, highlighting the successful integration of all the components and the impressive outcomes achieved by implementing our production-ready solution.

In the upcoming chapter, we will examine the concepts behind the latest and greatest AI technology in the market.

" *The key to artificial intelligence has always been the representation." - Jeff Hawkins*

https://github.com/OrangeAVA/Ultimate-Neural-Network-Programming-with-Python

## CHAPTER 11

Latest Advancements in AI

The final chapter of this book discusses a few very important AI technologies in the last few years. This chapter primarily focuses on advanced AI concepts used in technology such as ChatGPT and DALL-E 2. This is a particularly tough chapter to follow and might require a good understanding of many basic AI components.

Structure

This chapter covers the following topics:

- Context of RNN, LSTM, and Self-Attention for NLP
- Using Self-Attention for Transformers
- Understanding the object detection and components of YOLO
- VAE, GANs, Diffusion models, and understanding DALL-E 2

Transformers: Improving NLP Using Attention

The emergence of diverse data structures made the need for specialized models to handle different data formats increasingly evident. While Convolutional Neural

Networks (CNNs) and Multi-Layer Perceptrons (MLPs) excelled in dealing with image and tabular data, sequential data was yet to find its perfect match. This is where Recurrent Neural Networks (RNNs) and LSTM stepped in, promising to revolutionize sequential data, such as text and time series.

Recurrent Neural Network (RNN)

An RNN is an artificial neural network designed to recognize patterns in data sequences, such as numerical time series data originating from sensors, stock markets, and government agencies, or text data in which sequences of words or characters make up the fundamental structure.

To understand the essence of an RNN, consider it as a network with loops where information can persist. This loop allows information to be passed from one step in the sequence to the next, essentially giving the network a form of memory. This distinct feature is what makes RNNs unique and powerful in modeling and predicting sequences.

However, RNNs have their challenges. Training these networks often led to what is known as the vanishing gradient problem, where the contribution of information decays geometrically over time, hence making it hard for the network to learn and connect distant past information to the present task.

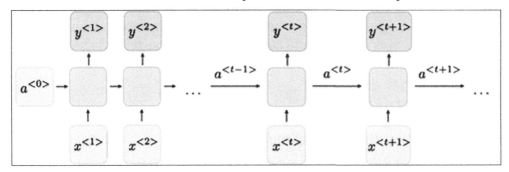

Figure 11.1: *RNN architecture*

Please visit the following link for a great lecture on RNN from Stanford:
https://www.youtube.com/watch?v=6niqTuYFZLQ&ab_channel=Stanford UniversitySchoolofEngineering [28]

Long-Short Term Memory (LSTM)

To counteract the problem encountered by RNNs, a new variant called Long Short-Term Memory (LSTM) was introduced. LSTM networks, a type of RNN, are explicitly designed to avoid the long-term dependency problem or the vanishing gradient problem.

In an LSTM, the information flows through a mechanism known as cell states. This mechanism has various gates regulating the flow of information, effectively controlling what is remembered and forgotten. This selective memory feature makes LSTMs significantly more effective at capturing long-term dependencies.

A typical LSTM unit comprises a cell, an input gate, an output gate, and a forget gate. The cell remembers values over arbitrary time intervals, and the three gates regulate the flow of information into and out of the cell.

While RNNs had the right idea for handling sequential data, LSTMs brought the necessary refinements to make it work in practice. By combating the vanishing gradient problem, LSTMs opened new possibilities in the world of sequence prediction problems.

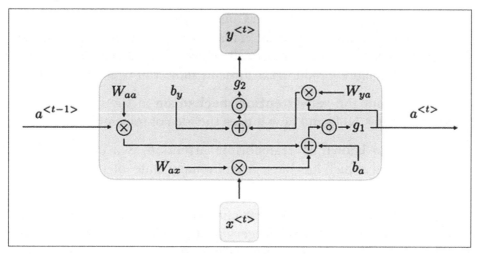

Figure 11.2: *LSTM block*

To solve all the problems of the RNN and LSTM, we introduce Transformers. Lately, everything in the field of AI has been transformed using Transformers, from image classification to audio processing, from text prediction to video generation. The introduction of Transformers was the biggest innovation in the last few years of AI research. One of the biggest AI products, ChatGPT, also uses Transformers only. You can find Transformers-inspired things everywhere in the market. In this section, let's try to break down the components behind this amazing feat of engineering and design.

Please visit the following link for a great video on LSTM by StatsQuest YouTube channel: **https://www.youtube.com/watch?v=YCzL96nL7j0&ab_channel=Stat QuestwithJoshStarmer [29]**

Self-Attention

Let's try to understand the idea of attention by first discussing the concept of reweighting.

Example to understand the concept:

Reweighing is a method where you adjust the importance of data. Let's use a simple classroom example to understand it. Imagine you have a class of students who are all studying for a final exam. The final exam covers five subjects, each with an equal weightage of 20%. This means that all subjects are equally important for the final score.

Now suppose after analyzing past exams, one subject tends to be more difficult for students, and they usually score lower in that subject. To boost overall scores, you decide to spend more time on that difficult subject and less time on the others. In effect, you're giving more weight to the difficult subject in your study schedule.

Now, let's talk about the **self-attention mechanism** in the context of natural language processing (NLP) and how it uses the idea of reweighting.

Self-attention, also known as Transformer attention, is a component of the Transformer model, which has been used in many state-of-the-art models for NLP tasks, like BERT, GPT-3, and others.

Imagine you have a sentence: **The cat chased its tail.** The word **its** refers to **The cat** in this sentence. When processing this sentence, the self-attention mechanism in the Transformer model allows the model to associate **its** with **The cat**.

Here's how it works:

1. **Embedding:** Each word in the sentence is first converted into a vector representation (or embedding).

2. **Attention Scores:** The model then calculates attention scores. These scores determine how much focus should be on each word in the sentence when trying to understand a specific word. For instance, when trying to understand **its**, the model will put more attention (or weight) on **The cat** and less attention on the other words. This is the **reweighing** part.

3. **Context Vector:** The attention scores are then used to create a weighted combination of the word vectors, resulting in a context-aware representation for each word. This means that the representation of **its** now contains information from The cat.

This process allows the model to understand the context and relationships between words in a sentence. The self-attention mechanism helps the model understand each word in isolation and the context of other words in the sentence. The following diagram shows the representation of the entire process.

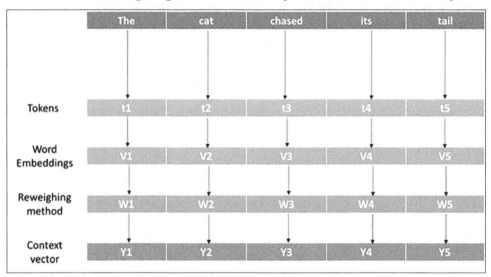

Figure 11.3: *Getting context vector using some reweighing method*

But now the question is: What are these W's? How do we get these, and where is learning involved in all of this?

W1 = [w11, w12, w13, w14, w15];   ...;   ...;   W4 = [w41, w42, w43, w44, w45]

w11 = V1xV1;   w12 =V1xV2;   w13 = V1xV3;   w14 = V1xV4;   w15 = V1xV5

Here, we see how we are just doing basic maths and doing multiplication of the embedding vectors with each other and themselves. Small note here, we need to normalize the W1 vector.

Let's use this information to build upon our context vectors:

Y1 = w11xV1 + w12xV2 + w13xV3 + w14xV4 + w15xV5

...

Y5 = w51xV1 + w52xV2 + w53xV3 + w54xV4 + w55xV5

We used the initial embeddings of all the tokens, multiplied them with each other, and then used them to rescale the initial embedding vectors.

Is there anything more to it? Definitely, yes, we still haven't made these trainable; right now, we are assuming the fixed, predetermined vectors here. Also, proximity has no influence here. This is the basic idea behind Self-Attention.

Understanding Key, Query, and Value

Now let's look into how we make our weights trainable and understand the concept of key, query, and value. Let's first understand it through a simple analogy before becoming more technical.

Example to understand the concept:

The concepts of key, query, and value come into play in the context of the self-attention mechanism in Transformer models, which is used for tasks like understanding language.

Imagine you're at a party full of people, and you're trying to find your friend, Bob. In this scenario:

Query: *This is you asking, "Where is Bob?" The query represents what you're looking for.*

Key: *These are the name tags people are wearing. When you approach someone and look at their name tag, you compare your query "Bob" to the key (the name on their tag).*

Value: *This is the information or characteristics associated with each person. Once you find Bob (where the query matches the key), you gain access to all the value information about him, like his conversation, his outfit details, etc.*

Now let's apply this to Transformer models in the context of a sentence : **The cat chased its tail**.

Query: When processing the word **its**, the query is a representation of **its**.

Key: These are representations of all the other words in the sentence. The Transformer model compares the query to these keys to find matches.

Value: These are also representations of all the words in the sentence. The associated value is used in the output when a match is found between the query and a key.

In the self-attention mechanism of Transformers, for each word (like **its** in our example), the model creates a query, a key, and a value. It then calculates a score by comparing the query of the current word to the key of every other word. These scores are used to weigh the values (which is the information from each word) before summing them up to produce the final context-aware representation of the current word.

In simple terms, the Transformer uses these queries, keys, and values to figure out which words in the sentence are important to each other, helping it understand the context and meaning of each word.

Let's see this in the idea of keys, queries, and values in more detail.

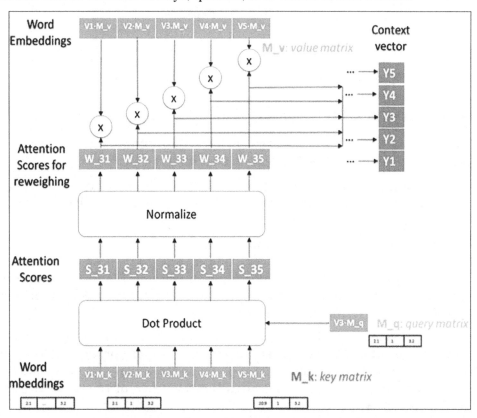

Figure 11.4: *Understanding keys, queries, and values*

In the preceding image, we have three matrices that we train for M_k (key matrix), M_q (query matrix), and M_v (values matrix). After feeding this through the backpropagation, we get the optimized value of these three matrices. An important thing to note here is that the architecture of self-attention can be written completely without trainable weights, all we need to do is remove these matrices and it still works completely fine. The following diagram shows the self-attention mechanism as one single trainable module.

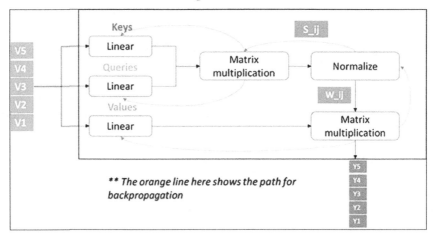

Figure 11.5: *Showing the Self-Attention mechanism as one unit*

Let's summarize the Self-Attention module.

Let's break down the attention process in a transformer model into easy steps, using the preceding sentence: **The cat chased its tail**.

- **Embedding**: First, each word in the sentence is converted into a vector representation or embedding. These embeddings are learned as the model is trained on lots of text data.

- **Generation of Query, Key, and Value pairs**: For every word, the model generates a Query (Q), a Key (K), and a Value (V). These are created by transforming the original embedding of the word with three different weight matrices that the model learns during training. So for the word **its**, we will have **its_Q**, **its_K**, and **its_V**.

- **Score Calculation**: The model calculates an attention score for each word with respect to the word it is processing. If we are processing the word **its**, the model calculates a score between **its** and all the other words in the sentence. The score measures the relevance of the other words to the current word.

   o This score is calculated by taking the dot product of the Query vector of the current word with the Key vector of the other word. For example, when processing **its**, one score would be calculated as the dot product of **its_Q** and **The_K**.

- **SoftMax**: The scores for each word are then passed through a SoftMax function, which converts these scores into probabilities. The sum of all these probabilities equals 1.

- **Weighted Sum:** The model then multiplies the SoftMax scores with the corresponding Value vectors and sums these up. This sum is the output of the self-attention mechanism for the current word, and it represents the context around that word. For example, when processing **its**, this output will contain more information from **cat**, because the attention score (and hence the SoftMax score) was higher for **cat**.

- **Repeat for all words:** This process is repeated for each word in the sentence. So, each word gets a new vector representing its context within the sentence.

- **Feed into Feed-Forward Neural Network:** Finally, the context-aware word vectors are fed into a feed-forward neural network for further processing.

This self-attention mechanism allows the model to focus more on words that are relevant to the current word and less on words that are not relevant. For instance, when trying to understand **its**, the model can pay more attention to **cat** and less attention to **chased** or **tail**.

What we describe above is a single module of self-attention, but in reality, we always use multiple modules in parallel, called multi-head attention. The following diagram shows the architecture of multi-head attention. There is nothing new in multi-head attention, it's just that this captures more context and can work better for longer sequences especially.

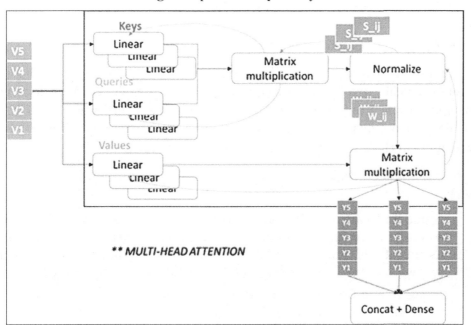

Figure 11.6: *Multi-head attention module*

Transformer Architecture

Let's talk about transformers with the attention mechanism out of the way. Transformers are nothing but a DL architecture that utilizes the power of self-attention to perform several tasks. If you look closely at the following diagram, you'll see a lot of multi-head attention blocks with a few additional things like positional encoding, Norm layers, and skip connections.

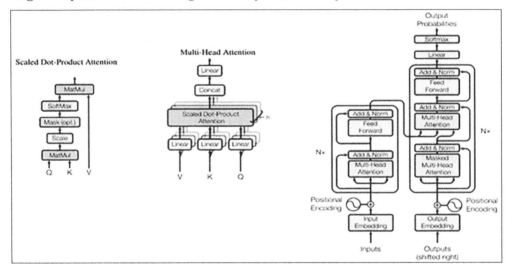

Figure 11.7: Transformer architecture and its component

Let's simplify the Transformer architecture

A Transformer is a type of model architecture used primarily for handling sequence data like text for Natural Language Processing (NLP) tasks. The primary innovation of the Transformer architecture is using **self-attention** mechanisms that allow the model to weigh and emphasize the importance of different words or elements in the input when making predictions.

Here's a simplified breakdown of the entire breakdown of entire Transformer model:

- **Input and Output:** The Transformer takes a sequence of tokens (for example, words in a sentence) as input and produces a sequence of tokens as output. This makes it suitable for tasks like machine translation, where you want to transform a sequence in one language into another.

- **Encoder and Decoder Structure:** The Transformer model has two main parts: the Encoder and the Decoder.

  o The **Encoder** takes the input sequence and processes it step by step, capturing the contextual information from the entire sequence. This part is about understanding the input.

o The **Decoder** then generates the output sequence step by step, using the information from the Encoder and its own inputs (previous output tokens). This part is about generating the output.

- **Self-Attention Mechanism:** Both the Encoder and Decoder use what's called a **self-attention mechanism**. This allows the model to look at other words in the input sequence to get a better context for the word it is processing, which leads to a better understanding of the sentence.

- **Positional Encoding:** Because the self-attention mechanism treats all words equally (meaning it doesn't consider their position in the sentence), the Transformer adds a **positional encoding** to each word's vector representation, so it can also understand the position of a word in a sentence.

- **Layered Structure:** Both the Encoder and Decoder are composed of a number of identical layers (the exact number can vary based on the specific model, but it's often in the range of 6-12). Each layer in the Encoder and Decoder performs the self-attention mechanism and then a simple feed-forward neural network.

- **Final Linear and SoftMax Layer:** In the Decoder, after the output has gone through all its layers, it's put through a final Linear layer and then a SoftMax function to generate probabilities for each possible output token (for example, each possible next word in a sentence).

Overall, the Transformer model has been revolutionary in NLP, thanks to its self-attention mechanism and scalability with sequence length. It forms the basis for many state-of-the-art models like BERT, GPT-2, ChatGPT, Llama, and more.

ChatGPT/GPT Overview

Building upon the foundation of self-attention mechanisms and the Transformer architecture, ChatGPT and similar models represent an evolution of these principles, offering a blend of scale and refinement. The GPT series took the original Transformer model, which had both an encoder and a decoder, and emphasized only the decoder for language modeling. Such a decision streamlined the architecture for generative tasks, allowing for more efficient and effective training.

Yet, the core principles remained. Stacked layers of transformers, positional encodings to compensate for the model's lack of inherent sequence awareness, and the combination of multi-head self-attention with feed-forward networks – all encapsulated within layer normalization and residual connections – served as the architectural backbone.

Training Paradigm with RLHF

GPT's training evolved further with the introduction of Reinforcement Learning from Human Feedback (RLHF). While it still maintained the two-step strategy of unsupervised pre-training on vast text corpora followed by fine-tuning on task-specific datasets, RLHF introduced a crucial enhancement. This paradigm involved collecting human feedback to rank different model-generated responses, and then using this feedback to fine-tune the models further via Proximal Policy Optimization. The inclusion of RLHF allowed for iterative refinements, where the model could be continuously improved based on specific human feedback, thereby making it more aligned with human values and desirable outputs.

The autoregressive nature of the training, where predictions are made based on prior context, further refined the model's ability to generate coherent and contextually relevant text.

The Leap with GPT-3

GPT-3's monumental scale, boasting 175 billion parameters, marked a significant shift. This wasn't merely an incremental growth in size; the sheer scale endowed GPT-3 with **few-shot** and **zero-shot** learning capabilities. Such abilities were unheard of in earlier models. GPT-3 could understand and execute tasks with minimal instruction, sometimes needing no prior examples at all. This was a stark contrast to earlier models, which required extensive fine-tuning for each specific task.

In essence, GPT-3' s advancements and capabilities are a testament to the interplay between advanced architectures, sophisticated training paradigms like RLHF, and the sheer scale of parameters, all of which combined to push the boundaries of AI-driven language understanding and generation.

Please visit the following link for a great lecture on Attention and Transformers from MIT: **https://www.youtube.com/watch?v=ySEx_Bqxvvo&ab_channel= AlexanderAmini [30]**

And also another lecture on the same topic from Stanford: **https://www.youtube.com/watch?v=ptuGllU5SQQ [31]**

Object Detection: Understanding YOLO

Object detection, a subfield of computer vision, focuses on identifying and locating objects of certain classes within an image. Going beyond image classification that can only tell what objects are present in an image, object detection also determines where these objects are by placing a bounding box around each detected object.

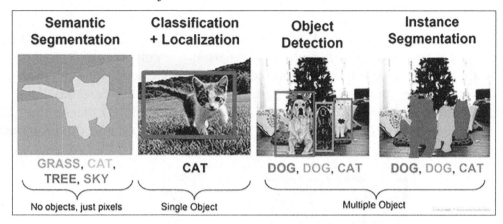

Figure 11.8: Different Computer vision tasks (Img Src)

All the tasks shown in the preceding image are powered by various machine learning models, such as R-CNN, Fast R-CNN, Faster R-CNN, SSD, and YOLO, each with its own strengths and trade-offs between speed and accuracy.

Object detection, a crucial technology in the realm of computer vision, finds extensive use across myriad industries. In security and surveillance, it aids in the real-time detection of unusual activities or prohibited items, proving to be invaluable in CCTV footage analysis. Autonomous vehicles leverage object detection to recognize pedestrians, other vehicles, traffic signs, and lanes to ensure safe navigation. In the healthcare industry, it's applied to identify diseases or anomalies in medical scans, such as MRIs and CT scans. Retail businesses use it to analyze customer behavior, manage inventory, and detect instances of shoplifting. Object detection is also beneficial in manufacturing, where it's employed for quality control to identify defective products on assembly lines. In agriculture, it assists in monitoring crop health, detecting pests, and even automating the harvesting process. Furthermore, it plays a critical role in Augmented Reality (AR) applications, aiding in identifying real-world objects to overlay digital content. Hence, object detection forms the backbone of a wide range of applications, contributing to automation and efficiency improvements across sectors.

How does object detection work?

To understand object detection, imagine that we have a photo and overlay a grid of squares on top of it. This grid splits the image into smaller sub-images, each square being a separate cell. The size of the grid is defined by the dimensions S×S (for example, 13×13 or 19×19), depending on the complexity of the image and the level of detail required.

In the object detection method, each cell in this grid is responsible for identifying an object if the center of that object lies within the cell. Each cell predicts B bounding boxes (usually two) and provides a confidence score for each of these predictions. The confidence score ranges from 0.0 to 1.0, where 0.0 signifies that the model is certain there's no object in that cell and 1.0 means that the model is completely confident there is an object in that cell and the predicted bounding box is accurate.

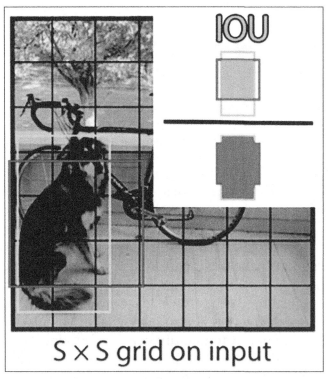

Figure 11.9: *Example of an IOU (the area of intersection of the ground truth and predicted box in green divided by the area of the union of the two boxes in purple. This will be between 0 and 1, 0 if they don't overlap at all, and 1 if they are the same box. Therefore, a higher IOU is better as it is a more accurate prediction)*

Each bounding box prediction consists of five components: the x and y coordinates (representing the center of the box), the width and height of the box (expressed as fractions of the entire image size), and the confidence score that represents how closely the predicted bounding box matches the actual bounding box (often measured using Intersection Over Union or IOU).

In addition to predicting bounding boxes and confidence scores, each cell also predicts the class of the object (for instance, 'dog', 'car', 'person'). This is represented as a one-hot vector of length C, where C is the total number of classes in the dataset. However, each cell predicts only one class, which is a limitation of the YOLO architecture. If multiple objects of different classes are within one cell, the algorithm may fail to classify all of them correctly.

Therefore, for each cell, the model's prediction is of the shape $C + B * 5$, which considers the number of classes and the number of bounding boxes. With $S \times S$ grid cells for each image, the overall prediction of the model is a tensor (a multi-dimensional array) of shape $S \times S \times (C + B * 5)$.

For example, in an image with a dog, the **object center** is the exact middle point of the dog. The grid cell containing this center point (highlighted in dark blue) detects and bounds the dog. The model's prediction will include the center, width, and height of the bounding box, along with the confidence score and class of the object. The class prediction will be a one-hot vector representing one of the several classes - in this case, the 'dog' class.

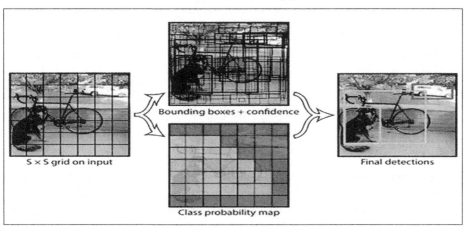

Figure 11.10: *Detecting different objects in a frame while showing class probability pas and bounding boxes*

Now let me introduce one of the most used object detectors in the world called YOLO. It is a very complex set of models designed to detect different types of objects. In this section, we will look at the core components of an object detection model like YOLO:

- Object detector architecture breakdown
- Backbone, neck, head
- Bag of freebies (BoF)

- Bag of specials (BoS)
- YOLO architecture selection
- YOLO BoF and BoS selection

Note: Object detection pipelines are extremely complex. We are introducing some key components from the object detection pipeline here so that we can talk about a few interesting ideas that you will keep seeing across different domains.

Object Detector Architecture Breakdown

The original YOLO (You Only Look Once) was written by Joseph Redmon in a custom framework called Darknet. Darknet is a flexible research framework written in low-level languages and has produced a series of the best real-time object detectors in computer vision: YOLO, YOLOv2, YOLOv3, and more.

- **The Original YOLO**: It was the first object detection network to combine the problem of drawing bounding boxes and identifying class labels in one end-to-end differentiable network.

- **YOLOv2**: It made a number of iterative improvements on top of YOLO, including BatchNorm, higher resolution, and anchor boxes. We discussed the idea of batch norm in the scaling of ConvNets.

- **YOLOv3**: It is built upon previous models by adding an objectness score to bounding box prediction, adding connections to the backbone network layers, and making predictions at three separate levels of granularity to improve performance on smaller objects.

- **YOLOv4**: It is a one-stage detector with several components to it. Each of its components will be broken down further in the later section. We currently have YOLOv8 in the market, but the core idea remains the same.

Here is the detailed breakdown of YOLO architecture:

- **Input:** There are three ways to feed input: **Image, patches**, **and Pyramid.**
- **Backbone:** VGG16, ResNet-50, SpineNet, EfficientNet-B0-B7, CSPRes Next50, CSPDarknet53, any one of these models can serve as the backbone of our Object detector.
- **Neck:** Again, we have many options to choose from for our neck as well, as follows:
  - ○ **Additional Blocks:** SPP, ASPP, RFB, SAM

- o **Path-aggregation blocks:** FPN, PAN, NAS-FPN, Fully-connected FPN, BiFPN, ASFF, SFAM.

- **Heads:** Lastly, a bunch more options for our head:

  - o **Dense prediction (one-stage):**

    - RPN, SSD, YOLO, RentinaNet (anchor-based)

    - CornerNet, CenterNet, MatrixNet (anchor-free)

  - o **Sparse prediction:**

    - Faster R-CNN, R-FCN, Mask R-CNN (anchor-based)

    - RepPoints (anchor-free)

We can see that YOLO can be implemented in any combination of input, backbone, neck, and head. Let's break these down even further.

Backbone, Neck, and Head

Backbone is the deep learning architecture that basically acts as a feature extractor. All of the backbone models are basically classification models. I assume that everyone is familiar with at least VGG16, one of the earliest deep-learning classifiers. There are three more models that we can use in the backbone other than the models mentioned earlier, namely SqueezeNet, MobileNet, and ShuffleNet. Still, these ones are meant for CPU training only, whereas the above one can be trained with GPUs. In previous sections, we have already discussed models like VGG16 and Efficient Net.

Within the object detection pipeline, the **neck** plays a crucial role as a subset of the bag of specials. Its primary function is to gather and consolidate feature maps obtained from various stages of the backbone. The neck acts as a feature aggregator, bringing together essential information for further processing. In subsequent sections, we will delve deeper into the intricacies of the neck and explore its significance within the object detection framework.

The **head**, also called the object detector, identifies the region where an object is likely to be present. However, it does not provide information about the specific object within that region. Object detectors can be categorized into two types: **two-stage** and **one-stage**. Further classification is based on whether they are **anchor-based or anchor-free detectors**. In the upcoming sections, we will delve into the intricacies of the head and explore its functionality within the object detection framework in greater detail.

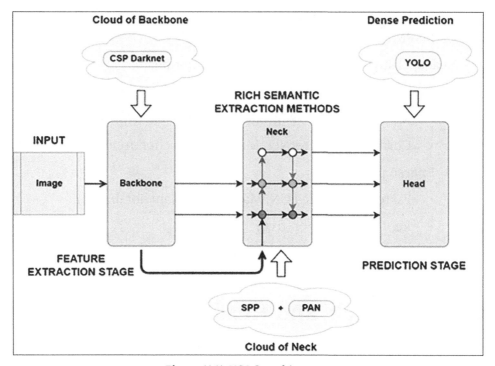

Figure 11.11: *YOLO architecture*

One-stage detectors are simpler and faster, directly predicting bounding boxes and class labels in a single pass through the network. They are well-suited for real-time applications and scenarios where speed is crucial. Examples of popular one-stage detectors include YOLO (You Only Look Once) and SSD (Single Shot MultiBox Detector). On the other hand, **two-stage detectors** have a more complex architecture and involve multiple stages. In the first stage, they generate a set of region proposals, which are potential object locations. These proposals are refined and classified in the second stage to produce final bounding box predictions and class labels. While two-stage detectors generally achieve higher accuracy, they are slower than one-stage detectors. Well-known two-stage detectors include Faster R-CNN and Mask R-CNN.

Anchor-based detectors, such as YOLO, SSD, Faster R-CNN, and RetinaNet, rely on predefined anchor boxes or priors. These anchor boxes act as reference templates and are matched to objects during training and prediction. They provide a way to handle objects of different scales and aspect ratios. On the other hand, **anchor-free detectors**, like CornerNet, CenterNet, and EfficientDet, do not use predefined anchor boxes. Instead, they directly predict object locations and sizes without relying on anchor matching. Anchor-free detectors offer simplicity and effectiveness in detecting objects.

Figure 11.12: *Showing different anchor boxes*

Bag of Freebies (BoF)

The term **bag of freebies** refers to methods that focus solely on altering the training strategy or increasing the training cost without directly impacting the inference stage. The diagram provided above illustrates a vast array of possibilities to explore, but we will concentrate on discussing the most crucial ones. These selected methods hold significant importance within the context of improving object detection and training efficiency.

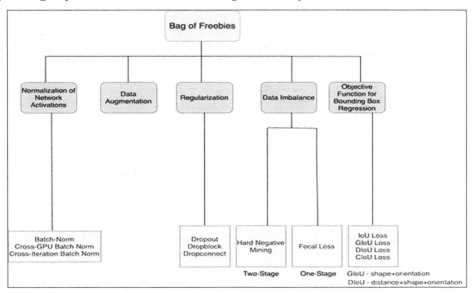

Figure 11.13: *Bag of Freebies*

Let's understand a few concepts from BoF, like new data augmentation techniques and improved batch normalization.

Mosaic data augmentation is commonly used in computer vision to train object detection models. It involves combining multiple images into a single mosaic image that is then used for training. The mosaic image consists of four sub-images randomly selected from the training dataset. These days you will see many similar data augmentation techniques being part of different AI pipelines. Other examples are cut&mix and random data erasing. These techniques make our models more generalized and behave better on unseen data.

Mosaic data augmentation aims to create more diverse and challenging training examples by simulating complex scenes with multiple objects and backgrounds. The model is exposed to a wider range of object placements, occlusions, and backgrounds by combining different images, helping it learn to handle various real-world scenarios.

The sub-images are randomly positioned within the mosaic during the process, and their bounding boxes are adjusted accordingly. This ensures that the model learns to detect objects in different spatial configurations, improving its robustness and generalization capabilities.

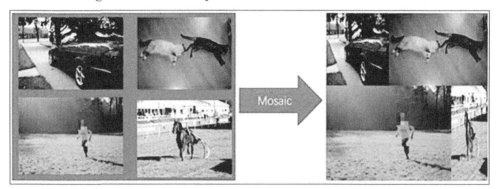

Figure 11.14: *Mosaic data augmentation*

CmBN: Cross-mini-Batch Normalization

Batch Normalization is a well-known technique used in deep learning, which involves normalizing the data within a single batch during training. However, Cross-Batch Normalization (CBN) takes this concept further by considering the mean and standard deviation of not just the current batch, but also the previous four batches. This means that the normalization process considers the statistics of a larger sample size, introducing some correlation between the batches.

Going a step further, CmBN (Cross-mini-Batch Normalization) introduces the idea of CBN within a single batch. Instead of considering the statistics of separate batches, CmBN combines the normalization process with mini-Batch Normalization, considering the statistics of smaller subsets within the batch. This allows for a more fine-grained normalization approach, capturing correlations within a smaller scale.

CBN and CmBN aim to improve the normalization process by considering a broader context of statistics, whether across multiple batches or within a single batch with mini-Batch Normalization. These techniques could enhance the training process and contribute to improved model performance.

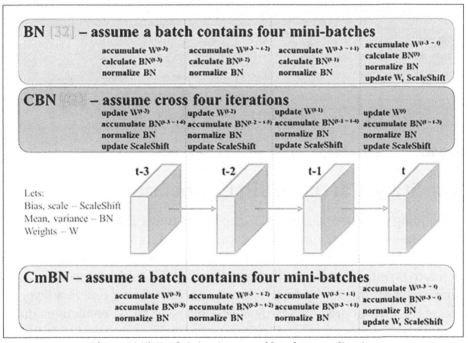

Figure 11.15: *Explaining improved batch normalization*

Bag of Specials (BoS)

The **bag of specials** refers to a collection of plugin modules and post-processing methods that introduce minimal additional computational cost during inference but can significantly enhance accuracy. These specialized techniques offer valuable improvements without significantly impacting the overall efficiency of the inference process. By incorporating these carefully selected components, one can achieve substantial gains in accuracy without compromising computational efficiency.

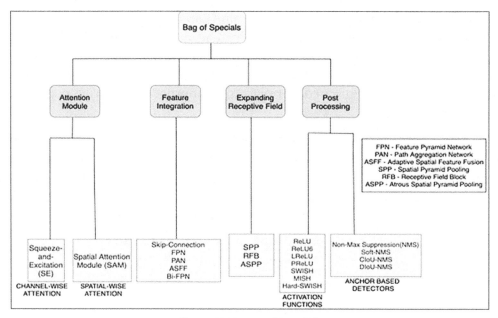

Figure 11.16: *Bag of Specials*

Let's take a look at a component from BoS called CSP.

Cross-Stage Partial (CSP) Connection

When building deep neural networks, the layers towards the end of the network may lose their ability to understand the context of features learned in the initial layers. To mitigate this issue, skip connections were introduced, allowing gradients to flow back to the earlier layers more effectively. DenseNet, a popular network architecture, incorporated skip connections between every layer, which improved the flow of gradients. However, DenseNet faced challenges due to its large number of parameters, making training and inference more challenging.

To overcome these challenges, CSPResNext50 and CSPDarknet53 drew inspiration from DenseNet while introducing modifications to enhance their performance. These modifications involved splitting the feature map of the base layer into two branches. One branch passed through the dense block as in DenseNet, while the other branch bypassed the dense block and directly proceeded to the next stage. This approach aimed to alleviate computational bottlenecks within the DenseNet architecture and improve the learning process by preserving an unedited version of the feature map.

To validate the effectiveness of this modification, experiments were conducted using cross-stage partial connections on ResNext-50. The results were striking, revealing a significant performance boost of approximately 20% compared to the original model. This improvement showcased the potential of the CSPResNext50 and CSPDarknet53 architectures in enhancing the performance of object detection networks.

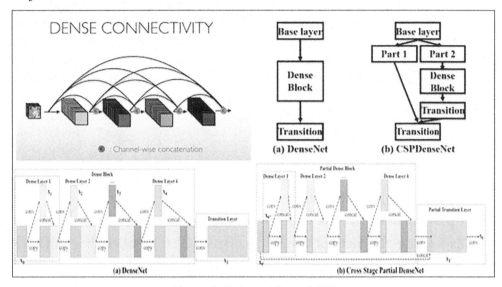

Figure 11.17: *DenseNet and CSP*

YOLO A rchitecture S election

When it comes to selecting an architecture, several factors come into play to ensure an optimal balance. These criteria include the input network resolution (input image size), the number of convolution layers, the number of parameters, and the number of output layers (filters). Additionally, there are additional blocks available to increase the receptive field, known as the **bag of specials**, and various methods to connect different backbone levels with detector levels referred to as **Necks**.

For instance, the final architecture in YOLOv4 is composed of:

- **Backbone**: CSPDarkNet53
- **Neck**: Combination of **SPP** and **PANet**
- **Head**: YOLOv3

Close competitors considered CSPDarkNet53 were CSPResNext50 and EfficientNet-B3, but CSPDarkNet53 exhibits higher frames per second (FPS) compared to the others, making it the preferred choice.

By carefully evaluating these aspects, one can determine an architecture that balances performance, efficiency, and accuracy.

Before delving into the discussion of **SPP** and **PANet** (both mentioned in Neck), it is crucial to address the impact of resolution. Unlike classifiers, detectors necessitate a higher input network size to detect multiple small-sized objects effectively. Additionally, more layers are required to achieve a larger receptive field capable of encompassing the expanded input network size. In essence, the detector demands more parameters to enhance the model's capacity to detect multiple objects of varying sizes within a single image. This ensures that the detector is capable of handling the complexity of object detection tasks.

Impact of receptive field size

The influence of the receptive field with different sizes is as follows:

- **Up to the object size** : allows viewing the entire object.

- **Up to the network size** : allows viewing the context around the object.

- **Exceeding the network size** : increases the number of connections between the image point and the final activation.

Spatial Pyramid Pooling (SPP)

The reason why we are talking about SPP is that a lot of new architectures, such as Efficient Net, use the concept of pyramidal-based inputs. In this fashion we are able to feed multi-scale input to our model, thus making it better by giving more context. So why not use a similar idea for pooling as well? Pooling is the layer where we generally lose a lot of context, but using SPP, we can preserve some more information and context than our standard max or average pooling.

In YOLO, an SPP (Spatial Pyramid Pooling) block is employed after CSPDarknet53 to enhance the receptive field and extract key features from the backbone. Spatial pyramid pooling involves taking an input image and using convolutional layers to extract its feature map. Subsequently, max pooling operations are performed with different window sizes, creating a pyramid of feature sets with varying dimensions in the height and width axes.

However, YOLO takes a step further by applying SPP in a unique manner. Instead of using SPP directly on the entire feature map, YOLOv4 divides the feature map along the depth dimension into separate parts. Then, SPP is applied individually to each part, resulting in multiple sets of pooled features. Finally, these individual sets are combined back together to generate an output feature map.

By utilizing this modified approach to SPP, YOLO can capture and leverage rich spatial information at different scales within the network, enabling enhanced object detection performance.

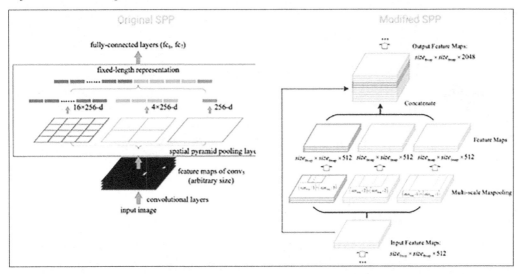

Figure 11.18: *Original and Modified SPP*

PAN Path – Aggregation Block

In the preceding section, we have already discussed the idea of better context using a pyramidal structure. Pyramidal base input generally leads to improved context; you will see this type of input feeding in a lot of new DL architectures. The idea behind all the new developments is to provide more context and flow during the training, and pyramidal-based input does exactly that.

Within the YOLOv4 architecture, the PAN (Path-Aggregation Network) block is selected for feature aggregation. Although the rationale behind this decision is not extensively elaborated upon, it is likely an area of ongoing research since NAS-FPN and BiFPN were mentioned concurrently. Notably, a modification made in YOLOv4 is the utilization of concatenation instead of addition in the PAN block.

PANet, which stands for Feature Pyramid Network, is crucial in extracting significant features from the backbone classifier. It achieves this by incorporating the SPP (Spatial Pyramid Pooling) technique, which facilitates the creation of an efficient feature pyramid network. The specific details regarding the rationale behind choosing PANet and its modifications in YOLOv4 may be areas of further exploration in future research.

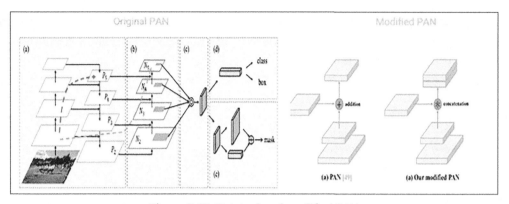

Figure 11.19: *Original and modified PAN*

And lastly, we have SAM or Spatial Attention Module.

Spatial Attention Module (SAM)

Now we have already used the word attention many times, but it is important to know that this can be applied in a lot of different contexts, thus requiring us to talk about this again and again.

To grasp the concept of the Special Attention Module (SAM) for object detection, it is important first to understand the Squeeze and Excitation Network (SENet). SENet focuses on determining the importance of each channel within a feature map block. It achieves this by analyzing the feature map and assigning a level of importance to each filter, as depicted in the colored feature block diagram (see *Figure 11.20*).

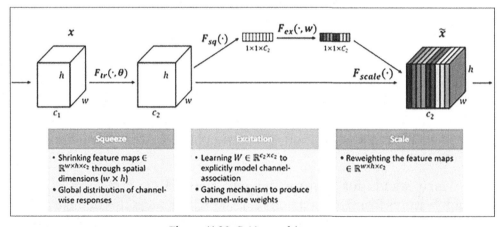

Figure 11.20: *SeNet architecture*

Returning to SAM, instead of compressing each filter to a single value as in SENet, SAM employs both max pooling and average pooling operations. This results in a reduced-size feature block in terms of width and height. This reduced feature block is then passed through a sigmoid activation function, generating a weight for each filter in the original feature map. These weights are then multiplied with the original feature map to obtain the feature importance of each filter.

What sets YOLO apart is its further advancement in attention mechanisms. In addition to the depth-based attention used in SENet and SAM, YOLOv4 introduces spatial attention, which focuses on both the filters (depth) and the spatial dimensions (width and height). This combination of attention mechanisms along with depth and spatial dimensions enhances the ability of YOLOv4 to capture important features across the entire feature map.

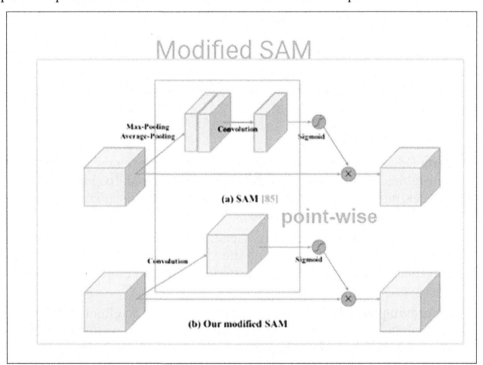

Figure 11.21: *Modified SAM*

And this marks the end of our discussion on Object detection using YOLO; in no way is this complete YOLO architecture but breaking down each component further is a book in itself. I understand this chapter is geared more towards people who already know a lot of AI concepts and ideas, but it is also important to show other readers that building something this big will have a sufficient amount of challenges and roadblocks. And often you will be using ideas from other subfields to improve upon the existing models and architectures.

Image Generation: GAN's and Diffusion models

Image generation in AI involves the creation of images based on text prompts, using random noise samples as a foundation. This process entails iterations during which each pixel undergoes modifications, gradually aligning it with the provided text prompt. Two primary approaches are commonly employed: GANs (Generative Adversarial Networks) and Diffusion.

Generative Adversarial Networks

Generative models, a branch of unsupervised learning, have seen a rapid rise in popularity in recent years. They've been instrumental in various applications, from image synthesis and text generation to improving cybersecurity. This surge in interest isn't accidental; it's a direct result of the models' capacity to learn and mimic the underlying data distributions, creating new data points with similar characteristics.

Why are GANs so popular?

- **Data Generation:** Generative models can generate new data that closely resembles training data. They've been employed to generate realistic images, write coherent text, and even compose music. This is particularly useful when access to real data is restricted or costly.

- **Learning Data Distribution:** Generative models aim to understand the underlying distribution of the data, which can provide insightful information about the data structure and dependencies among the variables.

- **Improving Data Efficiency:** Generative models can effectively learn from less labeled data, which is highly advantageous, considering the cost of data acquisition and labeling in many real-world scenarios.

- **Versatile Applications:** From super-resolution, image inpainting, and style transfer, to data augmentation and semi-supervised learning, generative models have wide-ranging applications.

Generative Discriminative models

Imagine you're at a pet store, and your job is to sort animals into their respective categories, such as dogs and cats. That's exactly what a discriminative model in machine learning does - it's a sort of **sorting expert**.

Just like you would use certain characteristics or features - like the nose's shape, the tongue's length, or the type of fur - to differentiate between a dog and a cat, the discriminative model does the same. It looks at a bunch of features, let's call them X, and then decides whether the picture it's looking at is a cat or a dog.

In other words, **Discriminative** models try to figure out the chances of the animal being a cat or a dog based on the features **X**. So, they're essentially asking, "Given these features, what's the likelihood that this picture is of a dog or a cat?" This is often represented as **P(Y|X)**, or the probability of a certain class **(Y)** given a set of features **(X)**.

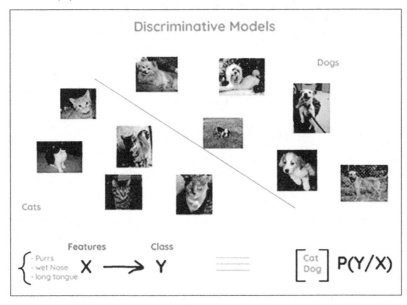

Figure 11.22: *Discriminative model*

But what if you could create a new image of a dog or cat instead of just identifying and sorting the animals? That's where **generative** models come into the picture. These models are like the artists of the machine learning world. They don't just stop at distinguishing between a dog and a cat; they actually aim to create a new, realistic image of a dog or a cat from nothing.

But how do they do that? They start with some random input, called noise (ε). You could think of this noise as a sort of raw material or a blob of clay that the artist will shape into a sculpture. Along with the noise, the model also takes an input of what class the image should be, for example, a cat or a dog **(Y)**. Using these two inputs **(ε, Y)**, the model then creates a set of features **X**, which make up the image of the dog or cat.

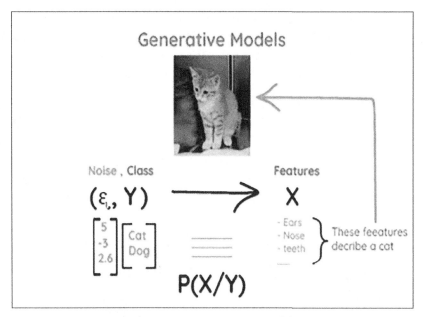

Figure 11.23: Generative model

You might be thinking, "Why do we need this random noise, ε? Why can't the model just create a cat or a dog without it?"

That's a great question! Random noise is crucial because it allows the model to create diverse and unique images. Without it, the model would keep producing the same image over and over again, which would be like an artist creating the same sculpture every single time - not very exciting, right? By using this random noise, the model can create a variety of realistic images for each class, truly living up to its name as a generative model.

Variational Autoencoders

The journey of image transformation in a VAE begins with feeding a realistic image into the encoder. The encoder's role is to effectively translate this image into a representation in a mathematical construct known as latent space.

Consider an example - a given image may be represented by a vector (5,-3,2.6) in the latent space, which we can visualize as a point. This latent representation, or a point in close proximity to it, is then passed on to the decoder.

In other words, the encoder part of a VAE takes the input data and transforms it into two different parameters in a latent space: a mean vector μ and a standard deviation vector σ. These vectors represent the parameters of a Gaussian distribution. The latent space is a compressed representation of the input data, which captures the essential characteristics necessary to reproduce it.

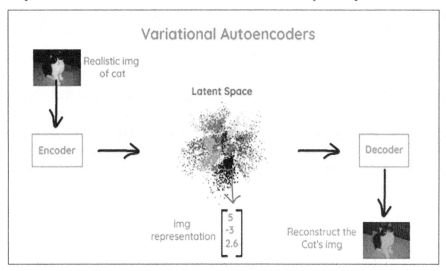

Figure 11.24: *Variational Autoencoder*

The decoder's challenge lies in reconstructing the original image from this latent representation. In the initial stages, the decoder might need help to create a convincing image of, say, a cat, based on the information it has. However, with training, its performance improves. Eventually, we can remove the encoder entirely and feed random points from the latent space directly into the decoder. Given enough training, the decoder can then generate realistic images, such as a cat, from these random points. The following illustration captures this intriguing process.

Now let's introduce the **variational** component, which brings a touch of randomness into the model and the training process. Rather than encoding an image into a single point in latent space, the variational approach enables the encoder to represent the image as an entire distribution. The samples drawn from this distribution then serve as inputs to the decoder, leading to the generation of realistic images. This addition of **noise** to the model through the variational process enhances the diversity and realism of the images generated by the VAE.

There are two more components to VAE, first, one is called the **reparameterization trick,** and it's loss function.

Reparameterization is a key step in the VAE process. To generate a sample in the latent space, we can't just sample from the learned distribution directly because backpropagation (the method by which we train the model) can't flow through a random node. So, instead, we sample from a standard normal distribution ε and then shift the sample by the mean μ and scale it by the standard deviation σ. This is represented as: $z = μ + σ*ε$. This allows us to keep the stochasticity necessary for a generative model while ensuring that the model remains differentiable and, therefore, trainable.

The loss function in VAEs comprises the reconstruction loss and the KL divergence. The reconstruction loss measures how well the decoder recreates the original input data, while the KL divergence measures how much the learned distribution deviates from a standard normal distribution. The aim of the training is to minimize this combined loss. It's important to note that we're not going into full detail about VAE because they are not industry standard anymore. However, it's still important to understand the basic idea behind these techniques and models.

Please visit the following link for a great video on VAE from YouTube channel called Arxiv Insights:

https://www.youtube.com/watch?v=9zKuYvjFFS8&t=530s&ab_channel=ArxivInsights [32]

GANs

Generative Adversarial Networks (GANs) are like an art contest between a forger and an art critic. In this duo, the forger is the **generator**, and the art critic is the **discriminator**. The generator creates fake images, aiming to mimic real ones as closely as possible, while the discriminator evaluates these fakes, distinguishing them from the real ones. It's a dynamic game of deception and detection, which leads to the generator producing impressively realistic images.

To begin this contest, you start with a collection of real images – say, famous paintings. The generator learns to produce convincing forgeries, and the discriminator becomes adept at spotting the fakes. This is an iterative process where both the generator and discriminator improve over time.

In a standard GAN architecture, the generator takes random noise ε as an input, generating **fake** images $\dot{X}$. The discriminator then takes these fake images, alongside real images X, and calculates the probability of each image being real. This results in an output, $\dot{Y}$.

The generator network G in GANs is typically a deep neural network that takes a random noise vector z as input and outputs a generated image $G(z)$. The generator's parameters are denoted as $θ_g$.

The discriminator network D, also a deep neural network, takes an image (either a real image from the training set or a fake image generated by **G**) as input and outputs a single scalar representing the probability that the input image is real. The discriminator's parameters are represented as θ_d.

The generator is trained to maximize the probability of **D** making a mistake, while the discriminator is trained to correctly classify images as real or fake. This setup is often described as a two-player minimax game with the following objective function:

$$v(D,G)_{\smile} = {}_{G,D} E\left\{x \sim pdata(x)\right\} logD(x) + E\left\{z \sim p_z(z)\right\} log\left(1 - D(z)\right)$$

Here, **E** is the expectation, $pdata(x)$ is the data distribution, and $p_z(z)$ is the prior input noise distribution.

The accuracy of the discriminator's predictions is measured using the Binary Cross Entropy (BCE) cost function, which compares the predictions $\dot{Y}$ against the true labels ($\dot{Y}$: 0 for fake, 1 for real). The discriminator's parameters θ_d are then updated to improve its accuracy, while the generator's parameters remain unchanged.

Understand that training GAN is quite tricky and has a lot of steps involved in it. There is a lot of maths that needs to be understood in order to implement GANs from scratch. A few concepts that you can look into to understand the idea behind GANs better are earth mover's distance, Mode collapse, training instability, unable to reach Nash equilibrium, and more. The idea here is to introduce readers to new concepts such that they can go on and learn these things in more detail on the internet.

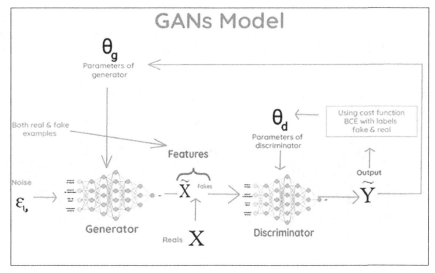

Figure 11.25: *Generative Adversarial Network architecture*

Here are a few different types of GANs that solve some of the mentioned problems:

- **Deep Convolutional GAN (DCGAN):** This architecture recommends certain constraints on the architectural topology of GANs, making them more stable to train. Notably, it suggests using batch normalization layers and strided convolutions instead of pooling to downsample, and using transposed convolution for upsampling.

- **Pix2Pix:** This GAN uses a conditional GAN architecture where the generation of the output image is conditional on an input image. In addition to the adversarial loss, Pix2Pix also uses an L1 loss to make the generated image as close as possible to the target image. This model is particularly useful for tasks like colorization, where an input image can be a grayscale image and the target image is the colored version.

Figure 11.26: *Results of Pix2Pix GAN (Img Src)*

- **CycleGAN:** This GAN is a breakthrough for unpaired image-to-image translation tasks. It introduces a cycle-consistency loss to the traditional GAN loss to enforce forward and backward consistency. If an image from the first domain is translated to the second domain and then translated back to the first domain, the double-translated image should be the same as the original image.

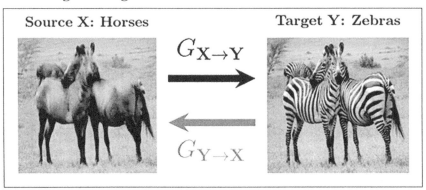

Figure 11.27: *Converting horses to zebras using CycleGAN (Img Src)*

- **Wasserstein GAN (WGAN):** This variant changes the GAN loss function to use the Wasserstein distance, providing smoother gradients and better training stability.
- **Spectral Normalization for Generative Adversarial Networks (SNGAN):** This architecture applies spectral normalization to the discriminator to stabilize the training of the discriminator network.

Please visit this link to see the power of GANs: **https://this-person-does-not-exist.com/en [33]**

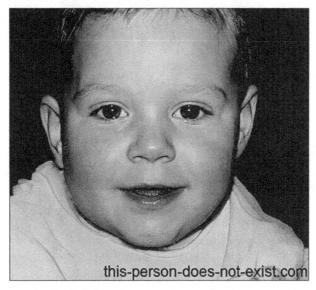

Figure 11.28: *This kid doesn't exist, it is completely generated using AI*

Please visit the following link for a great lecture on Generative models from Stanford: **https://www.youtube.com/watch?v=5WoItGTWV54&ab_channel= StanfordUniversitySchoolofEngineering [34]**

Another interesting talk of Ian Goodfellow from Lex Fridmans' Podcast on GANs: https://**www.youtube.com/watch?v=Z6rxFNMGdn0&t=656s&ab_channel= LexFridman [35]**

Diffusion Models

If you are impressed by GAN, wait until you see the Diffusion models' results. If you follow AI news, I'm sure you would have come across the name DALL-E or Mid Journey a few months ago. Both of these Image generative AI can create hyper-realistic images just out of the text. The results are so amazing that people now can't identify whether the images produced by them are real or not.

Recently there was a big controversy regarding these diffusion models. An artist fooled the entire world by winning the world's most prestigious photography competition organized by SONY. Later on, he refused the award because he didn't take the photo but created it using AI. The point was to demonstrate the insane capabilities of modern-day AI. Following is the image that won SONY's photography challenge.

Figure 11.29: *AI-generated photo wins SONY's photography competition (Img Src)*

But now, let's dive deeper into how this technology works. For understanding purposes, we'll talk about OpenAI's DALL-E 2 model.

DALL-E 2 is a text-to-image generation model developed by Open-AI researchers. It's the second installment in the series of text-to-image generation models. DALL-E 2 is an extremely capable model that can draw many images with unseen text prompts. DALL-E 2 can create images that don't exist on the internet, it's more like an actual painter who can paint anything with his/her imagination.

DALL-E 2 can understand images and text in great detail. Thus, it can not only create images out of the text but also create other versions of famous paintings, understand different art styles, and also understand the lighting conditions and create shadows accordingly. It can also be used for in-painting and has the capability to generate an image for almost any random text prompt.

DALL-E 2 Architecture

DALL-E 2, a groundbreaking model from OpenAI, features a distinctive two-component architecture comprising a **Prior** and a **Decoder**. The journey begins with converting a text prompt into an embedding, which the Prior then transmutes into an image-specific representation known as the image embedding. This image embedding is subsequently decoded into the final image representation.

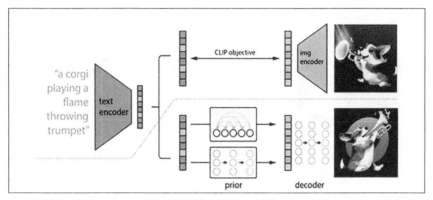

Figure 11.30: *A high-level overview of text-to-image generation models*

A key ingredient in this transformative process is **CLIP**, another brainchild of OpenAI. Working in reverse to DALL-E 2, CLIP links images to their most fitting captions, operating as a contrastive learning model, not merely classifying images but aligning them with appropriate text prompts.

The heart of CLIP lies in its dual encoder setup, which generates the essential text and image embeddings for DALL-E 2. An embedding is simply a carefully structured numerical array symbolizing an image or text. While reminiscent of the ASCII representation of characters and numbers, these embeddings are dynamic and learnable through the neural network, offering a more nuanced and flexible representation.

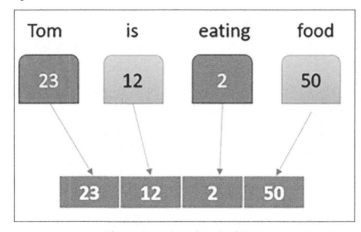

Figure 11.31: *Word Embeddings*

The following figure shows the CLIP matching the images to text prompts:

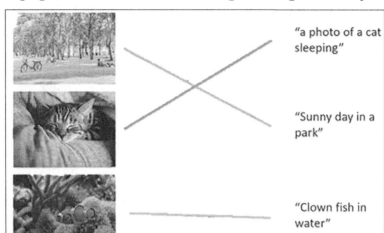

Figure 11.32: *CLIP matching the images to text prompts*

What does CLIP basically optimize?

CLIP primarily focuses on optimizing the correlation or similarity between text embeddings and image embeddings. Its goal is to maximize the similarity between the text and image embeddings. *Figure 11.33* illustrates the objective of CLIP during training. Ideally, the blue blocks in the following image should exhibit a very high degree of similarity, while the gray blocks should have a minimal similarity or low values.

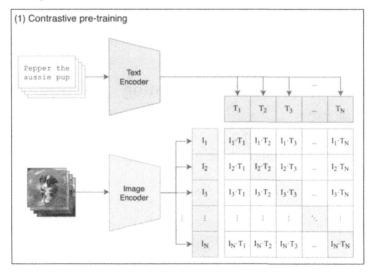

Figure 11.33: *CLIP creates a correlation or similarity matrix between image and text embeddings (Img Src)*

The Encoder: Prior Diffusion Model

To understand the text-to-image model in more detail, let's talk about **Prior**. In machine learning, the term **prior** generally refers to prior knowledge or belief about an uncertain quantity. Here, the two models for the prior, the **autoregressive model** and the **diffusion model**, are used to generate a prior belief about the data.

The **autoregressive model**, often used in time series analysis, predicts future data based on the data from previous time steps. For instance, it uses data from today and past days to predict tomorrow's weather or stock prices. It's built on the principle of regression, where one variable is predicted from previous values of the same variable. The model is known as **auto** regressive because it's a regression of the variable against itself.

On the other hand, the **diffusion model** is a stochastic model, characterized by randomness, used to represent how an image changes over time with the addition of noise. The noise is gradually added until the original image transforms into what appears as random noise. Then, the process is reversed, and the noisy image is converted back into the original image. This iterative procedure facilitates the network in learning how to generate images from noise.

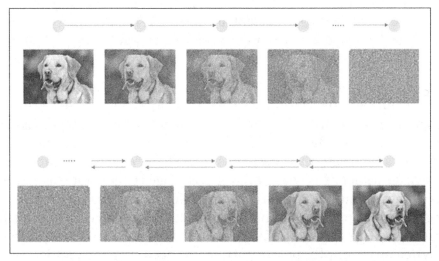

Figure 11.34: *Diffusion model learning to create images by adding and removing noise iteratively*

In the DALL-E 2, the researchers took advantage of the CLIP model, a large-scale, high-performance vision-and-language model developed by OpenAI. CLIP's text embedding was fed to a diffusion prior to generating an image embedding. Following this, the image embedding conditioned a diffusion decoder, producing the final image. Notably, during the training of the prior and decoder, the CLIP model needed to be updated, that is, it remained frozen.

The diffusion model showed a remarkable capacity to generate images, surpassing even Generative Adversarial Networks (GANs), a widely used class of models for image generation tasks. GANs, developed by Ian Goodfellow and his colleagues in 2014, are a class of artificial intelligence algorithms used in unsupervised machine learning. They use two neural networks, thegenerator and the discriminator, to generate new, synthetic data instances that can pass for real data.

The Decoder: GLIDE

GLIDE is an advanced image generation model that takes a noise-influenced image and progressively refines it through iterative stages. Notably, it relies on more than just the diffusion model's noise-to-image conversion process. Instead, it incorporates text embeddings into the process, significantly improving the generated image's overall quality.

Building on GLIDE's approach, DALL-E 2 goes a step further by integrating CLIP embeddings, another groundbreaking model from OpenAI that learns visual concepts from natural language supervision. When used with the diffusion decoder, these embeddings substantially augment the decoder's performance. This strategic enhancement allows DALL-E 2 to generate images that are more contextually aligned with the given text prompts and are of higher quality.

The image generation process in DALL-E 2 starts with a relatively low-resolution preliminary image, typically of size 64x64. This initial image is then progressively upscaled through a process called up-sampling. This process enlarges the image dimensions by a factor of four in two separate stages, leading to the final high-resolution image that measures 1024x1024 pixels. By employing this two-stage up-sampling process, DALL-E 2 manages to generate high-resolution images without requiring immense computational resources at the initial stages of the generation process. The final high-resolution images retain the quality and context alignment achieved through the diffusion model and CLIP embeddings, thereby demonstrating the potency of this advanced image generation technique.

Once again, it's important to remind all the readers that building systems like DALL-E 2 and ChatGPT requires millions of dollars and years' worth of training. There is no book in the world that can teach you how to make these systems; all you can do is grasp the ideas behind these great technologies. Also, it's natural not to understand every word on these complex AI models like DALL-E 2 and

ChatGPT. We have barely scratched the surface of these systems in this book. Understanding this in detail requires advanced knowledge of AI principles; honestly, it will be way beyond the scope of this book.

And this finally marks the end of the book. I hope you learned a lot about Neural Networks and got inspired, confused, and motivated to learn about the complexity of the field of AI.

Conclusion

This final chapter delves into the cutting-edge technologies that power the coolest AI advancements. We begin by exploring the context of recurrent neural networks (RNNs) and long short-term memory (LSTM) networks. From there, we swiftly transition to the fascinating concept of self-attention. We examine self-attention mechanisms, multi-headed attention, and their crucial role in the Transformers architecture. It is worth noting that Transformer's architecture is the backbone for groundbreaking technologies like ChatGPT, revolutionizing natural language processing.

Continuing our exploration, we focus on object detection and delve into the key concepts within the YOLO (You Only Look Once) framework. We dive into the detailed architecture of YOLO and discuss essential elements such as Cross-mini- Batch normalization, Path Aggregation Network, Spatial Attention Module, and Mosaic data transformation. These elements contribute to highly efficient and accurate object detection algorithms, enabling advancements in fields such as autonomous vehicles, surveillance, and image understanding.

Lastly, we broaden our discussion to include generative models such as variational autoencoders (VAEs) and generative adversarial networks (GANs). Additionally, we take a deep dive into diffusion models, particularly GLIDE, which forms the foundation for remarkable AI technologies like DALL-E 2. These generative models enable the creation of highly realistic and creative outputs, pushing the boundaries of AI-generated content in areas such as image synthesis, text generation, and creative arts. By exploring these state-of-the-art technologies, we gain insight into the forefront of AI advancements and their incredible potential.

" *We only believe in data; rest can trust in god*" – AIGuys

https://github.com/OrangeAVA/Ultimate-Neural-Network-Programming-with-Python

Index